The
Marjorie Rawlings
Reader

Books by Marjorie Kinnan Rawlings

THE MARJORIE RAWLINGS READER

THE SECRET RIVER

THE SOJOURNER

CROSS CREEK COOKERY

CROSS CREEK

WHEN THE WHIPPOORWILL

THE YEARLING

GOLDEN APPLES

SOUTH MOON UNDER

MARJORIE KINNAN RAWLINGS

THE
Marjorie Rawlings
READER

Selected and Edited

with

an Introduction

by

JULIA SCRIBNER BIGHAM

CHARLES SCRIBNER'S SONS
NEW YORK

The following stories appeared originally in The New Yorker: "Jessamine Springs" (1941), "The Pelican's Shadow" (1940) and "The Shell" (1944).

Contents

INTRODUCTION

Introduction

BY JULIA SCRIBNER BIGHAM

THE AIM of this book is to give the reader a representative selection of the best writing of Marjorie Kinnan Rawlings. It brings back into print her first novel, *South Moon Under,* and includes three stories, "The Pelican's Shadow," "Jessamine Springs," and "The Shell," which now appear for the first time in book form. It also gives the reader selections from *The Yearling* and *Cross Creek,* her two best-known books, and from her collection of short stories, *When the Whippoorwill.* It was difficult to make a choice among the short stories. This is a form in which she was especially happy, and there are many of them full of the individual flavor of her best work. The six here included were chosen to give an idea of the scope of these stories, from the hilarity of "Cocks Must Crow" to the poignance of "Gal Young Un"; from the bare simplicity of "Jacob's Ladder" to the sophistication of "The Pelican's Shadow."

In 1930 *Scribner's Magazine* accepted a group of sketches of Florida Cracker folk by an unknown author, Marjorie Kinnan Rawlings. The editor of the Magazine wrote asking to know something of her literary background and she answered: "I am not yet thirty-five but I have written consciously—actually—for twenty-four years. I have made my living off and on from advertising, publicity and journalism, all the time working at verse and fiction that came home to roost like carrier pigeons. . . . When I settled here, and the delights of this Cracker material fired me with enthusiasm—material vital past any straight fiction I could ever create—I made up my mind that if I could not interest one of the

ix

few topnotch magazines in it, I would deliberately put the torment of unaccepted writing out of my life. . . ."

The inspiration of the strange scrub country and her deep response to the Crackers who lived there were the ingredients needed to change Marjorie Rawlings' long struggle with creative writing from failure to success. The change was dramatically sudden and complete. When, early in 1931, the sketches appeared in the Magazine as "Cracker Chidlings," considerable interest was aroused by the work of this new writer. It even set in motion a campaign of abuse in certain Florida newspapers, which asserted that Mrs. Rawlings maligned the State by writing of "low" characters such as did not exist there. Actually, she worked so closely with real people and events that much of her work of this early period is more like inspired reporting than fiction. As she herself wrote: "I have gathered my facts firsthand. Most of the material is from my personal knowledge. The rest has been told me here and there in the locality and is equally authentic. Bits about this woman or that man, mentioned casually in the course of my ordinary conversations with Cracker friends and neighbors, make up, with perhaps some salient last fact, the outline of a life. A mere chance visit, as my literally recorded chat with a 'shiner's wife [in "Cracker Chidlings"], suggests the drama of a personality."

Encouraged by the acceptance of "Cracker Chidlings," Mrs. Rawlings wrote the long story or novella, "Jacob's Ladder." One of the chapters from *Cross Creek*, "Antses in Tim's Breakfast," has been included in this book, partly for the sharp insight it gives into the psychological genesis of "Jacob's Ladder" in particular, but indeed of much of her other writing as well. "Jacob's Ladder" confirmed Marjorie Rawlings' promise as a writer. The story, which appeared in *Scribner's Magazine* for April 1931, won second prize in the Scribner Prize Contest that year. From then on, her stories appeared regularly in *Scribner's* and later in *Harper's, The Saturday Evening Post, The New Yorker*, and other magazines. The lean years of rejection slips were over and the author received interested inquiries from several publishers about the prospects of a book.

In the fall of 1931 Mrs. Rawlings went to live, for several

weeks, deep in the scrub, with an old woman and her 'shiner son. During that time she hoped to gather material for a novel. On her return, she wrote a long letter to her editor, Maxwell Perkins. This letter is so interesting, not only as the background of the novel, but in its portrayal of how close she was to real people and events in her writing and in its revelation of the depth of her identification with them, that it is here included almost in full:

"About my novel of the scrub country—

"I came back recently from very absorbing weeks lived with the old woman and her 'shiner son, of whom I believe I wrote you. I have voluminous notes of the intimate type, for which the most prolific imagination is no substitute. I have also, well as I thought I knew the people of this particular section, an entirely new conception of them. I knew they were gentle; honest. I knew that living was precarious, but just how hand-to-mouth it is, surprised me. I was also astonished by the *utter lack of bleakness or despair,* in a group living momentarily on the very edge of starvation and danger. Whatever else my story turns out to be, it will not be a gloomy, morose 'novel of the soil.' I found a zestfulness in living, a humor, an alertness to beauty, quite unexpected, and of definite value to record, if I can 'get' it.

"These people are 'lawless' by an anomaly. They are living an entirely natural, and very hard, life, disturbing no one. Civilization has no concern with them, except to buy their excellent corn liquor and to hunt, in season, across their territory with an alarming abandon. Yet almost everything they do is illegal. And everything they do is necessary to sustain life in that place. The old clearings have been farmed out and will not 'make' good crops any more. The big timber is gone. The trapping is poor. They 'shine, because 'shining is the only business they know that can be carried on in the country they know, and would be unwilling to leave.

"The 'shining will have to be the main thread in my story. But I want to make it dramatic by an entire absence of melodrama. It is quite simply a part of the background; a part of the whole resistance of the scrub country to the civilizing process. The scrub, as a matter of fact, has defeated civilization. It is one of the few areas where settlements have disappeared and the scanty population is constantly thinning. Just this side of the Ocklawaha River, in the open range cattle country, the old-timers have recently heard their doom pronounced. The cattle must be fenced, which means the end of the old regime. A grand row has been raging there the past year, a Yankee family being whipped by the cattle men for not minding their own business, and I shall use the situation. Several of the old cattle men are 'kin' to the 'shiner families just across the river.

"There is no human habitation—there never has been and probably never will be—in the scrub itself. As far as I can determine, there is no similar section anywhere in the world. The scrub is a silent stretch enclosed by two rivers, deeply forested with Southern spruce (almost valueless), scrub oak, scrub myrtle and ti-ti, occasional gall-berry and black-jack and a few specialized shrubs and flowers, with 'islands' of long-leaf yellow pine. There is an occasional small lake with its attendant marsh or 'prairie.' The only settlement is here and there on these bodies of water, and along the river edges, where the natural hammock growth has been bitten into by the settlers' clearings. It is a fringe of life, following the waterways. The scrub is a vast wall, keeping out the timid and the alien.

"I have to go back again to stay another couple of weeks, for I need more information about the 'shining on the river of forty or fifty years ago, and the sources are of course scanty. I don't intend to dwell at any length on the past—the story will be one of the present—but I want to take the old woman of the book briefly through two or three generations of 'shining; it will indicate, as nothing else could do, the profound instincts that motivate the present generation. The 'shiner boy will be the chief protagonist.

"When I facetiously urged you not to bail me out if I was caught at the still, I wasn't too far off. Just the week before I went over to stay, a cousin of my 'shiner friend betrayed him, with two others, to the federal agents, and his still was torn up and burned. I had one experience I would not have missed for a great deal—a discussion of a group of the 'shiners and their friends, of various plans for dealing with the traitor. Nothing definite has been done to him yet, for reasons too involved to go into, but in one way and another they are closing in on him, and some day he will simply disappear.

"Possibly you wonder how I gain the confidence of these people without being a cold-blooded spy who intends to 'use' them. It is so easy for me to live their life with them, that I am in some danger of losing all sophistication and perspective. I feel hurried sometimes, as though I must get 'written out' in this country within the next few years, because so much is no longer strange or unusual to me. The life in the scrub is peculiarly right. While I was there, I did all the illegal things too; stalked deer with a light at night, out of season, kept the family in squirrels, paddled the boat while my friend dynamited mullet, shot limpkin on the river edge and had to wade waist deep in cypress swamp to get him (if you haven't eaten roast limpkin, you just haven't eaten, but you can go to county, state and federal jails for shooting them). But with food scarce, these people kill, quite correctly, I think, what they need. Incidentally, *only* what they need for food. The hunters with their licenses, on the other hand, kill a greater quantity during the legal season, and much of it is absolutely wasted—all of it entirely un-needed.

"I helped the old lady do her work, helped her wash her heavy quilts that had gone two years without washing, to her despair, because she had no help with them, and can no longer lift them alone from the water and get them on the line. (She cried when I left!) They live cleanly and decently, and have one sheet on the bottom of the bed. For cover, they use quilts, hand-pieced, of course, summer or winter. One bed had a counterpane instead, which the occupant used over him in place of sheet or quilt, and the phrase was used, 'to quilt with the counterpane. . . .'

. . . "Many expressions are very beautiful. The fish and deer, in fact most of the game, feed 'on the moon'—at moon-rise, moon-down, south-moon-over and south-moon-under. The people are conscious at all times of the position of the sun and moon and stars and wind. They *feel* the moon under the earth—south-moon-under. The simplicity of speech is most effective. Old Granny Brinson, whom we went to visit one night by way of row-boat down the river, described what you might call the state of consciousness between life and death. She answered the old lady's inquiry about her health, with the true and simple statement, 'I'm sick, Piety, an' dyin',' and told us of her 'spells': 'I go off into the twilight; into some lonesome-looking place.'

"The story is clear in my mind, and I am beginning the actual writing this week. Its success will depend, I should say, almost altogether on how real, how vivid, I am able to make the individuals whose lives move along with the 'shiner boy's. The background and small details are fool-proof, but tremendously hard work in delineating each character will be necessary to make the story anything like a reality. The final effect should be one of utter absorption in the people and their lives. For that reason, the title is giving me some difficulty. I don't like to call it 'Yonder in the Scrub,' as the Crackers in my own section do, for the title is detached, looking at the scrub from the outside. I want a complete submersion from the very beginning. An objective treatment, of course, but submersion. And I can't call it 'The Scrub' or 'Big Scrub,' simply, for the word to any reader in the country outside of Florida suggests foot-ball! It annoys me to work without a definite heading. . . ."

South Moon Under (the origin of the title is evident in the letter), the first fruits of that stay in the scrub, appeared early in 1933 in the blackest depths of the depression, just before the bank holiday. It was a selection of the Book-of-the-Month Club and was well received critically, but early 1933 was, certainly, about the worst moment possible for the appearance of a young writer's first novel. It is a fine book that deserved a better birthday and it is a pleasure to bring it back into print again. The writing lacks the finish that Marjorie Rawlings achieved in her later books, but the characters, in their integrity and vitality, are second to none that she created, and their lives, and the country itself, are wonderfully vivid and full of life in this portrayal.

The first mention of the book that was to become *The Yearling* occurs during the summer after the publication of *South Moon Under*. *The Yearling* is undoubtedly the best known and most loved of Marjorie Rawlings' books and perhaps the reader may be interested in the complex and often amusing story of its growth and evolution from idea to book.

Mr. Perkins wrote Mrs. Rawlings, rather mysteriously, that he had "another possible plan" for her "in connection with writing" about which he would like to speak with her when she next came north. She wrote back that "the only possible plan that I can conceive of your having for me 'in connection with writing,' would be that you'd like to have me do a text-book for your educational department on 'The Principle and Practice of Moonshine Liquor.' " This reply forced Mr. Perkins to reveal his plan, that between novels she might do a book for younger readers—something that would use material similar to that in the nature and hunting and fishing parts of *South Moon Under*, which would appeal to boys. She answered:

"I really didn't intend to bait you into telling me about your plan for me 'in connection with' writing—which, incidentally, is an entirely accurate phrase for what you have in mind! Such a book had never occurred to me. My first reaction was one of sheer distress, and then on second thought I was quite intrigued.

"Your suggestion has brought back a whole train of memories of my Washington childhood, that I hadn't thought of in years and years. They are memories of spring and summer evenings and nights when I sat on the cool stone steps of a Baptist church and told stories to the other children. We'd usually play our strenuous running games in the long twilight, and then when Tony the Italian lamp-lighter had

lit the red-glass gas lamps all along our street, we'd gather deliciously
close together on the church steps and I'd 'cut loose.' I can remember
very distinctly the feeling of smugness that came over me when one
of the youngsters would run up the street calling to any stragglers,
'Marjorie's going to tell stories!' and the hauteur with which I refused
to begin until everyone was there. There was a tumultuous Irish child
that shrieked and screamed if any of the details depressed him—particularly what I realize now must have been my very celebrated imita-
tion of a wolf howl. He got to be such a nuisance that I recall saying
sternly, 'You'll have to take Jimmy home now—there's going to be a
wolf in the next one.'

"It comes over me that I have always had a predilection for wolves
in a story. I believe I protested so your making me take a wolf out of
the scrub book, because it was really quite a serious repression! I think
I should almost be willing to do the book you speak of for the sole
purpose of getting in that wolf again.

"It really would be interesting to see if I could recapture whatever
quality it is that gives glamor to stories for the young mind. We'll
certainly have to talk about it. . . ."

Mrs. Rawlings then went to England, in part to get background
for her next novel, and when she returned in the fall, she was
undecided as to which book to do first, the novel or the boy's
book. Mr. Perkins advised the boy's book as being the shorter and
easier project and allowing her additional time for the novel to
ripen in her mind. Accordingly, she went to stay in the scrub with
an old hunter and his wife, and to listen to his stories of hunting
and life in earlier days. She wrote of this: "I hope you can see his
place someday—in the very core of the scrub where he has lived
since 1872—falling into decay under the exquisite mantle of flowering vines. They are hard put to it to make a living, principally
because the deer and foxes eat their crops almost faster than they
can raise them. They are in the forest preserve and are not allowed
to kill game. When I asked Mrs. Long what to bring with me she
chuckled and said, 'Something to eat.' . . ."

The visit was not altogether successful. The old man's stories
came slowly and the book did not take shape in Mrs. Rawlings'
mind. She wrote asking, how big a book—for children of what
age? Mr. Perkins replied, perhaps not really a book for children
but a book about a boy that both adults and children would enjoy,

such as *Kim,* or *Tom Sawyer.* Mrs. Rawlings retorted, "Do you realize how calmly you sit in your office and tell me to write a *classic?*" Meanwhile, the pressure of the novel was becoming greater and since the boy's book seemed to offer stubborn resistance, she set it aside and began work on the novel.

The novel, *Golden Apples,* was published in 1935 and proved less successful, perhaps because the author had not the same instinctive sympathy with the main character, a young Englishman, that she had with the country itself and the Crackers. That fall, somewhat let down after her struggle with what she termed "the inherent disharmonies" of *Golden Apples,* she wrote: "I don't know what to say about the boy's book. At the present I don't have the enthusiasm. Looking over my notes, my material seems thin. . . . I'll have to let it take its course." Not long after that came a short note, scrawled large in excitement: "The feeling for the boy's book, the particular thing I want to say, came to me. It will be a story *about* a boy—a brief and tragic idyll of boyhood . . . it would be a long story, say 50,000 words."

As Marjorie Rawlings set to work and gathered more material, *The Yearling* began to grow beyond her intentions. She worried whether she should try to hold it to her projected length or let it have its way, but it would not be held and she wrote: "I wanted to tell you that the material for the boy's story has been mounting. On two grand bear-hunts I have met another old pioneer who is full of animal and nature stories, and I have a growing pile of fascinating material. It only lacks the introduction of a few more characters than I had already conceived who will make their own plot as they go along—and I have had to resist them in the back of my mind as it was—to make a full book. . . . I am very happy in my material, Max, and by taking my time I feel sure I can do a very moving and harmonious piece of work. . . . Anyway it will simply have to be a full-length novel." Mr. Perkins replied: "Let the boy's book, as we call it—though I can see it may turn out not really to be that—take the form it ought to have, and then we'll study how it ought to be handled." There followed then these two letters, so illuminating of the writer-publisher relationship:

"Dear Max:

"I can see that you're disturbed about my feeling that I had better take full-length for the boy's book.

"It will positively be as we both first conceived of it. I have in front of me your letter of October 27, 1933. You say, 'I am thinking of a book about a boy.—A book about a boy and the life of the scrub is the thing we want.—It is those wonderful river trips and the hunting and the dogs and guns and the companionship of simple people who care about the same things which were included in *South Moon Under*—'.

"Until lately, I have had in mind one incident, almost, that would make a complete long-story in itself, about a boy. I wanted a bear-hunt in the story, for it fitted in with the other, and I have been prowling all over trying to find somebody who was actually bear-hunting, for I felt I had to see one to get what I want from it. By the merest accident, I met, and was taken into the confidence of, a perfectly marvelous old pioneer living on the St. John's river—the beautiful broad river I took the trip on [this trip is recorded in "Hyacinth Drift"], and which borders the scrub on the east side. This old man, a famous 'bad man,' but honorable and respected and at one time prosperous, too, took me bear-hunting twice, and in a few days I am going over to live a while with him and his wife and go hunting and fishing with him. So much material has come from my contact with him, and there is so much more there—anecdotes, hunting incidents, people— that I realized before I went to North Carolina that I had at hand a mass of stuff—and as always, the facts have suggested imaginary characters to me who fit in with the true ones—that couldn't possibly go in the simple 50,000 word narrative that I was ready to do. I had to resist constantly the thought of all these other things. . . .

"I don't want to write you about the actual stuff—I could talk to you for hours about it and not do harm. But if I try to express in a few sentences in a letter what I mean to do, it has a paralyzing effect— making the stuff *congeal* in a quickly-said form, when I want to take all those pages and pages of a book to say it. I can't sum it up like a review, without spoiling my pleasure in working it out right. But the short narrative I had in mind will make my culminating point—my climax and my point, and a very stirring point it is, too.

"It will be absolutely all told through the boy's eyes. He will be about twelve, and the period will not be a long one—not more than two years. I want it through his eyes before the age of puberty brings in any of the other factors to confuse the simplicity of viewpoint. It will be a book boys will love, and if it is done well enough otherwise, the people who liked South Moon will like it too. It is only since Golden Apples that I realize what it is about my writing that people like. I don't mean that I am writing *for* anyone, but now I feel free to luxuriate in the simple details that interest me, and that I have been so amazed to find interested other people—probably just from the element of sincerity given by my own interest and sympathy. . . .

"Now please don't write me another of those restrained 'You must do it as seems right to you' notes. Tell me what is really in your mind."

"Dear Marjorie:

"We seem to have got into confusion about the boy's book. Those sentences from my letter that you quote are exactly the way I have always thought of it, but when I write in that do-as-it-seems-right-to-you way, it is because it has always been my conviction—and I do not see how anyone could dispute the rightness of it—that a book must be done according to the writer's conception of it as nearly perfectly as possible, and that the publishing problems begin then.—That is, the publisher must not try to get a writer to fit the book to the conditions of the trade, etc. It must be the other way round. I know that you think this yourself. . . . But I do feel sure that you have the best possible idea of the book, and I do think that the rivers, the hunting adventures, the characters, and the ways of life, ought all to be in. I know that a writer ought not to give summaries of what he means to do, and that with some, even telling the story and talking about it, makes it so that they cannot write it. It is often that way, and it is not hard to see why. But I have the most complete confidence in the quality of this book. I would not be a bit surprised if it were the best book you have done, and it might well be the most successful. . . ."

From here on *The Yearling* went forward steadily. The author says: "Max, I am going simply delirious with delight in my material as the boy's book takes shape in my mind. The most delicious people are in it. Wait till you see Grandma Hutto. A little impudent, infidel, sharp-spoken thing with gold circle earrings and Spanish or Minorcan blood who scandalized the staid inhabitants of the scrub and who tells the boy wise and impudent things. . . . I am very happy and confident about it as it forms. None of the fear and torment of *Golden Apples.* . . ."

It is perhaps the author's joy in her work which carries through to the reader so strongly the vitality of the characters and the gusto one feels in their hard and dangerous lives. There is much hardship and sorrow and tragedy in the book, but here, possibly more than in any other of her books, Marjorie Rawlings has conveyed the quality of these people who drew her sympathy—their gal-lantry, their grace of spirit and the joy in living that they find in lives which appear, in the facts, to be merely bitter struggles for survival.

The Yearling had an immediate and widespread success when it was published in 1938, and was the Pulitzer Prize Novel of that year. It has been read in translation all the way round the world. At home it seems to be comfortably established in the literature of America, partly for its contribution to our knowledge of our own country, but most of all as "a story about a boy." The chapters here included form a particularly satisfactory narrative unit. They give the true flavor of the book and introduce us to the main characters.

Cross Creek, published in 1942, is in essence a long love-letter to a place and the people who live there, the place which became so truly Marjorie Rawlings' home, and of which she wrote three years after coming to live there: "My past years have become somehow unimportant to me. They are a shadow, against the satisfying substance which is life in the heart of the Florida hammock." *Cross Creek* is a collection of essays, character sketches, narratives and short stories written and accumulated over a period of many years, always with the idea of this special book in her mind. It is truly a labor of love and, as such books generally are, is a delight to read. It is warm, full of laughter, of outrageous and touching characters and of the exotic beauty of the Florida interior.

It is clear that the scrub and the hammock and, above all, their inhabitants, the Florida Crackers, were the well-spring of Marjorie Rawlings' inspiration and the lodestone of her writing talent. The best of her writing is that which is close to this land and to these people whom she understood so deeply because of her love for them. Through her they have gained a place in the literature of their country, and through them that literature has been enriched by the achievement of an outstanding writer.

SOUTH MOON UNDER

South Moon
Under

I

NIGHT entered the clearing from the scrub. The low tangled growth of young oak and pine and palmetto fell suddenly black and silent, seeming to move closer in one shadowy spring. The man told himself there was nothing to fear. Yet as he walked towards his cabin, naked and new on the raw sand, darkness in this place seemed to him unfriendly.

He thought, "Time I get me a fence raised tomorrow, maybe 'twon't seem so wild, like."

Light still hung raggedly above the hammock west of the cleared acres. Here and there a palm shook its head against the faint orange of the sky, or the varnished small leaves of a live oak were for a moment luminous. There was an instant when the hammock reared back against the west; when the outline of each tree-top was distinct; when the clearing gathered about it the shreds of twilight. Then there was no longer scrub or clearing or hammock. Blackness obliterated them with a great velvet paw and crouched like a panther on the cabin doorstep.

The man tested the security of the split rails that formed a temporary pen about his hogs. The grey mule was hobbled and the scrub milch cow tethered. The chickens clacked and fluttered in the coop that must hold them until a proper roost was built. After the fence was raised, they could all run free. He stood by the coop a moment. His thoughts stirred uneasily in his mind, milling like the fowls. He could not be sure that he had done well to move his family here, across the river. He had not made a good

3

living in the piney-woods. Only the knowledge of his native Florida wife and of his neighbours, her kin, had kept him to the few crops that would yield on that grey shifting land. His family of five was of an age now to help with the crops. He had exchanged pine-land for scrub, with a precarious fringe of hammock.

The Florida scrub was unique. The man Lantry recognized its quality as well as its remoteness. There was perhaps no similar region anywhere. It was a vast dry rectangular plateau, bounded on three sides by two rivers. The Ocklawaha, flowing towards the north, bounded it on the west. At the north-west corner of the rectangle the Ocklawaha turned sharply at right angles and flowed due east, joining, at the north-east corner, the St. Johns River which formed the eastern demarcation.

Within these deep watery lines the scrub stood aloof, uninhabited through its wider reaches. The growth repelled all human living. The soil was a tawny sand, from whose parched infertility there reared, indifferent to water, so dense a growth of scrub pine—the Southern spruce—that the effect of the massed thin trunks was of a limitless, canopied stockade. It seemed impenetrable, for a man-high growth of scrub oak, myrtle, sparkleberry and ti-ti filled the interstices. Wide areas, indeed, admitted of no human passage.

In places the pines grew more openly, the sunlight filtered through and patches of ground showed bald and lichened. The scrub was sparingly dotted with small lakes and springs. Around these grew a damp-loving hammock vegetation. Or a random patch of moisture produced, alien in the dryness, a fine stand of slash pine or long-leaf yellow. These were known as pine islands. To any one standing on a rise, they were visible from a great distance.

The scrub rolled towards its boundaries like a dark sea. It cast itself against the narrow beach of swamp and hammock that fringed the rivers. The two types of growth did not mingle, as though an ascetic race withdrew itself from a tropical one and refused to inter-breed. The moisture along the rivers gave a footing for the lush growth of cypress in the swamp; of live oak, magnolia, hickory, ash, bay, sweet gum and holly that made up the adjoining hammock.

The western edge of the scrub plateau was high. The Ockla-waha ran forty or fifty feet below, so that its scrubside bank rose from the river swamp in a steep ledge. Here Lantry had come, clearing land in the narrow strip of hammock along the top of the ridge. The scrub adjoining in front of his cabin had been recently burned over by forest fire. The bush was young and low and he could see across it for a mile or two.

He had high hopes of the hammock soil. He had a deeper hope of what should pass for security; a sense of safety achieved through isolation. For ten miles, north or south, there were no other settlers. Behind him the river ran, deep-banked and swift of current. Before him lay the scrub. Miles on miles of scrub rolled impenetrable between his clearing and the rising sun and moon.

He picked up a gourd foaming with the night's milk and moved to the house. Light from a fat-wood hearth fire flickered through the small-paned windows on three sides of the cabin. He lifted the wooden shoestring latch of the door. The clatter of cooking utensils on the clay hearth, bitten into by the snapping of the fire, was the only sound in the room. The woman, the three boys and two girls seemed frozen, waiting for his return, like a vixen and her litter in a den. They stirred to life as he closed the door and handed the gourd to his daughter Piety.

"Ol' cow know she's done been moved," he commented. "Didn't give no more'n the half o' what she belongs to give."

Relaxing, they looked at him where he stood massive across the door. The man Lantry was tall and bulky. He was red-brown, full-bearded. There was a stiffness about his beard and hair, so that the firelight darting across them gave the effect of sunlight on brown pine needles. His eyes were red-brown, deep-sunk like pools of cypress water. He made on strangers an instant impression of violence, but no one in the country could report him as anything but quiet.

The Lantry woman was small and fox-faced. She sat on her haunches before the fire, her long nose pointed over a black Dutch oven steaming with squirrel stew. Her scant streaked hair was twisted in a tight knob at the nape of her neck. Now and then she lifted a claw-like hand to smooth a wisp back of her ear. She turned her head to Lantry over her shoulder.

"You jest as good to put your 'baccy back in your pocket," she said, "for supper's that near done hit'll be to spit out and waste."

He continued to pare a shaving from his twist.

He said, "A short chaw's twicet as good as a long un."

The boys dragged straight wooden benches and split hickory chairs from against the walls to make seats along a rough deal table. The girls laid the table with a red cloth, white English crockery and heavy knives and spoons. They handed plates to their mother, which she filled with the stew, with soft-cooked grits and white-flour biscuits. The yield of corn had been poor the previous summer across the river and they had long since been out of meal. They drank heartily of thick coffee, thrice boiled since morning. The sugar, of their own making, was brown and sticky but of good flavour.

There was little talk while they ate, but the meal was shot through with excitement. There had been cold lunches eaten at the clearing while they worked on the house, but this was the first family supper cooked on the new hearth. This was to be the first night of sleeping in the scrub. They were here at last to stay, yet the place seemed more unfamiliar than before. The accustomed dishes were strange. They had moved in actual distance no more than twenty-five miles. But they had crossed the river into the scrub. The clear dark stream divided one world from another.

Mrs. Lantry was the first to finish. She was insensitive to change, so long as the major matters of food and bed were not interfered with. She sat at the end of the table nearest the fireplace, her hands folded in her lap, until the others should be done with their plates. The boys had bolted their meal. They teetered back in their chairs, seeing who could lean the farthest. Young Thaddeus suddenly spilled backwards, and the older two, Zeke and Abner, were on him like terriers. The woman had no interest in their tumblings. Lantry laughed aloud, wiping the red mouth above his beard with the back of his hand.

The girl Piety said, "Them crazies!"

Her look darted from the wrestling boys to the father; to the mother. She was alert to their thoughts.

She said to her sister Martha, "Wouldn't we ketch it, iffen we was to toss and mess that-a-way!"

The mother said, " 'Tain't mannerly, no-ways."

"Sho, hit's good for young uns," Lantry said.

He rose from the table and moved his chair close to the hearth. He stirred the coals, adding a log of live oak, and spat into the fire. His wife scraped the plates, opening the door a crack to put out the scraps for the hound whimpering outside. The girls laid away the red cloth and washed the few dishes in a pan on the table.

The boys threw themselves on the rough pine floor before the hearth, watching the flames. The girl Piety went to the east window and pressed her forehead against the pane. She stood some time, looking out into the blackness of the late winter night.

Lantry asked, "What you studyin', Py-tee?"

"Nothin'. Lookin' to see is there ary thing to study."

"You look out. You might r'aly see you somethin'."

Mrs. Lantry said, "She wouldn't keer no-ways. She's a perfeckly cur'ous young un."

Young Thaddeus spoke eagerly.

"Pa, what-all you reckon's here in the scrub? Varmints and snakeses and sich?"

The man looked long into the fire before he spoke. His red-brown beard shone. Thoughts beyond the immediate question rippled across the deep pools of his eyes. Piety watched him closely, her eyes small and bright. He answered slowly.

"I dunno. I dunno what-all's here. The same as on 'tother side o' the river, is what I been tole. B'ar, likely, same as there. Catty-mounts and lynxes and wild cats. Ol' man Wilson, your daddy," he nodded at his wife, "done tole me there was oncet hundreds o' wolves, quare-lookin' and pieded."

The boys fidgeted in delight.

The woman said with some animation, "I mind me o' him tellin' all that. Him and the ol' timers say there were a day when 'twa'nt safe to dress a beef in the woods and tote it home alone."

Abner said belligerently, "They ain't no wolves now. Leastways they ain't none in the piney-woods yonder."

Lantry nodded. "That's it. Ol' man Wilson said one day the wolves was here, hundreds. The next day they was gone. Jest plumb gone. No man kin say where they goed. They mought o' died o' some sort o' plague. Folkses mought o' got too thick for 'em here in Floridy and they mought o' taken out one night and goed off to Texas."

He stroked his beard.

"They's mighty leetle here to harm a man."

There was a defiance in his voice. There was something underneath what he said, Piety thought, like a trout thrashing around under what seemed still water.

He said, "A panther kin worry a man. I wouldn't want no panther trailin' me nor trackin' me. But they ain't attackded much more'n young uns, when it comes to humans. I ain't much afeerd of a b'ar. A wild hog's bad, now, and rattlesnakes."

He was talking aloud to himself. He rose from his chair and paced up and down the room, his chin sunk in his beard, his hands behind his back. His voice was heavy in the room, like thunder.

"The worst things I knows of is rattlesnakes and some kinds o' people. And a rattlesnake minds his own matters if he ain't bothered. A man's got a right to kill ary thing, snake or man, comes messin' up with him."

Piety thought, "He's afeerd o' somethin'. Somebody interferin'."

It chilled her, that Lantry was afraid.

Mrs. Lantry said, "I'd orter be piecin'. You gals had orter be piecin'." She said after a moment, "I'm too wore out, movin' over and all, for piecin'."

The family was silent. Thought of the change was a common holding. Lantry and the woman and the boys and girls drew close to one thought. It was a smouldering fire among them. Now and then a fresh blaze flamed into speech. Each one fed a few words to the fire.

Zeke said, "I reckon ever'thing's a mite different."

Abner said, "Seems to me they's cat-squirrels this side o' the river, 'stead o' fox-squirrels."

"You kin lay to it, they's a reason," Lantry said. "You jest don't know the reason yit."

Mrs. Lantry said, "You-all kin set up if you're a mind to. I'm fixin' to git into the bed. I be wore out."

She let down her streaked thin hair and braided it over her sharp shoulders. Her nose was peaked between the braids.

Abner said in a low voice, "Ma looks somethin' like a varmint with her hair that-a-way."

Zeke and Thaddeus guffawed. The woman gathered a swift vixenish energy to slap the boy across the face.

"You be mannerly, you!"

Lantry frowned.

"You boys turn your backs now while the girls gits undressed."

Piety and Martha took off their garments as far as cotton undershifts; slipped on muslin gowns with long sleeves and high necks; plaited their soft young hair like their mother's. Mrs. Lantry undressed.

"Ary one want to wash their feet?"

The day's work had been cleanly. Feet were not soiled. Mrs. Lantry padded about on bare soles with a hand basin of warm water from the black iron kettle on the hearth. Each took a turn at washing face and hands with the coarse washrag. Lantry and the boys undressed as far as their undersuits; stretched their toes, cramped from heavy home-made cowhide boots, before the fire. Lantry and his wife went into the adjoining room and between quilts into a large pine bed. The girls followed into the same room, taking a smaller bed at the other end. The boys were left, three to the one bed, in the main room of the cabin. They called luxuriously to their sisters, thrashing their cold feet under the covers.

"Py-tee! Marthy! We got the farr! You-all never figgered on the farr!"

Mrs. Lantry called wearily, "You boys shut your mouths now. The girls is warm as you."

The fire crackled. The light played jerkily over the high new rafters. The Lantrys were warm under thick hand-pieced quilts. Mrs. Lantry snored thinly, like a cat. There was no other sound but the sputtering fat-wood.

In the night Lantry awakened with a start. The chickens were cackling in alarm. The hound, huddled under the doorstep, was rumbling. The man threw on his jacket, examined his 11-gauge muzzle-loader and went out of the cabin into the yard. The hound crouched close at his heels. The chickens quieted as he came to the coop. The night was chill and black. He could see nothing. He walked around the house, wishing that he had brought a fat-wood splinter torch. The hound reared against him, licking his hand. Whatever the intruder, it was of little consequence. He felt his way to the front stoop. A small figure in a long white gown stood there.

"That you, Py-tee?" He knew in the night that it was she. "The night airs 'll do for you, child."

"I wanted to see what-all were stirrin' out here."

She walked down from the stoop, her bare feet white against the sand. She stood by him, close under his shoulder, her arms crossed over her thin breast, shivering. They listened together.

"You wa'n't afeerd to foller me, Py-tee?"

"I wa'n't no-ways afeerd."

As they stood, the blackness dissolved. The sky was a mass of stars, close and bright. The starlight spread towards the earth, so that as they watched, the chicken coop was visible. The thick line of hammock behind the clearing moved in sight. Stars clustered about the chimney-top like silver bees in swarm.

The girl said, "The longer you studies, the more you kin see in the dark, like."

He turned her ahead of him into the house.

" 'Twa'n't nothin' out here but a varmint. A 'possum or sich arter the chicks. They needs a roost."

The man looked at the straight figure, diminutive in the long gown.

He said softly, "Leetle ol' scrawny cur'ous young un."

Over his shoulder, closing the door, the cabin stood in the

clearing like a house on an island. He thought that he heard the river running below the ledge. The river was a wall for his back. In front of the clearing the scrub rolled in, lapping at the edges of the bare sand like a vast sea.

II

A<small>N HOUR</small> before sunrise the girl Piety was awakened by the throaty cries of hoot-owls. The great night-birds had seldom sounded in the piney-woods. The bare pines were not to their liking. They preyed on small creatures that fed in the richness of marsh and hammock. Their cry was stirring, like a thick sob. It rose in a rhythmic crescendo of four major notes, subsiding in agony in a minor key.

It had a pattern and a tune. It was, strangely, a dance step. A bass fiddle was playing a schottische. Piety had seen a man and woman from Virginia dance the schottische. Slowly; one-two-three-four. And then a quick running step; *one-two-three!*

She slipped from the bed and dressed fumblingly in the darkness. She laid a fire in the main room, blowing the embers to life under fresh fat-wood splinters. The boys breathed heavily in their bed. The coffee pot was empty of liquid and she added new coffee and water from the kettle to the stale grounds. In the bedroom behind her she could hear her mother creaking from the bed. Lantry's deep voice sounded in a question.

The girl hurried from the cabin. Voices would soon populate the rooms. The sun would fill the earth with the sounds of birds and creatures. Men would come shortly after sunrise to help Lantry raise his fences. Women would bring food and gossip; children would run across the clearing. There was a need for hurry. For a few moments she could listen to the hoot-owls, vibrant in the grey daylight.

As the slow light felt its way towards the house, she saw the scrub recede, as though darkness were going out like a tide. It was the hammock that was black now. The scrub unrolled towards the east in mist-filled valleys. The thin young pines and palmettos were no taller than she. She could look far across them to the horizon, pink and purple like the petunias they had brought with them to plant. She was startled—where she looked, the scrub was moving. The motion was almost imperceptible, yet the pines before her had changed their position. Against the east appeared a set of antlers; another. The smooth unhorned heads of does lifted in the mist. Piety ran across the clearing into the house. She cried out to the Lantrys.

"I seed deer! A hull mess o' deer! 'Most as many as cattle!"

They stared at her, absorbed with the day's beginning. Abner guffawed.

"A body'd figger you r'aly seed somethin'," he said. "Deer's plentiful."

Lantry stretched his long legs, lacing his boots by the morning fire.

"Hit's one thing to know," he said, "and 'tother thing to see. You kin know deer's plentiful all your life-time, but it ain't like seein' 'em clustered-like, the way Py-tee jest done."

She looked at him with bright eyes, breathing quickly. She had heavy lids, like a turtle's. They moved up and down over the direct hazel-coloured eyes. Her hair was hazel-brown. It still hung in the night's plaitings. Slowly, looking into the fire, she unbraided it. Mrs. Lantry was frying hot cakes on a long oval griddle propped on bricks over the flames. The smell of lard and batter and coffee was sweet in the room. Piety forgot the deer.

The fire on the hearth was golden in the sunlight that came in through the front windows. The room was quick with the vibrancy of change. The night's sleep had made the place familiar. The Lantrys had slept in their own beds in this house and it became overnight their home. The woman and her children accepted the cabin, as squirrels accept a nest in new feeding grounds. Only Lantry paced up and down the room before he went about his chores, his chin sunk in his beard.

The boys fed the chickens in their coop; the mule and cow at their stakes. The feed was a coarse corn fodder. The animals were fed from troughs hand-hewn from cypress. Lantry milked the cow. He leaned his face against her warm flank, his long fingers rippling over the teats. She was a heifer with her first calf, and skittish. He spoke to her now and then, his voice deep in his beard.

Piety and Martha tidied the cabin, hanging garments on nails behind the doors. They swept the floors with a new broom-sage sweep. The old palmetto broom had been left behind, for it was unlucky to move it. Mrs. Lantry busied herself with the day's dinner. She had protested the day of the fence-raising as coming too soon after the move. She had had no time to bake and stew. Lantry was anxious to fence, and sent the word up and down the river, ignoring her.

He said, "Folkses 'll carry rations."

"I don't want to be scarce with the table," she said.

The Wilsons, Mrs. Lantry's kin, appeared at the river end of the clearing before Piety had the stoop swept. They had come by rowboat across the river. The hammock immediately behind the house had been cleared as far as the top of the steep river bank. The Wilsons' heads bobbed abruptly over the edge of the clearing, as though they had been in hiding all night behind the ledge. They walked splay-footed, bent a little forward, pushing against the shifting soil. The women carried baskets among them. They were dressed in neat cotton prints with large hats of woven palmetto strands. The men wore their ordinary boots and breeches or blue denim trousers.

They hailed Lantry with reserve. The tall massive man who had walked with great strides into their section some twenty years before and had married their kinswoman was still unknown to them. They did not have with him the ease of intercourse they had among themselves. The women went into the house. Piety lingered at her sweeping on the stoop. The men in the yard called, "Howdy, Miss Py-tee," and she answered, "Howdy."

Old man Wilson said, watching Lantry at a pile of cypress slats ready for the fencing, "I favors a split-rail fence myself. Good heart pine."

Lantry said, pointing, "I got split rails laid out yonder. I aim to fence the yard with slats and split-rail the rest. I like a yard fenced in so's a stranger cain't jest step over."

Wilson nodded. "That's a good idee. A man kin step over a split-rail fence."

They handled the wood, discussing grain and quality. The men meandered about the clearing, making free comment. The scrub was unknown to many of them who had seldom crossed the river. They remarked the sharpness of the line where hammock ended and scrub began. Spudd Wilson hunted here.

He said, "Hit's the river. Hammock follers the water. Here's the river and the swamp and the bank. Hit's plentiful wet. The hammock follers the wet. First foot you gits away from the river damp, and into the white sand and the sand soaks, nothin' won't make exscusin' palmeeters and that sorry pine."

Jack Wilson said, spitting, "And rattlesnakes."

They guffawed, their mouths wide.

"I mean!"

Old man Wilson said, "I don't like the scrub. This hammock piece here is fine ground, and game plentiful. But I wouldn't keer to live with the scrub shuttin' me in this-a-way." He added profoundly, "But it's ever' man to his taste. I got nothin' to say."

The sun was an hour high before other families reached the clearing from Big Saw Grass, Tobacco Patch Landing, Turner Farm, Mill Creek and Moss Bluff. They came largely by river. The Lantry landing at the foot of the bluff was boggy and the visitors arrived with wet and mucky shoes. The women and girls sat down in the yard and took off their shoes and stockings with relief. They were accustomed to going with bare feet about their own homes. It was good to stretch their broad strong toes in the clean sand. Piety placed their shoes in a row. They walked with curiosity through the cabin. Many expressed disappointment that Mrs. Lantry had nothing new in the way of chairs or tables; that the windows were bare of curtains and that there was no kitchen. She was not offended.

" 'Tain't nothin' special," she agreed, "but we kin make out 'til the crops gits a-goin'."

Piety led them outside to the western wall. The two windows here had no panes, but were fitted with wooden shutters that could be swung to at night.

She told them, "Pa promises faithful when the spring crops is made, him and the boys'll put a blow-way here and another bed-room to the side and a kitchen yonder."

They approved the prospect.

"Hain't nothin' like a kivered blow-way for comfort."

"Yes," Ella Martin complained, "but the men-folks keeps 'em so littered with their contraptions, their ol' trapses and sich, they ain't no room hardly to set and shell peas."

"Well, when the guns and the trapses gits too thick, I pitches 'em off the place," Annie Wilson said.

"Yes, and Annie wouldn't be past pitchin' off the men their-selves."

They laughed together in a soft cackling. The woman Annie Wilson laughed with them with a rich sound. She was heavily built, deep-voiced and deep-breasted. Her hair grew thick and low, the shining black of gallberries. There was a dark down on her upper lip and on her large arms. She took everything com-fortably, as it came. Piety darted her quick look from Annie to the others. She thought that it was easy to distinguish the women who did field work from those who did not. The women who helped their men to plough, to hoe, to cultivate, to harvest, were stripped gaunt and lean, stringy as an overworked horse. Only the women of more casual natures, like Annie Wilson, or of better circumstances, like the Fikes and Jacklin women, grew stout in middle age.

At eight o'clock late-comers came in wagons from Ft. McCoy, Orange Springs and Eureka. They had crossed the river by ferry at the Springs and by bridge at Eureka. They plodded up the sandy road that bordered the river between scrub and hammock. They found the fence-raising in full swing. The men joined the others already at work. Twenty-five or thirty men and boys swarmed about the split rails, the gates, the stakes and the posts that were to put the mark of civilisation on the clearing.

They worked leisurely, stopping short, dropping their hands to boast of strength and speed; to tell a derisive anecdote of one of them. Yet while they were in movement they worked deftly. When Mrs. Lantry was occupied, Piety slipped away to watch the men. The fencing of fields was of greater interest than house matters. The slat fence about the yard went slowest. A group of six, familiar with such a style of fencing, toiled most of the day at the smaller area. Post-holes were dug, posts driven deep, slats nailed between with square nails and at last, breast high to Lantry, a flat top was nailed on for finish. These men worked quietly. The job was exacting.

Most of the men worked at the split-rail fences around the cleared fields. The type of fence was familiar to the youngest boy and it went up rapidly. Lantry and his sons, labouring all of their spare time for two years, had wrestled twenty acres of ground clear of the jungle hammock. Now in a little while, between sun and sun, a handful of men was shutting it in.

They tussled with the grey, seasoned wood, but there was an abandon in the familiar motions. They sweat and jostled and jested and threw a fence carelessly about what had been so recently a virgin wood. The fence went in a zig-zag pattern. The eye of old Wilson, overseeing, was true. Where men piled the rail-ends at the corners, interlacing them like the fingers of two hands, there became evident an undeviating straightness.

Some of the women left the house and came to the fields to watch. Piety trailed them. Annie Wilson climbed ponderously into a wagon to look down the fence line, which wavered insolently, like a drunken man, along the pushed-back edge of hammock. The men dropped the rails to watch her, large and rich and black-headed. She put her hands on her broad hips.

"How we comin', Annie?" they bellowed.

She bellowed back at them.

"A heap neater'n I figgered you'd git it!"

They roared with laughter.

"Looks jest like feather-stitchin'," she called, "dogged if it don't."

Mo Jacklin yelled, "You come take a hand, Annie, see kin you feather-stitch with split pine!"

She eased her heavy body over the wagon wheels and rested

a hand on Piety's shoulder as she jumped. She ran to the men on small agile feet. Her teeth were white in her dark face. Beads of sweat were like crystals across her forehead and her downy upper lip. She lifted an armful of rails and hurled them at the men. They warded them off or dodged them or caught them from her in the air.

"I'll feather," she panted, "and you-all kin stitch!"

Spudd Wilson protested, doubling up with laughter, "Iffen you'd please to feather with somethin' light, Ma'am——"

Old man Fikes, her uncle, broke a switch from a myrtle bush.

He said, "Annie, it's been thirty yare since I whopped you when you was a young un, and you 'bout four time the size you was then. But dogged if I ain't man enough to do hit agin. You git back to the women-folks and leave the men raise their fences."

She left them, turning a broad amiable back. Mo Jacklin called after her.

"When we're ready to stake and rider, come on back, Annie, and set on top o' the stakes and they'll be no need o' drivin' 'em."

She joined the women, puffing and chuckling. Most of them were pale and quiet. Her robustness was a rank growth, like a huge ragweed flowering in a worn-out field. The thin women dropped their eyes.

Ella Martin said querulously, "Iffen you worked hard as I do, Annie Wilson, you'd have no strength left for sich foolishness."

Annie linked her arm in Piety's and they walked together to the yard. Piety saw her mother's face sharpen. The long nose seemed to grow more pointed. Mrs. Lantry reproached her cousin.

"I'll say to your face, Annie, what I'll say behind your back. 'Tain't mannerly no-ways to go scaperin' acrost to the men-folks that-a-way."

The big woman laughed.

"I always gives them fellers as good as they sends," she said. "They perfeckly enjoys it," she added complacently.

The women called in some of the younger boys to help lay plank tables on the south side of the house. Romping children and sprawling babies were pushed aside to make room. Mrs. Lantry brought out a long white tablecloth. The others protested its use.

"No use lettin' them dirty men smutty it."

Gratified, she sent Piety to return it to her trunk in the bedroom. The guests had brought more food than twice their number could eat. Each woman flushed with satisfaction over her splint hickory basket as the others insisted she had brought too much. Mrs. Lantry was providing pork backbone and rice for the crowd. The last of the winter's butchering had been done before leaving the west side of the river. Sausage casings had been stuffed and given a first smoking. Hams and shoulders and sidemeat had been put down in barrels of salt brine. The fresh backbones were simmering in the black iron wash-pot, the smell sweet and heavy on the thin March air. As the sun rose high, rice was added. Piety was told to stir the pot.

Annie Wilson said, "Leave Marthy do it. Then mought be she'd git Syl Jacklin to he'p."

Mrs. Lantry said, "I don't aim to encourage Marthy courtin'. She ain't but sixteen."

Annie said easily, "I'd buried me a man time I were seventeen. Sho, Py-tee here ain't too young—what you, honey, fifteen? Leastwise, to make a beginnin'. Twelve ain't too young jest to let the boys come a-settin' around. A gal young un o' twelve's mighty near growed."

"Well, mought be, but Marthy's my big he'p in the house. Py-tee's a purely willin' worker, but she's the biggest crazy for field work. Always a-follerin' her daddy to the field, totin' a hoe since she were so-big."

Ella Martin said, "Lantry's lucky. Them boys is big enough to take out for theirselves. 'Twon't be too long 'til they're done gone. Iffen Py-tee's a good hand in the field, I say, Lantry's lucky."

The women warmed up to their talk as the day warmed. They buzzed and clacked as they spread out the food, tasting one another's samples. Dinner was not at noon, because the men found that by working steadily they could raise the fences without dividing the day in two.

"Le's be done when we be done," old man Wilson suggested. "I aim to eat hearty when I sets down to eat, and they ain't a mite o' pleasure in eatin' good and then carryin' your pore full belly to the field agin."

Young boys carried river water to the workers. The new-split rails were spotted with the sweat of men. Hands were blistered and splintered. The lean tanned faces were grimy from a constant wiping away of moisture. There was no more jesting. The work went doggedly. The rails swung into place at the end of long arms, precisely, rapidly. There was no pause except to drink from hollow gourds or to bite off a fresh mouthful of tobacco.

The women nursed their babies, the breasts hot and pendulous. The babies slept. Children whimpered and were quieted with sips of water and squares of cake, yellow with eggs and strong with meat-drippings. At half-past three the men plodded in from the north-east corner. The clearing was girdled with good fence. The mark of order was on the Lantry lands. The men washed their hands and faces, rubbing their hair with damp towels. They went to the plank tables and seated themselves. Lantry towered over them. The sun glinted in his eyes and beard. He cleared his throat.

"Men," he said, "I cain't eat a bite without I say I'm powerful proud to have me a noble fence like this un. I'm much obliged to you all, I'm shore." He hesitated. "Ary time I kin do the same for ary man he'ped me, I'll be proud to have him call on me."

The words were a fixed form. Piety saw that they tortured him. His teeth were tight together; the muscles in his neck constricted. All he asked was that these men go away now and leave him alone. Old man Wilson, helping himself to a fried squirrel head before he sat down, answered for the others.

"That's jest all right, son Lantry. Proud to he'p, and you'll be called on, never fear."

The women served the food, hurrying around the tables with hunched shoulders, bending a little forward from years of walking in the sand. They had put on their shoes again for the occasion. There was a hesitancy in beginning, although several had filled their mouths.

Mrs. Lantry said uncomfortably, "Reckon somebody had orter give thanks——"

"I'll ask the blessin'," Mo Jacklin proffered gravely.

He rolled his eyes and nudged Spudd Wilson. He bowed his head.

> *"Good God, with a bounty*
> *Look down on Marion County,*
> *For the soil is so pore, and so awful rooty, too,*
> *I don't know what to God the pore folks gonna do."*

There was a silence, a lifting of heads. Spudd Wilson covered his mouth to stifle a gulp of mirth. Young Johnny Martin giggled and poked Piety, standing behind him with a plate of biscuits. Annie Wilson's broad shoulders shook. Most of the women were vaguely horrified, looking at one another. They sat down with the men.

"That's a powerful quare-soundin' blessin'," Ella Martin complained. "Don't know as it's safe to eat under the sign o' sich foolishness."

The men came stoutly to Mo's defense, shovelling in fried chicken, pork backbone and rice, sausage, beans, grits, corn pone and biscuit.

"Ary thanks for rations is good thanks," said old Fikes. "I figger the Lord know when a man's thankful, and He ain't a-goin' to snatch the victuals outen his gullet jest account o' he don't mention 'em ser'ous."

"I mean! When a feller ain't proud to set down to table, and plenty on it, time to git worried over what-all God's fixin' to do to him."

"Pass me the rabbit stew," Annie Wilson said. She helped herself generously. "I'm a slave to rabbit."

The women, for all their leanness, ate as much as the men. Talk increased as the eating grew slow. They were labouring at the food. The men picked and chose among the desserts; pound cake, lard cake, sweet potato pone, pies of canned blueberries and peaches, wild orange preserves, guava paste and cassava pudding.

"Must be I got a bait," Mo Jacklin said, "I be gittin' kind o' pertickler."

The men drifted away from the tables. The women scraped plates indolently. Groups of men squatted on their haunches on the shady side of the stoop, others sat on the edge with legs suspended, chatting idly. Clusters of boys threw knives at the young live-oak at the northwest corner of the house. The well-aimed blades quivered in the wood.

Ella Martin called, "You boys'll kill that tree."

Piety said quickly, "They ain't barkin' it none."

The crowd was replete. Here and there a man lay back on the sand, his hat over his eyes, and dozed. The smaller children slept inside the house, curled like kittens on the beds and on quilts on the floor. Their dirty bare feet twitched. Now and then a woman came in quietly to look at them. In the late afternoon a southerly breeze brought a sound from the road. Piety heard it first and pulled at her father's sleeve. Lantry lifted his hand.

"Be still!" he said.

Spudd Wilson winked.

"I figgered them fellers'd be moseyin' along 'bout now."

"Who is it?" Ella Martin asked. "Sounds like a wagon."

Spudd said, "Willy Saunders and Buck Hinson and them."

The crowd stirred. The men sat upright. The women fluttered like disturbed hens. Mrs. Lantry spoke indignantly.

"Them Moss Bluff rowdies!"

"Easy, daughter!" Old man Wilson lifted his eyebrows at her. "They likely bein' sociable. They got the same right as ary man to be friendly."

Lantry listened closely, his eyes fixed on the blue haze across the river, as though the approaching sound might be of men from distant hills. The creaking of wheels came closer. As the wagon emerged from the forest growth, the men riding on high seats waved wide black felt hats and called lustily.

"Hi-yuh! How's the work a-comin'?"

Lantry walked to the new gate to meet them. The others straggled after him. He hailed the wagon.

"Git down, men, and come in."

The newcomers were four: Saunders, Hinson and two strangers. They were markedly of a different breed from the men who watched them jump down from their seats. They were more heavily built and swarthier, as though a thicker blood ran through them. Not all the men knew them. Spudd Wilson greeted them in the casual tone of intimacy.

"You-all's right peert gittin' to a fence-raisin'. Fence is done raised."

"That's good news, boys." Saunders cocked his head at his companions. "We studied on the correck time to go to a fence-raisin', and we figgered 'twere when the work was done done."

He slapped his leg and roared with laughter. The rest grinned, spitting. Hinson reached in the wagon and lifted out two brown crockery demi-johns with corn-cobs for stoppers.

"We didn't want you should think hard of us, Mr. Lantry, and we carried somethin' we figgered 'd make us a sight more welcome than the work."

Lantry said nothing. Old man Wilson looked at him and moved forward.

"Men, you're mighty welcome jest-so, we had he'p and a plenty, and we're proud to see you. But now see here, iffen ever' man figgered that-a-way and carried what I reckon you-all carried, and come late with it, what I say is—where-all'd be the fence-raisin'?"

Hinson uncorked a jug.

"There shore wouldn't be none," he said, "but there'd be a mighty merry time."

The crowd laughed and edged in towards the jug. Each man drank from the narrow mouth. Lantry hesitated a moment, then tipped the jug far back and swallowed deeply. He wiped the drops from his mouth.

"That's fine, sir. That's prime corn liquor." He opened and closed his mouth, judging the after-taste. "Sprouted corn or meal?"

" 'Pears to me the feller made it, mentioned meal," Hinson said demurely.

The whiskey was of his own distilling, as all knew. They snickered in appreciation.

"Come to the house, men, and set down to the table."

Lantry waved them through the gate.

"We had dinner, but we kin drink and set," they told him.

They moved to the house with the demi-johns. Spudd Wilson

introduced the Moss Bluff men to the women, gathered together.

"Ladies, these here is Mr. Saunders and Mr. Hinson and their friends."

"How do."

Here and there a woman greeted them, lowering her eyes. Piety was afraid food would not be offered them.

Mrs. Lantry said stiffly, "Won't you set down and eat cold rations?"

They refused food, but invited the women to drink. They declined for the most. Those who accepted said, "A mighty leetle. Seems like hit goes to my head." Piety noticed that the older women drank with greater gusto. Grandma Jacklin said, "Yes, I'll have a good big swaller. I were raised on it, and when hit's good, hit he'ps my stummick." Annie Wilson, too, drank with pleasure.

Mrs. Lantry said, "I got good scuppernong wine I made last summer, iffen you ladies prefers it. Go fetch it, Py-tee."

The lassitude of the men vanished. The liquor, sweet and raw, burned their throats. It struck through them, hotter than the noon-day sun, drawing the sweat from them. They complained of the quality of the last whiskey sold by the Eureka storekeeper. It had no strength, no virtue. The price was high. Fifty cents a quart was unreasonable. It paid a man to make his own.

Old man Wilson said, "I always figger to git me a barrel made from cane-skimmin's in the fall."

The sun dropped below the hammock. Twilight came unnoticed. Suddenly they were aware of the darkness. Willy Saunders shouted for lights. Piety and Martha brought torches of fat-wood splinters. They held them while Lantry and the boys did the belated chores. The Moss Bluff crowd was out-drinking the others two to one. The women made ineffectual sorties at their men, hinting of home. The men ignored them.

"We ain't a-goin' home 'til we've done danced with all you ladies," Buck Hinson called.

"That's right! Make us a leetle music for a breakdown!"

Three of the men brought their instruments from the house. Old man Wilson, as crack fiddler, struck up a tune, "Sugar in the Gourd." One of the Moss Bluff strangers, a little tipsy, picked the strings of a banjo, and Mo Jacklin played the harmonica. They played lustily, somewhat out of tune. The music jangled and the men clapped their hands. The women could not resist patting their feet.

Annie Wilson said, "A feller cain't dance to 'Sugar in the Gourd' is purely ailin'."

Suddenly Lantry leaped into the light of the torches.

"Take your partners!"

He whooped and cried out a verse of the song.

> *"Sugar in the gourd*
> *Goed on the ground—*
> *Way to git it out*
> *Is to roll the gourd around."*

He was calling the set. No one knew that he was familiar with the figures of the dance. They looked at one another. Piety edged in close to watch him. She followed the big figure with shining eyes. Some of the women murmured a protest at dancing with the Moss Bluff men. Annie Wilson was kicking off her shoes. Tittering, others of the women removed theirs. They came slowly to the light and men seized them. Lantry snapped Annie Wilson towards him as easily, Piety thought, as though the woman were a sapling. There were shouts of laughter when Buck Hinson, instead of gathering in one of the pretty girls, swooped on Grandma Jacklin and swung her into the circle forming for the square-dance.

"Older they be, the more they knows!"

The old woman showed the hit-or-miss pattern of her teeth and cackled shrilly. She followed until she was out of breath.

"I got to quit," she gasped. "Listen to me hasslin'."

Then Hinson swung out a girl. Annie Wilson and Lantry were dancing furiously. He called the figures with a roar.

> *"Take two back!*
> *Promenade all!*
> *Hold that calico*
> *From the wall!"*

The pair scuffled hugely in the sand, the woman's bare feet

kicking up a spray behind her. The bearded man and the big woman cast vast shadows that followed them grotesquely in the smoky light. Both were sweating. When the set was ended, Annie dropped near-by on the sand and fanned her hot face. Piety slipped to her side and sat close against her. A warm sweet steam came to her from the woman's flesh. She saw a streak of grime across Annie's wrist where Lantry had pulled her towards him.

Lantry called to his wife to dance the next set with him. She refused curtly. He blew through his beard and drank again from the demi-john.

Piety heard one man say, "Never did see Lantry that sociable," and another, "No, nor I never seed that much corn liquor into him, to make him sociable." She was pleased that her father danced and sang. Old man Wilson began to fiddle again. Lantry stood in front of Annie Wilson and Piety. He hesitated. Then he held out his hand to the girl.

"Time your daddy was learnin' you somethin' besides ploughin', honey," he said.

She followed him, dizzy with pleasure in the hold of his hot hand on her arm. When he called the set, swinging her gallantly, he howled the name of a figure that was strange to the dancers. They continued to shuffle their feet in time to the music, but did not advance, watching him with puzzled faces. He danced the figure and some of the quicker men followed his steps. Others dropped out of the set. He fell back on familiar figures. They sashayed, swung their partners.

"Swing or cheat!"

The set was ended. Lantry indicated that he was done for the evening. The tune-makers put up their instruments. The demi-john passed around. There was excited talk of the new figure. Groups knotted here and there outside the light, talking of Lantry. The Moss Bluff men nodded to one another.

"That feller's from a good ways off," they said wisely.

"Lantry," Willy Saunders said, moving close to him, "where did you l'arn that figger?"

Lantry did not look at him.

"I dis-remember. I reckon some knows it and some don't."

"Don't nobody know hit in these parts. Where-all you come from, man?"

Saunders asked the question in apparent innocence.

The man Lantry seemed to expand. The deep chest swelled, like a bull breathing before a charge. The vast shoulders lifted higher, the great arms lifting with them. The red-brown eyes smouldered like coals about to blaze. Above his beard clenched teeth bared white for an instant. Instinctively the crowd shrank away. Piety blinked at him in a sudden panic. She had never seen him so. Saunders faced him, swaying a little.

"Mought be you ain't a-sayin', Mr. Lantry."

There were murmurs. It seemed to those who knew Lantry that they had waited twenty years for this moment. Lantry would bring down his fist like an axe-head. Willy Saunders would go down like a rotten fence post. Through his tipsiness the Moss Bluff man felt their fear. He rubbed his eyes and his mouth with the back of his hand. Lantry was staring beyond him. The big man's pent breath burst out in a sigh. He dropped his arms. The deep voice rumbled.

"Where I come from, Willy, men ain't impudent nor nosey. They minds their business and leaves the other man mind his."

He turned his back. Saunders laughed nervously. Hinson spoke sullenly.

"Le's go."

The Moss Bluff men took their jugs and wavered to their wagon. They rattled off without leave-taking. Mrs. Lantry's friends spoke indignantly after their going.

"Them fightin' jessies come jest to stir up a ruckus. Lantry had orter crawled his frame."

Old man Wilson said, "No, they come sociable. Leave 'em go that-a-way."

The women gathered up the sleeping children. They had divided the food by daylight, each one filling her basket with scraps of another's cooking. A plentiful supply was left for Mrs. Lantry. They said to her, "Hit's hard to cook, and you no more than moved." They were tired and sleepy. The men were half-blind with drowsiness. They moved silently to their wagons at the gate; through the clearing, the hammock, down the bluff to the river landing, into their rowboats. They closed Lantry's new gates after them. He had fenced his land in. One or two among them understood as well that he had fenced them out.

Lantry watched them disappear into the darkness. Their voices died away. Far down on the river there was the click of an oarlock. The man threw back his head.

"Well, you had a plenty this evenin'," Mrs. Lantry complained.

"Git into the house, woman!"

The woman and her children were as alien to him as the rest. He herded them away. Piety did not move. She watched him, her hand half over her mouth. He could never be strange to her, nor far away.

She said, "Cain't I he'p free the creeters?"

He stared at her. He moved to her, laying his arm across her thin shoulders.

He said gently, "Yes, Py-tee, we'll turn 'em loose tonight."

They went together to the animals. The chickens were asleep in their coop. They did not disturb them. They untethered the mule and cow and removed the rails from around the hogs. The creatures snorted but did not stir. The mule understood that he was free and galloped across the clearing. The hogs grunted and shifted. Lantry tried the slats here and there.

A feeling of elation swept him. He panted, like a man who has run a long way in the sun and has now flung himself down in the shade to rest. He looked over the fence into the scrub, invisible with night. There was no sound but the stir of the pines. He spoke in the blackness to his daughter.

"I think we'll git along all right and make a livin'." He hesitated. "Honey, I got a idee this place be safe."

III

FIVE YEARS of planting had levelled the soil of the clearing. Sugar-cane and corn had flattened the fields. Sweet potatoes had been hilled and the hills knocked down again for the digging. Planting, growth and harvest; planting, growth and harvest; they had smoothed the sandy loam to a counterpane flung down between scrub and hammock.

Lantry was late with his corn. It was April. The whippoorwills had been calling for a month. The cane was well advanced, but he was only now planting his field corn. Crows made question and answer in the neighbouring hammock, waiting for the seed to fall. The birds interrogated raucously the man and mule moving steadily, sideways to the high sun. The corn dropped like gold nuggets from the one-horse planter. The crows would drift down like shining leaves of burned paper and would dig it up again.

Hearing them, the man felt an instant of despair. If there were not crows to fight there was drought; if not drought, insects, incessant rain or mildew. Yet he had prospered in his five years in the scrub. The fringe of hammock soil had produced with a lushness startling to his experience. Corn had grown higher than his head, so that he had moved through it like a bearded prophet. He raised a small patch of tobacco for his own use. It had a fine flavour. Yams had grown bigger than Piety's thigh. His money crop, the cane, had made sugar and syrup of choice quality. But he had had three sons at home to fight with him. Now they were leaving him.

Abner, the alien among them, had married a cousin and moved back across the river to the piney-woods. Zeke was homesteading half a mile to the north, duplicating his father's clearing. He had married and built a one-room cabin soon after New Year's. Thaddeus was courting. He had promised not to leave until the spring crops were well along, but he worked half-heartedly. Martha was of little use at field-work. His wife he discounted. She helped to plant and hoe and dig potatoes, but her querulousness was a constant offense. He preferred to leave her in the house and yard, complaining over her pots and pans, throwing water at the chickens in a sudden pet. After this spring, only Piety would be left to him.

The girl was turning beds for sweet potatoes in the north clearing. She drove a pony-like white horse and small plough. The plough handles pulled at her armpits, so that her shoulders jerked at every roughness and her bare feet flew up behind her. She held the plough steadily and the lines of her beds were true. Lantry watched the small figure on the other side of the clearing as he turned his corner. As he looked, the plough point caught a root and bucked. The girl plunged forward in a somersault. The man dropped his lines to run to her, but in a moment she was on her feet. He could see her brush the dirt from her face with her arm and take up the plough-lines again.

He thought, "She don't weigh enough to hold herself down."

He heard the girl's high shrill voice call to her horse. She spoke seldom, and the small thin tones invariably stirred him. Hearing her, he felt for a moment that he was not alone in this place. He clicked to his mule. He finished his planting before Piety was done. There were two hours of daylight left and the April sun was warm. He fed and watered his mule at the shed west of the house, then turned the animal to graze in the fenced pasture. He went to the girl.

"Leave me finish here, Py-tee," he called to her. "The way the plough done wasted you, cain't be you got much breath left."

"Hit didn't harm me none," she laughed, shaking her small head at him. "Whoa!" She lay back on her plough-lines to stop the horse. "I ain't no-ways tired."

"That's what you say, honey. Then time you gits to the house, you're a-settin' to the table nigh asleep and a-drappin' into the bed like a sack o' meal."

"Well, I wants to finish. These is my pertaters!" She defied him, laughing.

"Look at you," he derided her. "A gal no bigger'n a hammock wren, standin' there a-claimin' a hull pertater field. Dogged if you ain't gittin' impudent as a cricket."

He squatted on his haunches and stuck a straw of broom-sage in his mouth.

"Go ahead, finish your hills. I'll wait on you and quarrel with you if you don't do it good."

The straight thin back marched away from him, the soles of the dirty bare feet turned back at him. He chuckled to himself, his eyes glowing, watching her pride in the evenness of her furrows. The broom-sage dangled against his beard. As she swung back at the far end and moved towards him for the turning of the last bed, he could see that her deep-lidded eyes were fixed far over his head. She had picked out a distant tree to run by. It made him lonely.

They walked side by side to the shed to put up the plough and care for the horse. The cow had come to the gate to be milked. Piety let her in and brought the gourd while Lantry fed her. The girl rubbed the hard head of the animal as the man milked. The sweet scent of the smooth-haired hide, the perfumed breath, mingled with the crunched corn and the sweaty acridity of the human bodies. In the cabin Mrs. Lantry lifted her voice above the kitchen clatter. Martha answered, her voice dull through the pine wall.

The milking was done. Piety took the gourd of milk in her two hands. They walked slowly to the house. The breezeway and kitchen had been added at the rear. At the steps of the breezeway Lantry said, "Hold steady now." He picked up the girl by the waist and lifted her high, the brimming gourd level in her cupped hands. Her bare toes reached for the floor as he set her down.

"That's the way not to waste no milk comin' up the steps."

They laughed at each other. Mrs. Lantry grumbled at them.

Martha said, "Ma, 'pears to me like you'd be used to them cuttin' the fool."

Lantry said, "Yes, Marthy, but she's used to quarrellin', too."

Mrs. Lantry said, "Py-tee, you he'p now."

There was no reality except the work of the house. The woman knew the field work was hard. Yet when the girl came into the house, she made an aggrieved claim on her.

Martha said in a low voice, "Supper's about done, Py-tee. You go set down. I'll finish."

The older girl was almost a woman, phlegmatic and maternal. She had Lantry's red coloring faded to sandiness. Her plain, solid face was spotted with yellow freckles. The younger girl sat on the top step of the breezeway, leaning her head wearily against the wall until supper was called. After supper Martha made her a sign that she would take care of the dishes. Piety washed her hands and face, her grimy feet and legs, and slipped into the dusky bedroom. Twilight filled the room with a shadowy coolness. She got into her nightgown and stretched her legs against the one rough clean sheet. She drew a quilt over her and lay drowsily while the twilight deepened into dark and bull-bats darted past the window.

Before the girl dropped to sleep she heard voices on the breeze-way. Zeke and his wife had walked the half-mile from their clearing to pass an hour before bedtime. Zeke was lonely after the bustle of a family. He came a little wistfully to offer the details of his homesteading for discussion. He was a tip-nosed, ash-headed little fellow like a faded chipmunk. He had bright small eyes of robin's-egg blue. Piety pictured his eyes as he talked, his hair turning up forlornly from his neck in pale drake's-tails.

Lantry listened as his son spoke of the stick-and-clay fireplace he had completed that day; of the cooking-rack in the yard, with hooks suspended to hold pots over the fire; of the hog-pen he would build, planning to make hogs his money crop. The animals ran wild in scrub and swamp and hammock, fattening on pine and acorn mast, on huckleberries and palmetto berries, large and black and low-growing.

Lantry asked a question now and then but gave no advice. Zeke was a man and able to run his own affairs. He knew as much of stock-raising and of farming as his father. He sometimes recognised in the older man the touch of the novice, so that he wondered how he had previously earned his bread. He did not ask.

Zeke's wife, Ella May, said to Martha, "I seed your feller when we was to Eureka Sat'dy."

The sandy face flushed.

"That sorry Syl Jacklin, I reckon."

"When you and him fixin' to take up together?"

Martha shrugged her shoulders.

"I ain't in no hurry. I ain't fixin' to take up at all, lessen he'll come live over here."

Lantry looked at her sharply. He had not understood that the courting had gone so far.

"None o' them Jacklins likes the scrub," he said.

"Well, they's one of 'em'll like it, or he won't git to marry me." She added, "And he better make me a livin', too."

Piety, almost asleep, thought, "I wouldn't figger that-a-way. If a man done his best."

She was aware by how narrow a margin Lantry had escaped disaster with his crops. There was something about the most fertile field that was beyond control. A man could work himself to skin and bones, so that there was no flesh left on him to make sweat in the sun, and a crop would get away from him. There was something about all living that was uncertain.

Ella May asked, "Where-all's Py-tee?"

Martha said, "In the bed. She's been beddin' sweet pertaters. I mean, she's give out. Field work's too hard on her."

Mrs. Lantry said, "Hit don't hurt her none. Seem to me she do it jest to git away from the housework."

Lantry rumbled angrily, "Don't none of you know what you're talkin' about. She perfeckly enjoys it. She's got a knack for it, hit comes to her natural. Hit's a heap harder'n the piddlin' ol' jobs to the house, but she likes it. I got to have me some he'p."

Zeke asked. "Where-all's Thad?"

"Acrost the river, he'pin' Abner round up some cattle. Ab's gittin' him a fine bunch o' cattle."

Zeke said, "Long as he don't keer whose calves he runs in along of his own."

"Abner wouldn't steal calves, no more than you and me!" Martha flashed at him.

Zeke began to whistle indifferently.

"Mebbe not."

He said after a moment, "Ab's got him one thing I'd give a pretty for. He had him more syrup and corn than he'll use, and he takened a couple o' barrels and made him the nicest ten gallons o' whiskey I ever did taste."

Ella May asked, surprised, "Did! Where'd he git the still?"

"Used the wash-pot to cook the buck. Fixed him a cypress cover and daubed clay around the edge to make hit tight. Fixed him a pipe outen the top, and a gutter for the pipe to run through."

"Well, I do know."

Lantry chuckled. "Ella May, I've seed stills made outen a lard pail, a hog trough and a gun barrel."

"Well, now!"

Mrs. Lantry complained, "Yes, and makin' ten gallons to a time, he'll be raisin' up as bad a fuss with it as them Moss Bluff fellers."

"Sho, hit's a sight better to make hit than to buy hit." Lantry stroked his beard. "You know what you're drinkin'. I'm fixin' to make me a few jugs, come fall, and my cane juice plentiful. I don't use much liquor, but fifty cents a quart comes high."

"You mighty right." Zeke nodded maturely at his father.

"Ain't it agin the law, makin' whiskey?" Ella May inquired. " 'Pears like I've done heard somethin' 'bout hit bein' agin the law."

"I dunno," Zeke puzzled. "I cain't see why. Cattle-stealin' is onlawful, and hog-stealin'. And murder. I cain't see no harm to makin' whiskey."

Lantry stretched his long legs.

"Why yes," he said, "hit's agin the law. They's a tax on whiskey, a gov'mint tax. You kin make it, but you belong to git a license and pay a tax. But sho, nobody don't pay no mind to a feller makin' a leetle jest to drink and enjoy and treat his friends and kin-folks."

He straightened, electric in the dusk.

"But now the gov'mint is mighty pertickler in Caroliny and West Virginny. The revenooers is just bounden determined nobody won't git to make none. But sho, they jest as good to stay to home and put their noses over their own pots. They cain't half ketch them fellers makin' moonshine up in them mountings. When they do come up with 'em, they're like to git buckshot in their breeches for their trouble. I mind me——"

"You been there, Pa?" Zeke leaned towards him eagerly.

Lantry drew a vast breath and was silent. He lit his cob pipe and sucked on it. The light glowed against his beard. His eyes were half closed.

"I'm tellin' you what folks has tol' me," he said reprovingly. "I'll quit tellin' you, do you interrupt me."

"Well Pa, revenooers don't never mess up with nobody in these parts, do they?"

"I never heerd tell of 'em botherin' ary man. Floridy is a fine state that-a-way. Folkses here is the best in the world to mind their own business and not go interferin' in nobody else's."

Zeke said, "Dogged if I wouldn't like to make whiskey for a livin'."

Mrs. Lantry slapped at her legs.

"I'll be layin' a fire in the smudge-pot, iffen you're fixin' to set up much longer. The skeeters is a-comin'."

"Don't make no smudge, Ma." Zeke and Ella May rose. "We got to be goin'. We got a half-mile between us and the bed."

Piety heard the talk trailing away like fog. She wanted to call after them, to say good-night to Zeke, but her eyes and mouth would not open. She could hear the frogs in the swamp, louder now than the voices moving towards the gate.

"Pa, how come you never made you no liquor from the cane juice before?"

"I dunno, son."

Lantry's deep tones washed over her in a last misty wave.

"Jest someway never got around to it."

IV

A FEW pine needles sifted down on the shoulders of the company assembled for the burying of Lantry's wife. The man and his daughter Piety stood together, a little apart from the rest of the family, as the last spadeful of sand spattered over the grave. In death the woman had been brought back across the river to the burying-ground in the piney-woods. Lantry had turned over the stiff, fox-faced body to her kin with something like relief, as though he were returning a mule or horse he had borrowed.

Old man Wilson, the dead woman's father, remarked brightly,

"Seven yare, nigh to the day, son Lantry, since you takened her acrost the river to live in the scrub."

Lantry nodded, stroking his beard, where a streak of silver ran like a thin shaft of lightning. Piety moved closer to him.

Old man Wilson continued, "You've prospered, son, and this pore dead creeter he'ped you to do so. Your young uns is all growed and raisin' families, excusin' Py-tee, and her almost twenty-two."

Lantry spoke to her under his breath, "Le's go, honey. Ol' Wilson's drunk."

They turned away through the pine trees towards the river. Their rowboat rocked among bonnet-pads at the landing. They stepped in and Lantry poled off silently. Martha and Zeke and Thaddeus and their families were to return to the scrub by wagon, crossing the river bridge at Eureka. They watched after their father and sister. Through a break in the trees they saw the big man bend to his oars. The young woman sat facing him, her small, childlike face cupped in her hands.

"Long as Pa's got Py-tee where he kin look at her," Martha said drily, "the rest of us kin live or die——"

On the scrub side of the river Lantry grounded his boat at his open landing. South of Otter Landing the river bluffs flattened, and scrub met swamp in a twisting moil of briers and rattan and moccasins. There was no fertile ledge of hammock. Only cypresses reared their feathery heads from gigantic bases. Lantry waved his hand towards the south. He gave voice to his uneasiness for the first time in seven years.

"Nobody won't never slip up on us that-a-way," he said.

Piety blinked at him, taking her thoughts from her mother. For Lantry, she sensed, there were other enemies than death. They walked together up the ledge. The trail passed up through the rich darkness of hammock, across a cleared field, and through a gate in the slat fence to the house yard. They crossed the breeze-way and lifted the latch into the front room. Piety looked about her. The house was no emptier than before. No place would be empty, she thought, with Lantry in it. The man's bulk, the fire of his presence, filled the room so certainly that his wife, returning from the grave, would have crowded it. Piety stared at the hearth, missing the accustomed sight of her mother sitting near the fire. It was as though a sharp-nosed, snappish bitch of long association was gone.

The burying had been at noon. It was now mid-afternoon. Lantry and his daughter longed to go to the interrupted work of the field. They sat stiffly on a bench against the wall. Her mother, Piety thought, had enjoyed so little.

In the sustaining of life were pain and pleasure. Her mother had only understood the pain. Piety and Lantry, and indeed most folk she knew, felt a sharp pleasure in the details of the precarious thing that was existence. Breakfast was good, and dinner and supper, and a little snuff afterwards. The tug of the plough at the arms was good, and the sight of new cane and corn sprouting green above the earth. Deer, big-eyed and curious, and their spotted fawns; fox-squirrels upside down on a pine tree, black-backed and glossy, flicking their tails; all the small creatures that crossed her path were good to watch. She had never understood her mother's grumblings.

Towards dark the creak of wagon wheels sounded down the scrub road. The rest of the Lantrys were returning to their homes; Zeke, lonely because he had lost his wife in childbirth in the fall; Martha, contented with her husband, Sylvester Jacklin, and her twin babies; Thaddeus, homesteading with his bride four miles to the north. The wagon halted a moment at the gate; then, as though its occupants had suddenly changed their minds, rattled on northward.

Piety and Lantry breathed deeply, rose from the bench and went together to the kitchen. Lantry sat by the range, tending the fire while she cooked their meal. They ate in their accustomed places across from each other at the kitchen table, the space empty at the end where Mrs. Lantry had sat. Lantry watched Piety as she washed the dishes at the water-shelf. She made quick, light movements like a quail. The man followed her with his eyes. When they left the kitchen he drew his hand across her soft hair.

"I'll move into the front room to sleep," he said. "You keep your mammy's bedroom."

They were exhausted and slept long and hard. In the morning she heard him stirring ahead of her. He was building the kitchen fire. She opened her bedroom door and peered into the front room. He had built a quick blaze on the hearth for her to dress by. Something more than the small fire warmed her bones. At breakfast Lantry moved to the place at the end of the table. They sat close together. He ate silently, moving his beard, his thoughts milling behind his eyes. Startled, he looked up to see Piety staring at him, her hands in her lap. She smiled, moving her head a little.

"What you studyin' about, watchin' your Pappy that-a-way?"

He poked his dull case-knife at her ribs to hear her quick laugh.

She wondered uneasily if he would go away to the field without her. She hurried to get the dishes done, the two beds made, the mosquito bars rolled back, the floors swept, the dog and cat and chickens fed, while he did the outside chores. He dallied over the stock feeding and milking until he saw her at the last of her work. He came to the breezeway with two hoes.

"We got a day's work fightin' the 'muda grass," he said.

The day seemed short. They hoed adjacent rows. The man's long arms swung the hoe faster than her small-boned ones. When he found himself too far ahead of her, he turned to her row and hoed back to meet her.

Mrs. Lantry's illness had interfered with the routine of the house. The next morning Piety felt obliged to catch up with the washing. She rose long before daylight and had the clothes half-rubbed and the black wash-pot boiling before Lantry was up. After breakfast he contrived to keep himself busy about the yard. He repaired harness; drew off a new axe-handle; sorted over the equipment for his muzzle-loading gun. Piety was using the pot-water to scrub the floors. The corn-shucks scrub swished noisily across the rough breezeway. Lantry filled his shot-bag with shot, his horn with powder; polished the hickory ramrod; gathered a handful of dried Spanish moss for wadding.

"You thu, Py-tee?"

"I'm thu."

"We best take the mule and wagon into the scrub for fat-wood."

She took off her wet apron, put on her palmetto hat and went

with him, leaving the clothes to flap on the line and the floors
to dry without the usual last process of shuffling back and forth
across them with a cloth under bare feet. The small thin figure
with its shoulders a little bent trotted beside the great bulky one.

The scrub had not burned in the seven years since they had
come to it. The mule threaded his way through young pines and
oaks higher than his ears. Lantry had not been glad to see the
heightening of the growth. He had liked to be able to see across
it for a mile or two from the cabin doorstep. The mule came to
a stop. He could go no farther into the scrub. The undergrowth
was a twisted treachery. Saw palmetto ripped with its barbs at
hide and flesh; the refuse of old fires cluttered the infertile sand
with matted limbs, stumps and logs, all laced together with thorny
vines. The man and woman climbed from the wagon and began
to sort out scorched pine trunks, whose cores would burn like oil.

"I gits a dream, sometimes," Lantry said in a low voice. "I gits
takened by surprise from the river. I belong to run. I runs acrost
the clearing and into sich a piece o' scrub as this."

The sweat started from his temples as he talked. All night, he
told her, when the dream rode him, he ran through the scrub, his
feet interminably enmeshed in its tormented tangle.

"I cain't someway put my hand to peace and comfort," he said.

Her heart beat hard. She braced her small feet in the high boy's
shoes.

She blurted, "Pa, what you been so feered of?"

He did not answer. His breath came and went like the air in a
bellows.

He said at last, "You jest as good to know. Mought be some
day—you and me alone this-a-way—you'd have me to hide out. Or
lie for. Honey, I killed me a gov'mint man in the up-country."

"How come you to do sich as that?"

The young voice was dispassionate, touched with a faint anxiety.

"I were makin' moonshine whiskey. The revenooers come
messin' up with me. I got my gorge up and I killed me one. I lit
out of the south. I been right smart oneasy ever since."

She remembered a drunken man from Moss Bluff, swaying in

the firelight on the night of the fence-raising, asking Lantry questions.

"Does folkses around here know?"

"Don't nobody cold-out know, honey, but me and you. But 'pears to me, times, like, here and there a man has someway got a idee."

"They ain't nary one takened out after you?"

"If they has, they ain't caught up with me." He added slowly, "But all my life I got it to study on."

Her heart thumped with his. She wanted to speak. She could not think of any words to comfort him. She went with him inside his fear, as though together they entered some lonely place of shadows. They rode home without further speech. They were warm and close. It was as though a skein of wool, tangled and torn, had been wound at last into a firm bright ball.

The spring proved dry, and in March they planted a garden at the foot of the bluff where the swamp merged with the river, and the ground was moist without need of rain. In a week turnips and collards and onions showed green against the black muck. One Saturday morning Lantry left her to work the garden while he rowed to Eureka to trade. When the dip of his oars was absorbed by the rush of the river she bent to her weeding.

She was aware, with a slight acceleration of her heartbeat, of the life going on around her; the movement of alligators floundering in the creek, the slow beat of the wings of herons, the catfish jumping. She worked quietly for so long that when she lifted her head she found herself looking into the close bright eyes of an astonished cat-squirrel. A black swamp rabbit hopped casually by a hand's breadth away. She straightened her back and walked to the lower corner of the garden to find where he had pushed through the loose rail fence. She came there on the recent track of a panther. She was not afraid by daylight. She bent again to her work. She stayed at the garden until the earth about the plants was combed as smooth as her hair, hoping that Lantry would come so that she might meet him at the swamp landing.

She returned to the house and started a fire for supper. Towards sunset she heard him coming. He was whistling as sweetly as a redbird. She went to the door and shaded her eyes against the westerly sun. Lantry was swinging across the clearing. His bearded head was thrown back, his arms hung free from the shoulders, his long legs moved in time with his whistling. He stopped whistling abruptly and broke into a song. It was his favourite, "Git along down." She heard him all the way across the clearing in a musical burst of thunder.

> *"Git along down, git along down,*
> *Git along down to Richmond town*
> *To lay my t'baccy down."*

She wondered where Richmond town might be, but by the time Lantry was at the house he was calling to her, waving his bags and bundles, and she did not remember to ask. He had gone to Eureka expressly to buy new strings for his banjo, hanging long unused under the rafters. Now they were alone, he might indulge his taste for music. He put the new strings on the instrument, tuned it and picked at it, trying its tone, while she cooked supper. He sat in the breezeway with the setting sun in his beard and tinkled softly against the clatter of the pans.

On the following Saturday he left her alone again. Time seemed to hang on her hands when he was away and she occupied herself with tasks with which she seldom concerned herself. She grated cassava roots and made starch and pudding. The pudding was translucent like gum drops. Lantry was fond of it. She went a short way into the scrub and cut boughs of Highland ti-ti for a new yardbroom. Lantry returned, his red-brown eyes glowing with a small accordion for her.

She preferred to listen to him rather than to play herself, but she turned earnestly to learning the instrument. It was harder than ploughing new ground to remember the difference between the two kinds of notes, and that the accordion was opened for one and closed for the other. She wheezed gravely in and out, her eyes on him, the tip of her tongue between her lips, following his directions. For more than a week she achieved nothing beyond distressing howls and wheezes. Suddenly Lantry guffawed with a great roar, as she had not heard him since he laughed with Annie Wilson at the fence-raising.

"Honey," he said, "quit a-twistin' that pore ol' sick tomcat's tail!"

They laughed together until they were faint from it.

"Here, honey, leave me show you——"

He took the accordion and closed his eyes and swayed his shoulders. The music seemed to flow into him and then flow out again. He played tunes she knew and tunes that were strange, songs anyone could tell came from a long way off. Some were lively. Others were sweet and infinitely sad. Then he opened his eyes and handed her back the instrument, showing her once more the way it went.

She learned finally to play with the patient steadiness of her shooting. She wheezed out the hymns very well, and slow measured pieces like "Nellie Gray." She had no feeling for rhythm. When she got into pieces like "Little Brown Jug" and "Run, Nigger, Run," she stumbled and tripped over her own notes. She was hopelessly lost in such dance tunes as "Hen Cackle." Sweating, with a desperate intent, she squeezed a random note here and there from the accordion in an attempt to keep the pace, until Lantry stopped her gently.

"Py-tee, no use to try sich as that no more. Dogged if you don't double back on your own track like a run wildcat."

He accepted her peculiar timelessness at the slower pieces and they played them together with mutual satisfaction. Through two springs and summers, into the second autumn, Zeke or Thaddeus or Martha, walking down the road to visit, heard the pair at their music. They came on them sitting in the breezeway or before the hearth-fire, absorbed in the magic of string and wind.

V

IN THE SECOND October after his wife's death Lantry ran a few quarts of liquor from his cane-skimmings. He was leaning over to put more fire under the wash-pot that formed the cooker of the small still, when he found it suddenly impossible to breathe.

Piety discovered him an hour later on the sand, still fighting for air. He had torn open his shirt and was clutching with one desperate hand at his broad hairy breast. She thought her own breath would stop.

The viciousness of the heart attack alarmed Lantry, not for himself, but for her. Lying weakly at rest on his bed while she left him a moment to fire the pot again, so as not to lose the charge, a picture came before him of that scrawny fearless figure marching through the scrub without him. The blood pounded again in his throat. This place of dark hammock, of swift brown river, of impenetrable scrub, became more than ever alien and unfriendly. He saw the vague dangers that had never materialised against him, swallowing her up, as he had seen an alligator seize a fawn at the river's edge and drag it under. There was nothing he could quite put his finger on, to be afraid of for her, but he could not endure to leave her here alone. She would have to live with Martha, or keep house for widower Zeke. That was no life for a woman.

He saw in the new light the stupid Jacklin boy, Willy—Sylvester's cousin—who had come half-courting Piety without encouragement from either father or daughter. Willy made a pretense of visiting his cousin, rowing across the river to the scrub. Then he walked up as if by accident to sit mutely with the Lantrys. He was slow and strong, with a black forelock that hung between his eyes.

The next time he came, when Lantry was recovered, the older man welcomed him with unaccustomed hospitality. He talked to him of crops, and finding that the youth had always worked at timbering, turned amiably to a discussion of trees. There was a rumour that a Palatka lumber company might buy cypress rights along the river and put in crews to timber and raft. Lantry brought out the straw-covered demi-john of his last whiskey and asked young Jacklin's opinion on its flavour.

The youth said, "I ain't much for it," but he tipped up the jug and took an obliging swallow. "That's noble liquor, Mr. Lantry," he said earnestly.

Lantry took a deep drink, wiped his mouth and beard, set down the jug and started away.

"I'll jest go on and visit with Marthy and Syl a whiles," he said. "I figger you young folks don't want no interferin'."

Piety's puzzled eyes followed him as he walked across the yard and out of the gate. When Lantry came home again, the moon rode high over the scrub. The narrow road was a silver ribbon. He was half-way home when he met Piety and Willy. He thought with satisfaction that it was a fine night for courting. Piety turned and walked back with him and Willy went on alone.

When they were out of hearing Lantry said, "That's a fine young feller. Couldn't git you no nicer young feller." The girl did not speak. "Honey, he done said ary thing yit about you marryin'?"

"Nary thing, Pa." She looked at him astonished.

He took her thin arm and squeezed it playfully.

"He jest been courtin', that it? Talkin' sweet? Puttin' his arm around you, or kissin', or sich as that?"

Her deep-lidded eyes were round. Willy had spoken two or three times after Lantry's going, and then only about the saw-mill at Palatka. He had not moved from the spot where Lantry left him, until she had suggested that they walk down the road and meet her father. He had jumped up then like a hound told to come or go.

"Well, I be dogged!" Lantry spat violently into the myrtle bushes. "I jest be dogged."

He said no more that night. Looking at him in the bright moonlight as they went up the lane to the house, she could not read his eyes. She went to bed in a daze. For the first time she did not understand him. The next morning Lantry paced the breeze-way after breakfast and did not go to his work. He waited until she had finished her straightening of the cabin.

"Py-tee! Come here."

She settled herself on the stoop while he walked back and forth, his hands clasped behind him, his beard sunk on his chest.

"You ever studied on gittin' married?"

"When Marthy married Syl, I studied some on it. Not lately, I ain't."

"Willy's foolishly fond of you, Py-tee." He glared at her sternly. "He jest don't say much, is all ails him, but he's rarin' to git you."

She blinked at him.

"Would you have him, iffen he was to ask you?"

"I dunno. I ain't studied none on it."

He paced up and down.

"You like him a'right, Py-tee?"

"I reckon I like him."

He took a fresh start.

"Honey, you like to be powerful lonesome thouten no young uns. Don't you fancy a passel o' the leetle fellers?"

She laughed. "I ain't much for dandlin' 'em. Always 'peared to me young uns don't love to be dandled. Time they gits some size to 'em, I likes 'em a'right."

The chill thought struck her that Lantry was lonely. Perhaps he intended to move down with Martha, whose family was begun. Perhaps he planned to go back where he had come from, to the strange places where he had learned the tunes he played and the songs he sung. Her throat tightened.

She asked bluntly, "You fixin' to go off?"

He laid his hands on her shoulders, so that the pulse of his blood warmed them.

He said gently, "Not if I kin he'p it, Py-tee. I don't aim to leave you long as I has the say. A man cain't always he'p hisself when hit comes to goin' or to comin' or to dyin'."

She understood. She nodded.

He said, "A man o' your own's natural. Seems like ever'thing go along better when you do what's natural."

She asked, "What you want I should do?"

"Nothin' you don't r'aly want to. But if Willy suits you, I say take him."

"He suits me good as ary feller, I reckon."

He held her shoulders an instant longer, then turned abruptly to his work.

Willy came again on Sunday evening, bringing a gift of bass

from the river. The older man met him at the gate. They walked together back of the house and began to dress the fish while the scales were moist.

Lantry said, "Willy, mebbe you know, Py-tee thinks right smart o' you."

The youth flushed. "I'm shore proud to hear it."

"I don't aim to ask you nothin' you got no fancy for answerin', but if she was willin', would you care for marryin'?"

"Yes sir, I'd be mighty proud."

"Well you jest say to her then, Py-tee, you say, hit's all fixed we should marry. And you see what she has to say."

"I'll do that thing, Mr. Lantry. Much obliged."

Lantry called towards the house. "Py-tee, fetch a pan for the fish Willy carried you." He set off for the road. He turned back. "Willy, you be foolishly fond of her, ain't you? You be rarin' for her?"

Young Jacklin shuffled his feet in the sand.

"I reckon, sir. Why, sho."

Lantry's uneasiness lifted. He went whistling to Martha's. When he returned, he found the matter arranged.

"Py-tee said, 'All right, then,'" Willy greeted him. He poked an intimate finger in her ribs. "Didn't you, Py-tee?"

"That's what I said."

Lantry said, "That's fine."

The three sat in silence on the stoop.

A month later Lantry fetched the preacher from Eureka by row-boat. Piety and Willy Jacklin were married at Martha's, with a few of the Wilson and Jacklin kin present from across the river. Abner and his wife came, bringing a gift of a quarter of beef and a bolt of unbleached muslin. Abner was doing well with cattle. He and his wife were growing stout and florid with prosperity. Martha had sewed new shifts and nightgowns and aprons for her sister and had cooked a wedding supper of chicken pilau and pound cake, served with elderberry wine. There were no festivities and the group broke up before dark. Willy and Piety walked back up the scrub road to the Lantry cabin. Lantry would stay a few days with Martha.

"Give the young folks a chancet to git acquainted and settle down to their reg'lar ways," he said. "Let 'em see do they figger on quarrellin', then I kin come in and say who's right."

There was no quarrelling. Willy went slowly about the work of the Lantry place, amiable and silent. Lantry came home a week later, as eager as a lost dog. Piety looked from her father to Willy and back again, as though to understand why Lantry had encouraged his inclusion in the family. She felt a detached affection for her husband, but when he was out of her sight she seldom thought of him. They had moved into the wide bed with the high mosquito bar that her father and mother had occupied. It seemed to her that she was picking up in the middle something that had been interrupted. But if there was a meaning, she could not find it.

Willy had a way of sleeping curled up like a dog, his head deep in his chest, one arm over his face. She awakened one night after Lantry's return, when the hoot-owls were crying in the moonlight, and looked at the doubled-up figure breathing beside her. She thought that it might just as well be a dog curled up in the bed, for all the difference it made to her, one way or the other. A good dog, that fetched and carried as she told him.

With Willy's broad stupid back bent easily to the harder tasks, Lantry felt a secret triumph. It was as though, with his back to the wall, he had stood up to the forces that beat against him and had defeated them. A man's life was not his own, nor the time or manner of his dying. He moved like a cedar chip on the breast of the river; like a chicken feather lifted by a high wind. The man felt, securing this safety for the child for whom he knew such tenderness, stronger than the river or the wind.

VI

LANTRY'S IMPATIENCE with Willy Jacklin began two years later when Piety's boy was born. It was as though in that moment the man's slow usefulness was ended. He infuriated Lantry on the day of the birth. Piety had mistaken her time. When, alone in the

house with his wife, a heavy agony overtook her, Willy's mind
was unable to accept the fact of her travail, since by the calendar
it was not yet due. The woman paced the floor of the cabin, her
small swollen figure teetering grotesquely. The man stood bewildered in the doorway, watching her knife-struck progressions.

He asked, "What you figger ails you, Py-tee?"

"Must be I'm took, Willy. I ain't never been with nary woman
when she was took. I'll see kin I walk the pains off."

The man twisted his hands together, his black forelock shaggy
between his eyes.

"Be it better?"

"Nary a mite."

Beads of sweat stood out on her temples.

"What you figger I'd best do, Py-tee?"

She must use her last breath, she thought, to order him to come
or go.

"Go call Pa."

He went to the landing where Lantry was repairing a boat,
calling him from the ledge as he came towards him. Lantry made
out the words, "Py-tee's ailin'," and began to run up the bluff with
long reaching strides. He was at the cabin ahead of Willy.

"Honey, what's it like?"

She gripped his sleeve and described the hot pain that swelled
to the unbearable, held its crest, like a kettle about to boil over,
and then in time receded.

"You're took, Py-tee. It were that-a-way with your Ma." He said
over his shoulder, "She's took, Willy." He felt her hands. They
were numb and cold. "You best lay down and git you warm. Hit
don't do to git all froze up, like." He settled her on her bed and
covered her with the white spread. "You kin quilt with the
counterpane 'til time to git you undressed."

He came to the door. Willy stood as he had left him. Lantry
roared at him.

"Great God, feller, don't stand there a-battin' your eyes at me!
Git to Doc Lorimer! Don't make no difference what he's doin',
carry him back here!"

Willy hesitated.

"Take the mule and wagon?"

"Oh, my God—hit'd take you all the day! Fetch him in the rowboat!"

Willy turned away. He had had time to reach the edge of the hickory ledge. Lantry saw him coming back towards the cabin. Willy called from the rear gate.

"Is the oar-locks in the boat?"

Lantry's blood surged into his head and pushed against his temples. His face was violent, the color of old beef. His red beard glowed, the streaks of silver like tongues of white-hot flame. His eyes were on fire. He ran to the farm-bell lashed to an eight-foot post and tolled it wildly. It would bring Zeke and Martha from their half-mile and two miles away. Martha would help Piety while he was gone.

He passed Willy at the gate in a rush. He was like a red bull ploughing furiously across time and space. Willy heard him in a few moments, clanking the chain of the rowboat, rattling the oar-locks. The oars dipped noisily into the shallow water by the river-bank. Then, an instant later, the deep whisper of the river current engulfed all sound.

Lantry was gasping for breath when he landed Lorimer at the foot of the bluff. He hurried him to the cabin, where the woman laboured with a child too brawny for her spare loins. Willy crouched unhappily on his haunches in the yard, flipping a knife into the sand. Martha moved quietly back and forth with hot towels. Lantry went into the bedroom.

"Is it bad, honey?"

"Hit's bad."

The turtle-like lids of her eyes were blue with pain. Lantry could not endure to look at her. He moistened his lips.

"You afeered, Py-tee?"

The small head moved a little on the pillow.

"I ain't afeered."

"Kin you stand it?"

"What don't kill you, I figger you kin stand."

He left the room precipitously. Martha's square frame passed him. Her eyes narrowed.

"You never had nary doctor for Ma in the child-bed," she said with a rare bitterness. "You made nary visit to me two years ago when my Cleve come, 'til he were a day-two old. Now the way you carries on——"

He said hoarsely, "She's so scrawny and so leetle."

The woman's voice softened.

"I know, Pa. Hit's perfectly piteeful."

The sun set, dropping behind the ledge. The full moon rose over the scrub.

Martha said, "Hit'll be a boy, comin' on the full moon."

Lorimer said, "I'll be dogged if I see how you women-folks figure the moon when it comes to birthin' young uns. Don't none of you go that high to get one."

Piety pressed her lips together, so that a sharp cry slipped out only now and then against her will. Moonlight filled the cabin. The boy was born. Martha wrapped the new Jacklin in old soft muslin. Lorimer joined Zeke and Willy in the kitchen. They ate cold rations and drank cold coffee; stretched and laughed and chatted. The job was done and they talked of other things. Birth and death were unimportant, being only a beginning and an end.

Lantry did not appear in the kitchen. Lorimer, wiping his mouth with the back of his hand, passed through the main room on his way again to Piety. He found Lantry half-conscious on his bed.

When he had eased the man, he said, "Shame to you, Lantry. Tryin' to get two treatments for the price of one. I've got the notion to charge you double."

Zeke said, "He like to rowed the guts outen him, I reckon, the time he made a-fetchin' you."

"Yes," Martha said shortly, "and railin' out at pore Willy didn't he'p him none, neither. Willy says he like to went crazy when he come askin' him was the oar-locks to the boat."

Willy offered mildly, " 'Peared to me like 'twere savin' time to come ask, 'stead o' gittin' there and findin' 'em back to the house."

Lantry smiled weakly, rubbing the sore battleground of his breast.

"I had no right to take on so, son. Hit jest put me in a blaze to see you standin' still."

Lorimer said, "Another of them pets'll finish you."

Lantry did not see Piety's baby until after sun-up the next morning. Then he was able, holding to Willy's shoulder, to walk slowly into the bedroom, breathing as though his breath were of spun glass. Piety lay still exhausted, her closed lids white over her eyes. The child slept beside her. Above the wrinkled face the silky birth-hair was the red-brown of Lantry's. The man slipped one cautious finger into the diminutive fist. The woman opened her eyes. She smiled a little.

She said faintly, "Reckon us kin make a livin' for him?"

"Shore kin. Ten-twelve yare, anyways, and then if we've done raised him right, he kin make it for us."

His deep laugh shook the bed.

"What you fixin' to name him, Py-tee?"

Willy shuffled his feet near the head of the bed.

"I studied some on namin' him 'Lantry,'" she said. "Kin call him 'Lant.'"

"Lantry Jacklin," he said slowly.

Piety spoke politely to her husband.

"That suit you, Willy?"

He twisted his black forelock.

"Hit's as good a name as ary other, I reckon."

"Hi-yuh, you leetle ol' Lant." Lantry stroked the baby's stomach. "Got you red hair like your grand-daddy, you booger."

A heat flowed through his body, through the woman, to the child. It was as though it belonged to him and not to Willy.

He said slowly, "Kin make him a livin' all right, Py-tee, if nothin' don't interfere. You got the say so fur, and then you got no say at all."

VII

L ANTRY and his grandson Lant sat on a fallen log beside the timber trail that wound through the upper swamp. At their backs the ledge of hammock sheered steeply against the sky. Piety was hunting squirrels in the hickories. Below them in the swamp and on the river sounded the racket of timbering. It was incredibly noisy after the years of silence. The Murkley Cypress Company had come up the Ochlawaha eight years ago, in the year young Lant was born. Their presence still irked Lantry. The blows of axe on cypress struck on his ears with a sharpness keener than sound. He shook his bearded head impatiently. Young Lant looked at him curiously.

At eight years of age the boy had his father's heavy forelock that dropped between his eyes, but it was dark red, like Lantry's. His neck was long and thin and the thick hair made him top-heavy. His head, with its red-brown eyes staring like those of a deer, might have gone on a twelve-year body. He was all head and eyes and neck. The spindling frame might some day equal Lantry's in height, but the massive bulk would not be there. Something about the country to which the grandfather had brought his blood to breed, pared down progeny to a square-jointed leanness. Lant edged closer to the old man.

"Le's go yonder to the timberin' and see kin we ketch Pa workin' on a jog-board."

"You set still. Your Ma won't know where to look for us, time she's done huntin'."

"I got no mind to set still," the boy said belligerently.

He glared at Lantry and for an instant the man glared back at him. They were much alike and the two minds met in mid-air, like gamecocks, and clashed. But Lantry was gentler, with his age upon him.

After a moment his red lips parted through his beard in a smile, and he said quietly, "Set right still and Grand-daddy'll tell you about the up-country. And about the world."

"What's the world?"

The man ruminated. His eyes twinkled.

"Well, son," he said, "I ain't never travelled no direction but south. But if so hit's the same in 'tother directions, why, all I got to say, the world's a big place and a lot o' people in it."

The boy frowned blackly.

"That ain't no tale. Tell me about niggers."

The subject fascinated the child, for there was only one Negro in the scrub, an ex-slave to whom his master had given land in Florida. The Negro kept to himself in an old house.

"Niggers," Lantry said, "is borned male and female, like squirrels and dogs and white folks. Niggers is all shades o' black and brown and yaller." He closed his eyes, as though recalling a picture. He sang softly:

> *"Massa had a yaller gal,*
> *Brought her from the South.*
> *She combed her hair so very tight*
> *She could not close her mouth.*
>
> *Her head was like a coffee pot,*
> *Her nose was like the spout.*
> *Her mouth was like the fireplace*
> *With the ashes taken out."*

The child shouted with laughter.

"That's 'Git along down,' ain't it?"

"You got it right, son. That's the song."

Lantry leaned his back against a palmetto trunk, scratching his shoulder blades.

"I mind me of a big buck nigger in North Caroliny, had one glass eye——"

He smiled to himself. The boy, watching him raptly, saw the lids droop, the big head nod. The old man had fallen asleep. Lant jumped angrily on a dry palmetto frond, hoping it would rouse him. His grandfather infuriated him. Lantry went to sleep with a story half-told. He was ignorant, too, of most of the things the boy wanted to know. He had wanted to ask him if squirrels could swim. He decided that his grandfather would only have said, "Blest if I know." He would ask his Uncle Zeke. Better, he would remember to ask old man Paine, the mighty hunter who lived across the scrub and brought them presents of bear-meat and venison.

He walked a few cautious feet away from the sleeping man. His movement went unheard. He wheeled like a yearling deer and ran down the trail towards the swamp. He picked a vantage point high on a cable trail. He could see the pull-boat anchored with iron stakes on the opposite side of the river. He could see the company house boat above Otter Landing. The boat lay quiet now, but last Saturday, after dark, it had been bright with lights and the sound of men singing and playing. His father had lived on the boat before the timbering came close to the Lantry land.

Through the dense upper swamp Lant thought he could identify a man driving a wedge into a cypress as Willy Jacklin. His father's hanging black forelock shook like a horse's mane with the force of the blows. The noise of the timber outfit hummed in Lant's ears. He heard the shouts of men above distant axes and cross-cut saws. The drum on the pull-boat chattered, the gears ground and creaked. A steam whistle blew, the engine puffed and chugged. The great cypress began to fall. Three hundred feet away he saw a trembling in the dark canopy that was the tree-tops over the swamp. There came a ripping, as woody cells, inseparable for a century, were torn violently one from another. The tree crashed, flattening everything in its path, and the roar of the fall went like a roll of thunder through swamp and hammock and scrub. The boy thought there was a hush after the last echo, as though the men waited before they began to trim and saw, watching the tree like a great prone animal that might not be entirely dead.

When he was a man, he decided, he would not timber. His father, his father's cousin Sylvester, and his Uncle Thaddeus had been timbering since the year he was born. They seemed stupid, puny creatures to him, to be felling and rafting the giants of the swamp. He would raise cattle, like his Uncle Abner; or become a hunter like old man Paine; or make whiskey as his Uncle Zeke was doing. The thought of hunting reminded him that he had not heard his mother's gun in some time. He scrambled to his feet and trotted back over the trail. Piety, coming down the hammock ledge towards her father, saw the boy moving in, with a curious air of rapt detachment, on a line converging with hers.

Lantry was still asleep. He looked old. His mind still ran pursued down dark roadways. This, she thought, and not the wear of time on the bulky body, had weakened him. She felt concerned about his frailty, as he had once concerned himself with hers. She was small and scrawny, as she had always been. But she felt within herself a rooted strength, like that of a small plant sucking at the earth with deep tentacles. Between her father and her son she was strong and comforted.

Lant's eyes shone as his mother fished out squirrels from the pockets of the man's jacket she wore. There were ten. The boy gathered the limp grey bodies together and tip-toed on bare feet to his grandfather. He piled them on the sleeping man's lap and against his breast. When he laid one on either side of Lantry's neck, the man wakened with a start and leaped to his feet, scattering dead squirrels like leaves. Piety chuckled and the child shouted.

"Dog take it," Lantry said, "I figgered I'd done woke up in a nest o' varmints."

The boy sobered.

"Squirrels is varmints, ain't they?"

"I reckon so. I had it right. A nest o' varmints is jest what 'twas."

They laughed together. The man and boy were friendliest when the woman was with them. A turbulent stream flowed into a quiet pond and another flowed out of it. One violence did not meet the other. The boy carried the squirrels against his chest. He went ahead of Piety and Lantry. Where the hammock met the clearing, he stopped short. He pointed with a stubby brown toe to fresh deer tracks.

"A doe and a fawn," he said excitedly. "Ma, le's track the boogers and you shoot 'em."

The fawn, in the early fall, must be past the spotted stage and at its best for eating. Piety turned to Lantry.

"Reckon hit's ary use to try and foller? I ain't much for trackin'."

"The boy's a fine tracker," he said indulgently. "Le's go a piece, anyways."

The trail led in plain sight along the edge of the clearing, across the road and into the scrub. Piety hung the squirrels in the crotch of a tree. They crept along in single file. Lant led the way, pointing out the tracks. They went a long way into the scrub. It was the farthest either Piety or Lantry had come on foot.

The trees grew thickly, like trees in a dream, and there were no shadows, because all the scrub was shadow. The scrub was unreal. They had left behind the road, the hammock and the river. Human life was left behind, and human safety. Nothing was here but thin pines and blackjacks, with scrub palmettos thick and hindering underneath. They could scarcely walk for the low growth. Piety could see no further track, but the boy insisted it was plain. Where the underbrush was thickest they heard once the faint whirr of a rattler. All three stood breathless for a long time. At last the boy, shaking himself free from his mother's hand on his shoulder, pointed a cautious foot ahead. There was no further sound. The snake had slipped away.

The trail led into the rough, a patch of ground that had been lately burned, and the fire put out by rains. The area here was as the scrub had been in front of Lantry's clearing when he first moved from across the river. The new growth was low and tangled, matted with stumps and burned trees. Because the strip was narrow, the three continued across it. It lead into old scrub; scrub whose tall pines were bent by the storm of '71. The pines grew openly, with stretches carpeted with coarse grass, dotted with the grey-green of sweet myrtle bushes, of rosemary and sea-myrtle.

The doe and fawn were here, bedding. The doe leaped up ahead of them. The fawn lurched to its feet and turned immense wondering eyes. Piety cocked her gun and levelled it; exerted her strength to pull the stiff trigger. She was slow. The fawn and doe were gone.

The child went into a rage. He stamped his foot on the ground like an infuriated bull yearling. He spat, as he had seen Lantry do. His red-brown eyes glared at his mother. He seized the heavy gun from her hands and tried to put it to his shoulder to fire in the direction of the deer's retreat. He could not lift it. He stared at it. His fury subsided as quickly as it had come.

Lantry said gently, "Never you mind, son. Grand-daddy'll git you a leetle gun you kin tote and shoot all by yourself."

The child nodded. "Then I kin trail alone."

They turned to go home. They walked silently for half a mile, each with his own thoughts. The child was in the rear, following without attention, his head poked forward on his long neck. Lantry halted.

"Py-tee," he said in a low voice, "this ain't right."

She looked at him, her hand half over her mouth.

"I cain't never find my way here, Pa," she said. "I figgered you knowed the way."

"I figgered so too. But I ain't never been much in these parts. I got no hankerin' to be in the scrub no time. Le's try up here a ways, see kin we hit us a trail back."

They went farther. The scrub deepened. They were lost. Lantry mopped his forehead with his bandana. Piety took out her snuff-box from her blouse and lipped a pinch for encouragement.

Lantry said, "No use, daughter, I got nary idee where we're at."

The child jerked himself out of his reveries.

"You-all fixin' to go home?" he asked abruptly.

"Soon's we kin find the way," Lantry answered.

Lant craned his neck.

He said, "Lift me up so's I kin see."

He pointed from Lantry's shoulder.

"Yonder's the river," he said.

He set out ahead of them. The man and woman looked at each other.

Piety asked, "Reckon he know?"

Lantry said, "How kin he know?"

But the eight-year-old back ahead of them had a surety that drew them. One way was as good now as another. In a brief time they came out on the road that marked scrub from hammock. They could hear faintly the sounds of the timbering. They had been near home all the time. The boy turned to the right, striding brusquely.

"Son," Lantry called, "how come you to know the way?"

The boy pointed to the ridge at his left.

"Why," he said impatiently, "I could see the tops o' them big trees yonder. Them's hickories. Ain't none o' them in the scrub. Ain't hickories nowhere excusin' right along above the river."

They retrieved their squirrels and approached the clearing.

They saw three women and some children waiting for them on the stoop. Martha came down the fenced-in lane to meet them. Behind her were Thaddeus' wife and Zeke's wife, Lulu. Zeke had married Dan Wilson's widow. He was a gentle step-father to her girl-child, Kezzy.

Lulu had not been friendly after she married Zeke. Piety and Lantry had not seen the girl in some months. Kezzy was ten years old, with a milk-white skin, great black eyes and smooth black hair that hung over her shoulders in stiff braids. She was square-built and quiet. Piety was struck at once with her resemblance to some one she had known and liked. Lantry studied the child, stroking his beard.

"Lemme see—Annie Wilson were aunt to this gal young un. That right, Lulu?"

Lulu said, primly belligerent, "Annie were Dan's sister, all right. Her and Dan's buried side by side right now. I were always proud Dan never had none of Annie's crazy ways."

"Annie Wilson were a fine woman," Lantry said quietly.

He turned to his daughter Martha.

"What you women-folks studyin' about? Clustered on my stoop like hens with your biddies."

Martha smiled, smoothing back her sandy hair. She laid a hand on the shoulder of her oldest living child, the boy Cleve. He was ten, the age of Kezzy; a pasty-faced boy, sullen, inclined to a round puffiness. Four younger girls twisted their hands into the woman's full calico skirt.

"Well, Pa," she answered him, "we been wonderin' wasn't you goin' to start Lant in to the school this year. If you was, we figgered couldn't we git you-all to tote the hull mess o' young uns acrost the river in the rowboat."

Lantry said, "We been talkin' about it. I been learnin' him since he were six. He do pretty good now at the readin'. I reckon 'tain't the same as reg'lar schoolin', though."

Lant said, "I cain't go to school. I'm fixin' to hunt this winter."

The man stroked the boy's head and studied him thoughtfully. Piety could not endure to have the boy all day across the river, sitting unwilling at desk and bench.

"He'll perfeckly hate it," she said. "You jest as good to put a wild cat to the books."

The boy Cleve grinned, exposing his gums.

"He'll be a varmint shore, if you don't learn him somethin' more'n runnin' in the scrub."

Lantry said, "We got it to do, Py-tee." He nodded at the women. "Leave us know the day school is due to commence. Have all the young uns is to go, at the Landin' soon of a mornin'. Py-tee and me between us kin tote 'em and fetch 'em back agin."

Relieved, they talked a while of the timbering, of fall crops and hogs, then took their leave. The girl Kezzy passed close to Lant.

She said in a low voice, "You won't hate it the least bit, time you git used to it."

Lantry watched after her, smiling.

He nodded to Piety, "She shore favours her Aunt Annie."

Suddenly Piety was watching again a big man and woman scuffling sand in the dance; fat-wood torches flickered and she was sitting close to Annie Wilson, hearing the rich laugh, smelling the sweet musk of the big sweating body. When the stoop under her took shape again, her eyes came to rest on the boy. His head was thrown back like a deer's at sound of the dogs. His nostrils quivered. He glared impartially at her, at Lantry, and in the direction of his kin plodding down the lane.

"I be dogged," he said, "if I aim to mess up with no school no longer'n I have to."

VIII

THE TWO YEARS of school on which Lantry insisted, passed for the boy Lant in a dull torment. By the spring in which he was ten years old, he had learned to read and write and to figure enough to make change in money. He had learned as well to pass the brief winter sessions in the unresisting aloofness of a caged animal that has found there is no escape.

The second year was over and done with. On an afternoon

in April he followed Kezzy and his cousins out of the schoolhouse and down the road through the piney-woods to the river landing, where his mother waited for them with the rowboat. The girl of twelve hummed under her breath. Cleve was hilarious and chased the smaller children around the pine trees. Lant was preoccupied.

He was thinking about squirrels. He had thought about them a great deal. He could tell young squirrels from old ones and females from males. There were squirrels in between that were neither male nor female. Old man Paine the hunter said it was to keep off too much fighting. The male squirrels were fighting now, for they were mating. That morning, coming through the hammock, he had seen one big grey male attacked by three. They had baited him one at a time, while the female watched bright-eyed from a crotch.

He had long wondered whether squirrels could swim; whether they could swim across the fierce sweep of the river current. Now, as the children settled themselves in the rowboat and Piety picked up the oars to swing out into the river, he saw that a grey cat-squirrel was rocking back and forth on the trunk of a palm, poising to jump into the water. The palmetto was fifty feet high and curved in almost as sharp an arc as a sapling trap. The bent top leaned part-way across the river. The woman settled to her rowing. The squirrel leaped. His jump, with his tail spread behind him, carried him more than half-way across the stream. He paddled madly the rest of the way to the east shore and was out of sight with a whisk. The boy grunted to himself.

"Kin swim like Hell," he said under his breath with satisfaction.

Kezzy asked, "What you see now?"

He frowned and dabbled his fingers indifferently over the side of the boat.

"Jest a ol' squirrel."

Piety said, "You young uns has got all your books and sich. I best to carry you thu the creek."

Kezzy said, "'Tis a sight closer, Aunt Py-tee, but I hates to see you polin' thu sich a thick place. Leave Cleve take the boat thu the swamp." She added, looking at him, "You big ol' lazy, you."

He grinned at her but did not repeat her offer.

At the entrance to the creek the woman laid down her oars and stood up in the stern to pole. The channel narrowed in the swamp. It doubled back on itself, winding about obstructions of rotted stumps and fallen logs. It was gloomy; almost without light. The boat slipped under the arching growth like a water-bug. The boy Lant drew a deep breath. He reached for a leaf of flea-myrtle and crushed its spiced sweetness against his nose. He leaned his cheek against the board seat so that he might peer into the ends of hollow logs for a sight of hidden alligator or coiled moccasin.

The creek spread flat and shallow in the overhanging swamp. Piety poled the boat between cypress knees. The children jumped out on hummocks of dark muck. Piety tied the boat to a cypress and laid the oars behind a clump of bushes. Lant gathered a handful of twigs and crouched a step at a time along the swamp edge. He drew in his breath and let it out again with a puff, hurling his sticks in the water. A gurgle sounded above the ripples he had made, and a wider ring spread across the brown water. Cleve called after him.

"What you chunkin' sticks at?"

"Leetle ol' 'gator."

"More'n likely a catfish," the older boy said.

Lant shook his head.

"I seed his big ol' eyes."

He cut up the steep ledge at an angle from the others, following a narrow trail among the live-oaks and hickories and magnolias. The April sunlight, so fiercely strident in the open, was defeated by the dark hammock and filtered in thin patches to the ground. The earth here was cool. Ferns were moist and sweet-scented and fungus sprouted, sometimes in alabaster sprays like unearthly flowers. He broke one off; smelled of its loamy must; touched his tongue to the stem, splintered like crystal; remembered old man Paine's warning against poisonous herbs and threw it down.

From the north the sound of the timbering came faintly. The crews had passed the Lantry land and were working beyond Zeke Lantry's homestead. Thad Lantry and Willy and Sylvester Jacklin still worked with them. There sounded the dull clang of wedges being driven. Then the boy heard the muffled crash of a tree. From the thickness of the sound he judged it to have been a dead-fall, taking the top of another tree with it. He reached the top of the ridge, where the hammock broke abruptly into the Lantry clearing. Piety and Cleve and Kezzy and the small children were entering the field below him. Ahead, he saw Lantry's tall form moving about the yard.

He was suddenly conscious that instead of the renewed activity that usually followed a felling, there had been a silence. Now he heard one man "Halloo-o-o-o," and another take up the cry. The steam whistle on the pull-boat burst into a long-drawn scream. Piety cupped her mouth with her small hands and called shrilly across the field.

"Lant! You go see what's the matter."

He dropped his books on the sand and loped down through the hammock towards the timbering. He had run half a mile when he heard the voices of men come close. On the trail he met his uncles, Thaddeus and Sylvester, and two of the piney-woods Jacklins. They were carrying among them a large bundle wrapped in their clothing. Thad was naked to his waist, white-skinned and thin. His blue work shirt with one sleeve dangling held the bundle under the middle. Blood soaked through it as from fresh venison in a sack. The men looked at one another.

Thad said, "Son, you jest as good to know now, hit's your daddy."

The boy blinked. He remembered the heavy crash of cypress.

"Was it him caught in the dead-fall?"

"It were him."

The men laid the bundle on the ground. Thad wiped the sweat from his throat; passed his hand down the hollow between his ribs, leaving a streak of grime; shook his hand, so that small drops spattered on a palmetto frond by the trail.

One of the Jacklins said, "I never figgered Willy no big kind of a man, but the pore feller's as heavy totin' as a buck in the scrub."

Another said, "It'll pussle us to git him home."

The boy stared at the bundle. Syl Jacklin looked at him.

"He were slow, son," he said solemnly. "Cousin Willy were always slow. Hit don't do to be slow too clost to no dead-fall."

Lant asked slowly, "Is he done dead?"

Thad said, "If we hadn't of knowed 'twas Willy was there, nobody wouldn't never of knowed who 'twas, after." He spat to the side of the trail. "Son, I don't know what Py-tee kin do about a fitten buryin'. They jest ain't enough o' Willy to fix nice in the coffin. Le's go, boys."

They lifted the bundle by its four corners. The boy followed behind. His stomach hurt him. He remembered his father, slow and quiet, with his black forelock between his eyes. He tried to imagine a man smashed by a dead-fall; he would be flat, like smoked mullet. He could make the two pictures of his father but he could not fit them together.

He ran ahead of the men to open gates for them into the clearing. They passed through the garden into the yard. His mother walked slowly towards them, twisting her apron between her hands. Lantry stood by a chair on the breezeway, holding to its back.

"Willy?" she asked.

Thad nodded.

"Take him in to the bed," she said.

Lantry watched after them, trembling as they passed him. In the bedroom the men hesitated.

Sylvester said, "Better git a ol' quilt to lay under——"

The woman said, "The mattress don't matter. Hit's jest corn-shucks."

Lantry came to the doorway, leaning heavily against the frame. "How come it to happen?" he asked.

"The pore feller were slow, Pa," Thaddeus said. "He someway wa'n't payin' no mind when the tree were throwed."

The blood in Lantry's face grew purple. His temples pulsed.

"God damn his sorry hide," he said hoarsely.

The men raised from their disposing of the lacerated mass on the bed. They gaped at him.

"Hit's jest like the fool to make a pore widder-woman o' Py-tee before her time. He's a no-account white man, dead or alive——"

His breath grew short. He choked. He put one hand to his

throat and clawed at his windpipe. Piety left the side of the bed and came to him.

"Pa—you're gittin' yourself in a turrible fix."

Lant, by the window, saw that she was more concerned for the living man than for the dead. She led him to his bed and loosened his shirt. The three Jacklins talked together in the bedroom. Sylvester came alone to the woman.

"Py-tee," he said, "we'll jest go on and take Willy acrost the river for the buryin'." He flushed. "A Jacklin ain't beholden to nobody."

Lantry was fighting for breath. The woman began to pour whiskey a drop at a time down his throat. His mouth was open, like a fish on a line. When his throat was full, the whiskey began to trickle out again. She called to her brother.

"Thad! You do what's right about Willy. I can't leave Pa. He won't never come out of this un."

He nodded to the other men. They passed through the room with the wet bundle. Lant heard their voices in the yard; then the movement of a mule and the sound of the wagon rattling down the road. He moved across the room to Lantry's bed. The man was black with agony. A few minutes before the end he drew a comfortable breath or two. He knew that he was done for. He clenched Piety's wrist until it swelled in his grip. He jerked his head towards the boy, big-eyed and white of face at the foot of the bed.

He said hoarsely, "He'll look out for you, Py-tee." He gasped. "This place—suit him. He kin make a livin' here—somehow."

He closed his eyes. His chin sagged, spreading his beard on his chest. Suddenly he reared bolt upright in the bed. Terror wiped out his pain. His red eyes rolled. He fell back on his pillow. A crafty expression came over the glazing face. He had, after everything, gotten safely away. He plunged panting into the cool dark retreat of death. He whispered over his shoulder to old pursuing phantoms.

"Run, you bastards, run!"

IX

SORROW was like the wind. It came in gusts, shaking the
woman. She braced herself. She closed her eyes against
the sight of the dead man. His set features were aquiline; the
yellow of bee's-wax above the streaked red beard. Safe from his
fear, he looked noble and at peace. Pain swept across her in a gale.
The deep-lidded eyes blinked. She shook her small head to be
rid of her torment.

Suddenly Piety remembered her son. He had gone away as
Lantry fought for his last breath. She went across the breezeway
into the kitchen. He sat on a low bench before the stove. He was
trembling as a frightened puppy trembles. She had not seen him
afraid before. Lantry's fear was tangible in the moment of his
dying, and a cold breath had blown in on the boy from a distant
land. She sat beside him. The wood-fire was almost out and she
reached across him for a stick of pine. He handed her splinters to
make a blaze and after they had sat together a while his trembling
stopped.

A little after sunset the front gate clicked and steps sounded
on the stoop. Zeke Lantry and his step-daughter Kezzy came into
the room and Piety went to meet them. Zeke took his sister's hand
gravely and walked with her to look down at his father. The
drake's-tails fluttered on his neck. His pale blue eyes watered and
he blew his nose. He had spilled fermented mash on his trousers
and the odour rose about him in a sour wave.

"I ran off a charge this evenin'," he said. "I were jest crossin'
the river from the outfit, jugs and all, when a raft o' logs passed
me and the men hollers to me Willy were dead and Pa were dyin'.
Hit takened me so I like to turned the boat over."

She asked, "Where's Marthy and Lulu and Nellie?"

"Marthy don't dast leave the house. She sent word you was
havin' trouble enough without she should take to the child-bed on
you." He blew his nose again. "Sis, my Lulu and Thad's Nellie,

they right-out say they'll not put foot in your house again. They both got Jacklin blood and they're sayin' mighty hard things about you and Pa. I say, Pa wa'n't hisself, and you cain't hold a dyin' man's words agin him. I say, you done right lookin' after him, with Willy to where mortal hand couldn't raise to he'p him. The dead's dead, but the breath o' life is the breath o' life."

He cleared his throat, pulled out a plug of tobacco, looked at it and shoved it hastily back into his pocket.

Kezzy asked in a low voice, "Where's Lant, Aunt Py-tee?"

"To the kitchen. The young un's had a perfeck fright."

The girl walked away with her eyes averted from the sight of Lantry. She found Lant feeding the fire and stroking the head of Lantry's small mongrel dog.

"Hey, Lant."

"Hey, Kezzy."

She went to him and put her hand on his shoulder, leaning over him so that her long smooth braids hung against his flat chest. He shook away.

"Git them ol' black snakes outen my way," he said.

They laughed. He drew a deep breath. He realized that he was hungry.

"Kezzy," he whispered, "don't nobody eat no supper when folkses die?"

"You ain't had nothin'?"

She was not familiar with the kitchen. Her mother had discouraged intimacy between the two families, through jealousy that the Lantry land was plainly to pass to Piety instead of the sons. But she foraged in the kitchen safe and fried the boy cold biscuits and warmed squirrel-meat and rice together. He ate ravenously. She lit a kerosene lamp and sat beside him. Piety and Zeke talked in low tones in the front room.

Zeke called to Kezzy and they went away. Lant sat alone in the kitchen until he nodded. Through the doorway he could see his mother sitting motionless. A shaft of lamplight lay across her pointed face and on the small knotted hands. He did not want to see his grandfather again. He moved without sound into his bedroom off the breezeway, undressed as far as his underwear and got into his bed. After a time he heard his mother stir in the front room. Then she too went to bed.

The woman was dropping off to an unhappy sleep when she heard a sound as of a small animal scuffling across the floor. The boy was at the side of her bed, slipping in under the quilt beside her. It was like having a wooden box in the bed, she thought. The buttons on his underwear were hard against her arm and his knees and elbows filled the bed. He was all bones and buttons. He had not slept at her side since she had weaned him. She felt with her hand until she had found his hard young knuckles. She drowsed. Towards morning she wakened and found that he had slipped away.

In the afternoon Willy Jacklin was buried on the west side of the river and Lantry was buried on the east. Several Lantry and Jacklin infants lay under the blackjack oaks of Martha's clearing and her husband Sylvester had given a grudging permission that for Piety's sake the old man should rest there too. The preacher and most of the family buried Willy. Even Abner Lantry had chosen to follow him. Only Piety and Lant, Martha and her children, and Zeke and Thad saw the sand fall on Lantry's home-made pine coffin. Martha was big with child and left the burying nervously as soon as it was ended. There was no ceremony. Piety thought bitterly that her father had come without the word of his fellows into an alien country and was gone the same way. Zeke walked with her and Lant down the road as far as his place.

"Sis," he asked, "you got money sufficient to do with?"

"I got money to do with for a whiles. Willy were rale good that-a-way. He give me his loggin' wages, what didn't go for rations, and I got some hid out. I'm gittin' corn and sweet pertaters in the ground soon's I kin. I aim to fatten hogs, come fall."

"You always was a great un for corn and 'taters and hogs. If I remembers, you always had your hogs so rotten spoiled to where they'd lay up near the house all day, scairt to go to rootin' off a ways for fear they wouldn't hear a year o' corn to drap."

She smiled a little. "Well, Zeke, I makes mighty fine hogs when the 'gators'll leave 'em be."

Zeke said to Lant, "You been wild as a jay-bird, son, runnin' the woods. You belong to he'p your mammy now."

They went on. The boy's long arms dangled at his sides. His big head, poked forward on his neck, moved from side to side, like a turtle's. He frowned, his eyebrows meeting over the red-brown eyes.

"Ma," he burst out, "I been studyin'. Grandpa wa'n't no farmer. Nor he wa'n't no trapper nor no timberman. What did he do for a livin' in the up-country where he come from?"

"He never did love to say, but he told me oncet 'twere makin' moonshine whiskey."

The boy nodded.

"The revenooers gits after them fellers up in Caroliny," he said wisely. "Grandpa done tol' me they was raisin' sand all the time."

His eyes turned to her and held, steady as a good bead on a target.

"What were he skeert of, here in Florida?"

She hesitated.

"I don't rightly know," she faltered.

"You do too," he said. "You do too know."

"I reckon he'd had trouble."

"What kind o' trouble?"

"If you got to know," she said desperately, "he killed him a feller and had to take out."

"Who was after him for killin' the feller?"

"I reckon the gov'mint," she said. "Hit were a gov'mint feller."

"Didn't nobody never come up with him, did they?"

"Nobody never come up with him here. He had it always to figger on."

The boy nodded.

"That's what he was skeert of."

He spat zestfully into the gallberry bushes by the road.

"I'll jest bet he had good reason, killin' that feller. Nobody better never come messin' up with me, neither," he said.

His maturity startled her.

"No, nor you'd better not go to gittin' biggety nor lookin' for a fuss. Your Grandpa nicked nary fuss in his life."

She had never tried to rule the boy, but she felt a new and frightening responsibility. Her small voice rose shrilly.

"Don't you go to rarin' back on your dew-claws!"

He swung a moment on the gate before galloping after her up the lane to the house.

"Ma," he coaxed her, "say now I ain't got to go to school no more, come fall."

"You got to learn somethin'," she protested.

"I've done learned a-plenty. I got to make a livin'." He blocked her way, standing with his thin legs spraddled, his eyes owl-like on either side of the ruddy forelock. "Say it now, I ain't got to go no more," he insisted. "Don't look to me to take keer of you if I got to go to school."

In spite of her heaviness, she had to laugh at him.

"If you're he'pin' make the livin', come fall," she promised, "you don't have to go."

She made hot cakes for his supper. She sat with her hands folded in her lap and could not eat. The boy poured the syrup thickly. There was no one to complain. The dog whined at the door and went unheeded.

They were both worn out. Lant thought it would be easier to sleep without Lantry's sharp yellow features lifted to the rafters on his death-bed, with the lamplight flickering over them so that he seemed to breathe. The woman and the boy were in their beds before the sunset melted into the river. The redbirds were still singing when they fell asleep.

A light rain fell during the night.

In the morning Piety said to Lant, "Hit's always so. You take notice, son, hit'll always rain after a buryin'. Hit's planned so o' purpose. The rain washes out the tracks o' the dead along with the tracks o' the livin'. Hit wouldn't do to have the earth all yopped up with the tracks o' the dead."

A sharp pain struck through her because she would never come on Lantry's footprints again.

After breakfast she dug some roots of coral vine to plant on the grave. She helped Lant with his chores and they walked together down the scrub road. They turned into the open blackjack and stopped short at the fresh tawny mound. Something had been digging at the grave.

The boy said excitedly, "Hit's small sharp tracks! Hit must be 'possums. They's dirty scapers."

The woman was faint. It was an obscene thing that Lantry's bones should not go unmolested.

She said, "Don't say nothin' to nobody. We'll come tonight and lay for it."

They went home and waited nervously for dark. They ate no supper, the woman for nausea and the boy for his excitement. He got out his father's 12-gauge gun and polished the sight. Soon after the sun had set they walked the scrub road again and squatted among the blackjacks and waited. Nothing came. They went home at midnight. The next morning the creature bent on its scavenging had dug deeper.

Lant said, "Mought be that wolf been seen around Lake Kerr." The tracks puzzled him.

Piety said, "We come too soon, that's what we done. The varmint done watched us and slipped up when we was gone agin."

The next night they did not go until two o'clock in the morning. As they crept up they heard the scratching of claws on the thin pine box. Lant waited for his eyes to become accustomed to the surroundings. In a few minutes the light colour of the fresh grave swung into focus. Then he made out a small dark form in movement. He fired. A thumping and a scrambling indicated that he had made a hit. When the motion ceased, they approached. The dead animal was Lantry's own dog.

Piety said weakly, "Mebbe he were lonesome for Pa and figgered he wa'n't dead."

"We ain't paid much attention to him the last two-three days," Lant said bitterly. "The low-down varmint were hongry."

He kicked the dog's body into the blackjacks. He was furious and frightened.

In the morning Piety caught Thaddeus before he went to his timbering and Zeke before he went to his still. Since the occasion was somehow extraordinary, Lant rowed across the river and brought back Abner. Abner was florid and pompous. He had cattle ranging on both sides of the river.

He said at once to his brothers, "You fellers buried the ol' man too shallow. Hit don't do to dig a grave too shallow."

Zeke said mildly, "We ain't had much practice, Ab."

They were digging a new grave for luck, throwing the red-gold sand against the sun. Thaddeus rested on his shovel.

"I don't know as a six-foot grave be needful," he said. "Four foot had orter do for ary man."

"Not for me, 'twouldn't," Abner said. "I aim to swell up when I die."

Zeke and Thad were doing the work. Abner strolled off to poke the body of the dead hound with his foot.

"On my side the river," he remarked, "some o' the folks was so foolishly fond o' Pa they'd say this were a case o' dog-eat-dog."

They guffawed.

Zeke said, "Pa were all right."

Piety sat near-by with her hand over her mouth. The boy watched with his hands in his overall pockets, scuffling the sand with his bare toes.

Abner said, "Why'n't you bury your dog?"

"He weren't mine. He were Grandpa's. I got nuthin' to do with him. Let the buzzards have him."

"Th'ow him out a ways then."

Lantry's board coffin was moved and the new grave filled in. Abner turned to the boy.

"You want you a rale good dog, son?"

"I wouldn't keer."

The man pondered. He never gave something for nothing.

"I tell you, son. I got nobody to look after my cattle this side the river. I got a pair o' young dogs has got no names, even. You come git them dogs and learn 'em to run cattle and you he'p round up and brand and butcher, and you're welcome to the dogs and a calf for your own."

Lant's face was eager. His eyes shone, as though sunlight moved swiftly across pools of cypress water. He had never had a dog of his own.

He said, "I'll come with you and git 'em."

His uncles laughed at his eagerness.

"You'd git there quicker to swim the river, Lant," Thaddeus said.

Piety watched him follow after Abner. She went back alone to the cabin. When dusk came, and the boy had not returned, and the hoot-owls cried, she hated the sound. She got out her accordion and played a hymn on it. Her throat swelled and she thought she might feel better if she played something lively. She began to play "Double Eagle" but she remembered Lantry playing it on the banjo with his head thrown back and she was obliged to put away the accordion. She sat with her hands folded in her lap, rocking in the buckskin rocker, lipping a little snuff. She thought of walking down the road to Martha.

" 'Twon't be the last time I'll set alone," she decided, and did not go. She had no existence, she thought, outside these two males; the one living and the other dead.

The boy returned after dark. She heard him talking softly to the new dogs. He was bedding them under the kitchen, tying them so they could not run away. She heard him go into the kitchen and get cornbread to feed them. She heard them lapping water. She strained her ears for the words he was saying to them. The boy came in the house and she laid out a cold supper for him. She stuffed crumbs of biscuit in her mouth, watching his face.

"Them's fine leetle fellers," he said. "One's black as a nigger and one's kind o' red-like." He stirred sugar in his cold coffee.

"I've done named 'em Red and Black, Ma."

She was grateful to him for telling her what he had named the puppies.

"Them's fine names for dogs o' sich colors," she said with enthusiasm. "You couldn't git you no better names for a pair o' dogs."

X

THE NEW puppies, Red and Black, barked with proper ferocity, rearing against the slat-fence. The horse-hooves coming south down the scrub road sounded nearer. Piety was in the back yard at the wash tubs and Lant went to the front stoop to watch. A grey horse, ridden by a stranger, drew up at the gate at the foot of the lane. Lant could make out the girl Kezzy sitting the horse primly behind the rider. She slipped down and opened the gate and the stranger dismounted and followed her.

"Hey, Lant!" she called.

"Hey."

The horseman spoke cordially.

"Howdy, son."

"Howdy."

The boy was braced, as though on a slippery bank.

"Where's Aunt Py-tee?" the girl asked.

"Back at the pot."

"The man here's lookin' for Zeke," she said, lifting her heavy eyebrows at him as she passed.

The boy's blood pounded in his throat. The stranger must be a revenuer; or, sent by the government, had tracked his grandfather down at last. He thought with relief that they were three months too late for Lantry. Then panic swept across him again. The man, of course, was after Zeke.

"What's your name, son?"

"Lantry Jacklin."

"You any kin to Zeke Lantry?"

"He's my uncle."

"Well, now," the stranger said, leaning forward, "you're just the fellow I want to see. Your uncle Zeke's at his still, isn't he?"

The boy did not answer. The man studied him. It irked him to have Zeke's family evade him. Zeke's step-daughter, alone at the house, had claimed no knowledge of his whereabouts. Zeke had already made excuses to keep him away from the still. When Pryde bought whiskey of a moonshiner, he liked to know where to find him.

"Come on, sonny. Tell me where your Uncle Zeke is right now. Just point which way."

The boy felt the coercion and threw his weight against it, like a young bull calf against the tug of the halter. His eyes glared but he did not move or speak.

"I'll just bet you don't even know."

There was no trap quick enough for the boy's instinct. He turned quietly into the house. He returned behind Kezzy and his mother. Pryde had seated himself on the stoop.

"How-do, Ma'am. My name's Pryde."

He asked his questions.

Piety said, "No, I got no idee where Zeke mought be."

"I'm the man buying that cane syrup of his," he said. "That syrup that makes a man feel so prime." He winked at her.

She said politely, "That so?"

A silence fell, in which the squirrels could be heard barking in the neighbouring hammock.

At last Pryde said, "Well, I'm mighty sorry to miss him. I had business with him."

Piety and Kezzy looked quickly at each other. It would be a pity to lose trade for Zeke. The stranger seemed all right. Piety believed him to be the man of whom Zeke had spoken. Pryde was the name, all right. She wanted to tell him to go down the road to Magnolia Landing and to halloo across the river to Zeke, who would answer him from Taylor's Dread. She was unable to do so. Caution dammed the words in her throat.

At last she said questioningly, "If you was to care to state your business now? If you was to say what-all you wants o' Zeke, mought be I could find him and tell him."

It was the best Pryde could do.

He said bluntly, "Yes, I'll state my business. Tell Zeke to put a barrel of whiskey on the *Mary* when she comes down Wednesday. Here's some tags to use. See, Florida Cane Syrup, addressed to the Southern Wholesale Grocery Company at Jacksonville. Tell him to put one on the barrel and to send a barrel every Wednesday until I tell him different."

The woman and the girl and boy blinked at him. The stranger turned away.

Piety said, speaking mildly after the vanishing back, "Mought be a good idee to smear a leetle rale syrup around the edge o' the barrel-head, like the juice were leakin' a mite."

Pryde said over his shoulder, "I don't care what he does to the barrel-head, as long as the barrel gets on the boat."

He mounted his horse and thumped off. Piety turned the tags over in her hand.

She said, "Reckon we better go tell Zeke. Mought make a difference, settin' up more mash, mebbe. I'll git me a hat."

She lifted the wide hat of woven palmetto strands over her head with a stiff gesture, bringing it down to sit high on her small head. The three walked across the clearing and down the hammock ledge to the open river landing. Piety took up the oars.

"I'll row down-stream," she said, "and you young uns kin spell me off rowin' back."

The rowboat moved rapidly. The river seemed to stand still while the banks slipped past. Here and there the tangled lushness bared to dry hammock, with saw palmettos visible, and yellow sand. Sometimes there was a break both in swamp and hammock, and broom-sage and brier-berries grew to the edge of the water. No one could have found the entrance to Taylor's Dread who did not know the landmarks: Hoop-skirt, the big cypress, on one side, and on the other a dead grey magnolia. The river here had the trick of sending a dribbling thread of current through a slice of mainland, making in effect an island. Yet between island and mainland the dividing creek was so tortuous and so shallow that a stranger would have called the island, swamp. Part way in, the channel merged hopelessly with swamp.

"I ain't been here in a good whiles," Piety said. "I cain't foller these creeks."

The girl said, "I cain't foller 'em."

The boy pointed to an eddy under an overhanging swamp laurel.

"Yonder 'tis."

"That's it," Kezzy agreed. "Last time we come, Zeke cut a limb there to string fish."

Piety swung with relief through the dimly marked opening. Black rattan, twisted about ash trees, scraped the boatsides as they slid through. At times it seemed as though they must be again mistaken in the channel, for there would come an obstruction. But a submerged log that looked solid would yield to the pole; a tangle of wild rose briers would open at the last instant so that, lowering their bodies flat to the boat, they could pass through. A quarter of a mile in, there came to their noses the sour sweetness of fermenting mash. They were opposite the still. Piety spoke in a low voice, questioningly.

"Zeke?"

The answer, as low, came startlingly at their elbows. They had been seen and heard. Zeke squatted behind a clump of palmettos.

"Py-tee?"

The woman turned the bow of the boat between cypress knees. Kezzy and the boy climbed out, drawing the boat high. Piety followed. Zeke stood up.

"Hi, folkses."

Piety asked, "Where's Lulu?"

He jerked his head.

"Yonder."

He was gathering an armful of ash wood for his fire. They picked their way through the swamp to the still. Lulu was there, tending the pot. She spoke curtly to Piety. A pile of bricks and two large sheets of copper stood at one side. Zeke planned to build a larger outfit now that business was good. There was a demand, even at town bars, for good strong corn liquor. Piety gave him the message from Pryde. She described the visitor. Zeke nodded.

"That's him, a'right. That's Pryde."

Kezzy said anxiously, "I jest didn't know what to do when he come to the house. All I could study on, was, leave Aunt Py-tee talk to him."

Zeke said amiably, "You both done jest right. I jest as lief he not come nosin' around here."

The boy was prowling around the wooden barrels of mash. He stood on tiptoe and stirred one with the long paddle standing there.

"You git out o' there, Lant!" Piety spoke sharply. "You'll spile your Uncle Zeke's buck."

"That un ain't hardly buck yit, Py-tee. Hit's slow, like. Hit ain't made a cap yit and hit's 'most due to run."

"Hit's been cold, nights," Lulu said.

"That's about it."

Zeke dipped a gourd in one of the barrels of seething mash. "You want some o' the beer, Lulu? How 'bout you, Py-tee?"

They refused. He gave a drink to the boy, his face in eclipse behind the gourd. They laughed at him. Zeke took the gourd and drank deeply.

"They got no call to laugh at us, son," he said to Lant. "Us knows what's good." He wiped the foam from his mouth. "I declare, this be the healthiest stuff to drink. How come me to drink it, hit's a pure nuisance to tote river water. And they's a taste to the creek water I jest someways cain't love. I tried the buck one day I were thirsty and felt kind o' porely, and it done me good."

The island was cool and dusky. The sunlight lay like lace under the palms and cypresses. The black moist earth smelled of leaf mould. Wild yellow cannas and blue iris bloomed around the brackish pools. The pot boiled, gurgling as it began. Its steam passed through a pipe and through copper coils submerged in water. The distillate began to drip slowly from a copper spout. The Lantrys leaned their backs against tree trunks and fell idle and silent. The boy climbed a tall sweet-gum and gathered a handful of the balls to play with. He settled himself in a high crotch where he could glimpse the river on one side, and on the other his Uncle Abner's cattle coming through the swamp to drink.

There was suddenly a commotion at the edge of the creek. Lant cried from his tree-crotch, "Hogses!" and half a dozen black shoats splashed through the swamp, throwing the muck and rattling palmetto fronds. They collided violently with one another as they discovered the group of humans, and fell in a heap. They were drunk. The boy laughed shrilly from the sweet-gum, throwing his prickly balls. Zeke shouted and lunged at them. They staggered to their feet and ran sideways, their ears flopping over hazed eyes. He drove them back across the shallow water of the creek. They ran grunting to the piney-woods beyond. Piety and Kezzy and the boy laughed, but Zeke was angry.

"Dog take them shoatses o' Posey's." He was out of breath. "They comes ever' day a-fillin' their bellies with my th'owed-out mash and gittin' hog-drunk to go back home again. Ary fool could back-track 'em here to the still. I got a good idee to move my outfit."

"You feered Posey'll call in the revenooers?" Piety asked.

"Hell, no. Ain't no revenooers in these parts, Sis. I'm skeert Posey'll come steal my whiskey."

Piety chuckled and rose from the ground to go. The boy clambered down from the tree. He ran ahead to climb in the boat and picked up the oars. It would be a long row against the current. He settled down in his usual silence, his eyes alert. On the way he might see many things; a buck crossing the river; an otter's smooth flat nose lifted above the sinuous streak that was the swimming body; always alligators and Poor Joes, and perhaps a water-turkey that at sight of them would drop from its limb as if shot, straight into the depths of the river.

Kezzy said, "Leave me take a oar, Lant."

"I don't want no big ol' girl rowin' side o' me," he said.

On Wednesday Lant heard the *Mary* whistle as she passed north and approached Two-Mile Landing above Taylor's Dread. Zeke was there, he thought, loading his barrel of whiskey with its syrup label.

"Sho," he thought, "I could tell the difference if I was a revenooer. Whiskey makes a thin sound moving. Syrup's slow and thick."

The barrel was not questioned, he decided, for three Wednesdays in succession he heard the *Mary* whistle and no news came of trouble. On a Monday the *Mary* went south up the river as usual. Soon after the last echo of the engines had been absorbed by the bends in the stream, Lant heard hoof-beats coming up the scrub road. He recognised Zeke, riding a bay mule, and ran to the gate to meet him. Zeke was small and frightened on the big animal. His pale blue eyes bulged and his mouth was tremulous.

"Hit happened," he said. "You tell Py-tee hit happened. I knowed it were a risk. The last barrel busted its hoops on the wharf at Jacksonville. Cap'n Turner's nigger boy th'owed me off a note in a bottle. Cap'n done the best he could for me. He had to tell where the barrel was loaded, but he let on like he didn't know my name. I aim to stay hid out 'til I see what comes of it."

"Where you goin'?" the boy asked eagerly.

"Son, I ain't tellin' nobody but my wife Lulu and her Kezzy— and you-all. I ain't even tellin' Martha and Syl, nor Thad. You tell your Ma I'll be at old man Paine's, and time she figgers they's no more risk, you come git me word."

He lifted his reins and the mule jerked forward.

"I'm jest dependin' on you, son," he called gravely over his shoulder.

The bay mule jogged off. The boy bolted up the lane and into the house to his mother. He repeated breathlessly his uncle's message.

"I mean, ol' Uncle Zeke is scairt," he said.

"He's got reason," she said thoughtfully. "But I some ways don't figger no revenooers'll never git fur into the Dread."

"They's nary man 'tother side o' the river would tell 'em the way to go? None o' Pa's kin what's mad at us?"

She shrilled indignantly at him.

"You got you no sense? Don't never leave me hear you say sich as that again. They's nary Wilson nor Jacklin that low-down and sorry, to turn a man up."

"Some of 'em's right low-down," he insisted, grinning.

That night he could scarcely sleep for excitement. Every sound in the night struck quickly, like a blow. Leaves fell from the live-oak on the shingles like fingers being laid on a latch. When Red and Black, chained under the house, changed position in the sand, it was as though strange men walked in the yard. He was out of bed as soon as his mother in the morning, hurrying her at the stove. He ate his breakfast in a deep absorption. He did his chores in a careless hurry. The woman heard him running down the road toward Zeke's clearing.

Lant slipped up to Zeke's back door. He wanted to see Kezzy. Her mother sometimes sent him curtly away. This time the girl herself came to the door, her square hands dripping with soap-suds.

"Hey, Kezzy," he whispered. "Where's your Ma?"

She laughed.

"She takened to the bed when the word come. She's worse scairt than Zeke. I ain't scairt. I jest got a feelin' nothin' won't come of it."

He stepped into the doorway beside her. For all his gangling length at ten, the girl at twelve was still a head taller. He stood on tiptoe to whisper in her ear.

"Did ol' Zeke leave ary whiskey to the outfit?"

"Three jugs, Ma said."

He frowned importantly.

"Kezzy, Uncle Zeke done tol' me to look out for things. He said he were dependin' on me. How 'bout me and you goin' in the boat and gittin' out that whiskey, if them gov'mint cat-birds goin' to come?"

She looked at him a moment. She took off her gingham apron, tossed it into the kitchen behind her and went with him without speaking. Her dark eyes shone. They walked flat-footed and silent until they were out of Lulu's hearing, then scurried for the road. They ran most of the half-mile.

Piety saw the pair cutting across the far corner of the Lantry clearing. It was not like Kezzy to come so close and not say "Howdy." The woman went to the fence and called to them. They stopped in their tracks. She could see them questioning each other. Finally they walked slowly towards her. Kezzy looked sheepish. The boy faced his mother boldly.

She scolded, "You jest better come when I call. I want to know what-all you young uns are up to."

Kezzy did not speak.

"We're goin'," the boy said, "no matter what you say. We're goin' to git out Uncle Zeke's jugs o' whiskey."

The woman was silent.

"You study about it right on," he said belligerently.

"The way I'm studyin'," she said, "hit's the thing to do. I been thinkin', mought be he had axes and sich could be proved was his."

"You got good sense sometimes, Ma," he said approvingly.

The woman and girl laughed together at him.

"I'll go along," Piety said. "You young uns cain't lift them jugs."

The rowboat was at the open landing. Paddling with the swift current, the boy reached the entrance to the Dread in a few minutes. It was hard poling through the creek channel and he could only go slowly. His high thin cheekbones were wet with sweat. All three felt hurried. They plunged across the swamp to the abandoned still. It stood bleak and cold. The mash had been ready to run the day before and was now flat. Zeke's axe lay in plain sight with his initials burned in the handle. Kezzy ran with it to the boat. The woman made three trips with the five-gallon demi-johns of liquor. They were heavy for her and at the creek edge she dropped the third jug. It struck a stump as it slipped and the crash reverberated back and forth across the Dread. It frightened them. They shivered in the dark swamp.

"Git the boat goin'," the woman said nervously. "We're fixin' to git caught ourselves."

Out of the swamp and on the open river, Lant allowed Kezzy to take one of the oars. Piety sat in the stern seat, her long full skirt spread out around her, covering the two jugs underneath. The boy took his thoughts from the swamp and river to watch his mother's small face, drawn with her fear. Half-way home, the chugging of a motor sounded down the current. A small launch swung suddenly around a bend and passed close to them.

Two strangers on board eyed them casually; nodded to the woman, the girl and the boy, and were gone, leaving a wake that rocked the light rowboat. The boy and girl continued to row, not daring to look at each other. The woman's thin lips were dry. They heard the launch stop at Two-Mile Landing. The boy

thought his heart would burst against his ribs. Safe at the river-
bank at the Lantry landing, he spoke.

"Reckon we kin tote them jugs up the ledge?"

The woman shook her head.

"Hide 'em under the palmetters and lay moss and trash on top."

They walked in single file up through the hammock.

Kezzy said, "I best be gittin' on back to Ma. She'll be rarin'."
She was subdued, but her mouth twitched as she left them. "You
Mister Lant, you," she said drily, "next time you git a idee you
jest keep it."

Piety sat down weakly in the breezeway. The boy sat beside
her, kicking his heels against the steps. He had set out proud and
bold. Now he felt limp and half-sick. Piety dipped herself a drink
of water.

"A ruckus like this takes the starch outen you," she said.

"Ma," he asked, "what happens if them gov'mint buzzards cold-
out ketches a feller?"

She blinked her turtle-lidded eyes and shook her head.

"Jest ain't no tellin'."

They passed a week of torment. Kezzy did not come to the
house. They were trying to make up their minds to walk down
to see her, braving Lulu, when Cleve Jacklin, who had been
visiting his Uncle Abner across the river, brought Piety a note
from him. Phrased discreetly, it passed the word that the revenue
agents had come and gone. They had questioned half the
men at Eureka. No one had heard of any moonshining on the
river. The revenuers had tried to find the outfit, working back
from Two-Mile Landing, but the swamp had been too much for
them. It was safe for Zeke to come home again. Piety might know
her brother's whereabouts; Abner did not. Cleve stood gossiping
with his aunt. The boy Lant slipped away.

When Cleve had gone, Piety found Lant saddling the mule.
Red and Black leaped about its heels.

"I kin go tell Zeke, cain't I?"

"Go ahead. Kin you make Pat's Island by night-fall?"

"Yessum."

"You want to carry cold rations?"

"Better wrop up some biscuits."

"What about your dogs? They're rarin' to go, but it's mighty fur for the leetle fellers."

"Call 'em back, time I'm down the lane."

He was gone, thin and bony on top of the mule, his elbows at angles.

As he rode the long miles to old man Paine's, the sand road shadowy under canopied pines, a load lifted from him. The river was safe, after all; intruders came, but they went away; and swamp and hammock and scrub were safer. When he reached the tall yellow pines that lifted Pat's Island high above the dry scrub country, and found Zeke and old man Paine smoking and chatting on the stoop; when they hailed him like a grown man; when he spent the night in a strange bed, with the smell of strange walls and bedding about him; and when the old hunter said at daylight, "Boy, you spend a week-two with me. Your mammy won't keer"; he forgot his fears. It was as though he had been away in a chill far land and had come safe home again to the good scrub.

Zeke rode away to join the timber crew. He was through with 'shining. The old man and the boy watched after him.

Paine said, "Zeke say you want to quit school and he'p make a livin' for your mammy. I got a bait o' trapses you kin borry. You kin trap all winter. You got a fine place for trappin'. You kin learn to shoot good and sell venison to them river-boats. Son, I'll learn you tricks about huntin' and trappin' will open your eyes like a nine-day puppy. I know the tricks."

He pulled his stringy whiskers and winked.

"A young 'coon for runnin'—but a ol' 'coon for cunnin'."

XI

OLD MAN Paine, sitting on the Lantry stoop with Piety and Lant, waved his catfish whiskers over his chew of tobacco. "Sun's jest fixin' to set over Simms' ledge," he said.

Lant said, "Moon-rise 'bout a hour after sun tonight."

The old man nodded.

"Finest kind o' time for the deer."

"Moon-down's jest as good," Lant said.

Paine gave him a push with his foot.

"You leetle ol' shirt-tail boy, you, settin' there tellin' me the time to hunt. How old you now, anyway?"

"He's fourteen," Piety answered defiantly. "You'd think he were a growed man. I declare I never knowed a young un so biggety."

The old hunter swerved to the boy's defense. They had become cronies, as close as the distance between them allowed. They visited back and forth several times a year. Paine had passed on to the boy his lore of scrub and hammock. Much was only corroboration of what Lant had guessed.

"Why, the boy's right," he said. "He knows the deer feeds on the moon, like most ary wild creeter. Four times the deer feeds. Stirs or feeds. Moon-rise and moon-down, and south-moon-over and south-moon-under. Come moon-rise, say, the deer's done been sleepin', ain't they? They comes out about a hour 'fore the moon. They feeds a while and frolics a while."

"And blows," Lant interrupted.

"And blows. Or sets lullin' around. Or walks around nibblin'. They fools around a good whiles." He spat from the stoop. "Hit's jest my idee," he added, "favourin' moon-rise. Seem to me the deer's hongrier and more keerless. Jest like I enjoys my breakfast afore sun-up the most of ary meal."

"The best time for deer," Lant said, "is after two-three days' rain."

"You mighty right."

"Why's that?" Piety asked.

"Why, the deer won't sleep in the rain. Time the rain stops, they beds down to sleep and you kin walk right up on 'em. Many's the time I could of drug off a deer by the scut, he'd be sleepin' that sound."

"I never knowed that," Piety said.

"Reckon not." Paine winked at Lant. "You ain't never lived here in the scrub, Miss Py-tee. You jest done been here."

They laughed. The old man clasped his hands behind his head.

"What I love the most," he said, "is fire-huntin'. Slippin' along in the dark, with my ol' fire-pan at the end of a pole over my shoulder, and the fat-wood splinters blazin' away—and then the light shinin' sudden in the ol' buck's eyes——"

The boy hunched closer, breathless.

"—and me balancin' the fire-pole under my right arm and h'istin' my rifle and takin' aim betwixt them two shinin' eyes——"

The boy rubbed his bony knees. The old man spat indifferently.

"—jest a pity," he finished, "the moon'll be too bright to fire-hunt tonight."

The boy's face fell. He gathered his lanky legs into his long arms, twitching in his eagerness.

"Le's go jest at moon-rise, then," he pled earnestly, "and kill us a deer in the Shanghai."

The old man, tormenting him, seemed to ruminate.

He said at last, "Iffen you'll guarantee to kill him."

"I'll kill him."

"Mind you do now. You got it to do, now you got your promise out."

The boy ran for his gun and shells. He shot a 12-gauge double-barrelled hammer gun. It was a heavy Belgian piece that must be cocked separately for the two barrels, but he handled it well. He was a better shot than any of his uncles. The dogs Red and Black sensed his excitement and jumped about him. He pulled their ears. Red growled when the old man laid a hand on him. Piety apologised for the dog.

"Black's right friendly," she said, "but Red won't even let me tech him. That Red's a wild un. Cain't nobody but Lant tech him."

They ate supper of cornbread, cold baked sweet potatoes, white bacon and coffee. Piety had an iron cook stove, but she still used over its open flame the Dutch ovens and kettles in which she and her mother had long done their cooking on the hearth. She offered white sugar and a bottle of Abner's cane syrup to Paine.

"Will you have long or short sweetenin'?" she inquired politely.

"I'll take the long, Ma'am," he said, pouring syrup in his coffee cup. "What a man's raised on, seem to taste better right on."

Piety said, "Don't ask Lant here which un he want—jest give him one whopped on top of 'tother."

The sun had set. The kitchen in which they ate grew black. The stove and table and kitchen safe loomed monstrous. The faces were large and white. The boy seemed to have only cheeks and eyes, for his hair was one with the ruddy dusk. He and Paine rose to go. He chained the dogs so they could not follow. Piety watched after them a moment. She would have liked to go with them through the soft night. She turned into the house. Before the man and boy reached the sweet potato field they heard the plaintive wheeze of her accordion making its faltering music.

Paine led the way. The boy felt proudly that he was following a master. The old man had killed many hundreds of deer in his day; trailing and stalking; fire-hunting by night; "tiling" a gun on a trail that led to a water-hole, gauging the proper height by the size of the tracks, so that the deer, tripping a line connected with the trigger of the concealed gun, fired the shot that killed it.

They climbed the high slat-fence at the south-east corner of the clearing, lifting their legs carefully to make no noise. Crossing the scrub road that skirted an abandoned field, Paine nudged the boy and pointed in the twilight to deer tracks. A large buck had fed twelve hours ago and had come out this way.

"He's likely layin' up right around here some'eres," Paine whispered.

They advanced slowly. The old man was sure-footed, putting his toe first to earth, so that if he stepped on a branch or twig that gave signs of crackling, he was ready-poised to withdraw his foot. The boy was inherently awkward. His body moved in spasms under his impassioned control. Once, laying down his foot on a dry palmetto frond, he threw out his long arms to balance himself against the halted step. He struck the boughs of a live-oak. They made the sound of a squirrel jumping. Lant held his breath until the blood pounded against his ears. There was no answering leap of startled game. He let out his breath in a puff and moved forward again. A prickly pear jabbed its barbs through his overalls. He made no sound.

The scrub lay behind them. The buck would come from the scrub tonight. The moon rose as they reached the potato field. Lant pointed to the vines, trampled and eaten. The man and boy moved an inch at a time. The buck had not come in.

Paine looked about him appraisingly. In the centre of the field stood a tall slash pine. The lowest branches were twelve feet from the ground. The boy had built a scaffold among them. Paine spoke aloud, but lightly. His voice was no more than the stir of one pine-bough rubbing against another.

"We'll climb the tree, son, and wait for the scoundrel up in your Shanghai."

He hunched up the rough tree trunk, agile as an old 'possum. The boy on tiptoe reached the guns up to him and hunched after him. They sat in the Shanghai, their legs dangling. The moon swung up over the scrub. The hammock was black velvet, but the field at their feet was silver. The sweet potato vines were silver-grey. There was no wind. Suddenly the hammock around the field seemed to be falling down. There was a crashing in the underbrush, then a thud-thud where the buck had leaped the fence. He was among the potato vines.

For a few moments he made no sound. He may have scented them faintly for he indulged in a deer's mysterious trick of standing still and striking his hooves to make a deceptive sound of running. Then there came, when he was satisfied as to his surroundings, a soft rustling. The boy could not credit his senses. The buck was here, almost under his feet, and he could not see him. He had heard of the things moonlight did to the bodies, but he could not have believed that a deer within twenty feet of him could elude his eyes. Paine eased his gun higher.

The rustling moved farther away. There was a break in the hammock to the north, where the field joined the rest of the Lantry clearing. The boy saw a black outline of antlers lifted an instant against the bright night. He fired blindly. A snort sounded by the fence, there was again the thud of the fence-leap, the buck's heels pounded three or four times and he was gone. Paine spoke in his normal voice.

"We jest as good to go home, son. You won't see no more deer tonight."

Lant was sick with his chagrin.

"Dog take it, I seed his ol' horns agin the fence-top."

"Yes, and you fired too quick and too high." Paine spoke mildly. "I seed him when you shot, and your fire plumb cleared his head. You got that to learn, shootin' up above this-a-way. You got to figger the same way shootin' on top of a rise towards a valley. You been used to shootin' on a level. Hit's the most natchel thing in the world, over-shootin'. Ne' mind, son, you'll git the hang of it." He chuckled. "I mean, the buck crashed thu like a lumber-cart."

Lant considered himself a good shot. It made him ugly to find there was still much he did not know. He did not want to go home with Paine. He lagged behind.

Paine said, "This time o' yare, a buck's a right dark grey color. You'd of done better to of waited. You'd of got used to him stirrin' in the moonlight, and first thing, you'd of seed him clare."

The boy stopped short. His heart beat violently. If that were true, he could see the deer playing tonight in Twin Sinks. He had only been able to account for the multitude of tracks there by deciding that the deer came in to frolic. He had intended to take old man Paine with him the next time he went, but he was ashamed and wanted now to go alone.

He said, "You go on, Uncle Frank. I aim to lay for a rabbit 'fore I comes in."

Paine thought he hoped to get another shot at a deer. He smiled to himself, nodded and went to the cabin. The boy watched him disappear and turned into the mottled half-light of the hammock.

A bright night made little change in the hammock. Where the sunlight was tawny, the moonlight was silver-grey. Sunlight or moonlight or the incandescence of sub-tropical stars no more than washed thinly through the live-oaks and magnolias. A pillared canopy kept the earth black and moist and cool. The boy smelled the spice of crushed fern as he walked. Over its aroma lay the lighter odour of palmetto bloom. He divided them in his nostrils, the one from the other. The trail sometimes turned up the sloping bluff; sometimes dipped without reason close to the swamp. The cypress men had perhaps made it so, deviating this way or that to avoid a fallen tree. It was familiar by reason of a certain hickory here, a clump of ash there, or a mere conjunction of tree and shrub and slope, the sum making something recognisable, as an assortment of features makes a face.

Lant kept to the lower trail along the swamp until he was directly below the Twin Sinks. Then he turned sharply and climbed the steep bluff. The trees grew larger, the hammock more open, as he reached the top. The deer might have come already; he approached the sink-holes cautiously. There was no evidence a short distance away of the great cavities. They yawned suddenly at his feet. Limestone underlay the section, honeycombed by subterranean springs and rivers. Every so often a shell of surface soil, eaten away from underneath, weakened by rain, gave way. What seemed solid earth one day was a gaping hole the next. Sometimes spring water filled it for a foot or two in depth; sometimes, as here, the hidden river having dropped insidiously to a lower level, the sink-hole was perpetually dry.

The deer had not yet come. Lant peered over the edge of the Sinks. When the earth had caved in here, some forty years before, a firm ledge a few feet wide had remained standing in the middle. On either side of the ridge lay a deep bowl, fifty feet deep, the almost perpendicular sides sparsely grown up with tall hickories and magnolias and sweet-gums. By daylight the boy had seen these walls so spotted with deer-tracks that it seemed as if a triangular hoe had worked the soil. At the bottom of the east sink were a gopher shell and a rattlesnake skeleton. The gopher had fallen in and had never been able to climb the slippery sanded slopes to the top again. The rattlesnake, if the stories told were true, had been killed by a deer. The skull of the snake was split neatly down the middle.

There was no wind. If he picked a proper position the deer would not scent him. At the brim of the west sink grew a magnolia tree. He climbed it, hoping that he would not leave too strong a taint behind him. He settled himself well above the lower branches. Through the broad varnished leaves the Twin Sinks showed plain. The moon, almost full and a quarter high, turned the gopher shell below to ivory. With the firm trunk of the magnolia at his back, the boy dozed.

He was wakened by the throaty cries of hoot-owls. The birds were sobbing in the trees around him. He had not heard them so close before. Their voices beat on him like the deep string of the banjo when he tore at it to make a fierce bass music. He heard the sweep of wings across the hammock, striking on the still air. The moon rode at its zenith, swimming through high clouds.

"Jest south-moon-over," Lant thought. "Feed time for them hootin' scapers."

He could only guess that the deer would come here to play. He could only pray profanely, clenching his square tanned fists, that the taint of him would not filter down to frighten them away.

He breathed deeply. "I hopes I don't stink to where them creeters kin smell me."

He could see nothing. The shadow of the magnolia lay on the earth. But there was motion. He sensed it, rather than heard.

"—slippin' in, the way they does," he thought.

Deer could move more silently than any bird. Quail could not stir among the brambles without a rustling, nor turtle doves fly from a pine without a whistling of wings, but deer, with hooves sharp enough to crack a snake-skull, could move without sound. The grey bodies were there in the bright moonlight. Perhaps they stood at the edge of the sink-hole, heads lifted, nostrils wide, as he had often seen them. He scarcely breathed. Then he heard a light thumping. The familiar snap of the cradled leap sounded below him. There was a jostling and a multitudinous thudding. He strained his eyes, daring to lean an inch or two to one side.

As though a rifle sight had been brought down accurately on an elusive mark, he saw them. An old buck was there, leading the play, with a doe and a yearling. The buck ran down the far wall of the east sink-hole, then bounded up the near side, stretching his legs in the joy of the climbing. The yearling followed. Sometimes they ran at once down the side of the same sink; sometimes they kicked up their heels a moment on the dividing ledge and plunged out of sight into the other. They raced and crowded one another. They blew and snorted. Once the doe stood at the bottom with wary lifted head while the buck and yearling frolicked. They were more like moonlit shadows than blood-filled animals. The boy could no more than discern them, nebulous as the ghosts of deer.

He longed for his shotgun. He had left it in a clump of palmettos. He wanted to kill. Yet the deer stirred him. If he had had his gun, he decided he would not have shot. They were strangely dear to him. They were a part of him, closer than his mother or his dogs or his bed.

The yearling butted at the doe. Lant drew in his breath and let it out again with the sharp "Hah!" he used in swinging an axe. The sound struck ominously on the hushed night. The deer threw up their heads in a moment of alarm and were gone in three directions as noiselessly as they had come. Far off he heard the buck blow, calling to the others. He heard them answer.

Lant slid down the magnolia trunk. He retraced his steps, the light so bright about him that he could see the shine of new green sparkleberries. His gun barrel glinted under the palmettos. He swung the gun over his shoulder and trudged home. It was not far from daylight.

On the way home he considered the deer and the moon. He considered the fish and the owls. The deer and the rabbits, the fish and the owls, stirred at moon-rise and at moon-down; at south-moon-over and at south-moon-under. The moon swung around the earth, or the earth swung around the moon, he was not sure. The moon rose in the east and that was moon-rise. Six hours later it hung at its zenith between east and west, and that was south-moon-over. It set in the west and that was moon-down. Then it passed from sight and swung under the earth, between west and east. And when it was directly under the earth, that was south-moon-under.

He could understand that the creatures, the fish and the owls, should feed and frolic at moon-rise, at moon-down and at south-moon-over, for these were all plain marks to go by, direct and visible. He marvelled, padding on bare feet past the slat-fence of the clearing, that the moon was so strong that when it lay the other side of the earth, the creatures felt it and stirred by the hour it struck. The moon was far away, unseen, and it had power to move them.

XII

THE WINTER in which Lant turned sixteen was an unhealthy one. The weather had been unseasonable since October, when the autumn storms failed to appear. The dry heat of summer had continued on past Christmas. The mosquitoes thrived through January and February, with no rain, no cold, to kill them. It was impossible to raise anything in the garden.

Early in March the influenza struck along the river. There were a dozen deaths on the piney-woods side. Then it crossed the river into the scrub. On the morning of the fifteenth Sylvester Jacklin rode to the gate, hitched his horse and walked up the lane. Lant and Piety met him at the front stoop. They went into the front room and sat by the hearth-fire. Sylvester was ill at ease. He sat on the edge of a hickory chair, twisting his wide-brimmed black felt hat in his hands. He had not been in the house since the day he had taken away the body of Willy Jacklin. Piety was glad to be friendly with her sister's husband.

"How come you not workin' today, Syl?" she asked.

"The Comp'ny knocked off the last crew a week ago," he said. "Them scapers got enough cypress stacked in the yards at Palatka to do 'em 'til my young uns is growed."

He twirled his hat on one finger and did not lift his eyes.

"I wouldn't be to work no-ways this evenin'," he said. He blurted out, "Py-tee, no man on earth hated to ask a favour worser'n me. But I got to ask you to come nuss Marthy. Her and two o' the leetle gals has got the flu."

"I tol' you that were Doc Lorimer's mare," Lant nodded at Piety.

"I thought 'twere Zeke's Lulu had takened it," the woman said. "Kezzy were here Monday and said her Ma were down."

"Marthy takened it from her, I reckon," he said heavily. "Doc says they're all in a mighty bad fix. Thad's down, too." He looked at her helplessly. "'Tain't nobody but you to go to. That passel o' young uns o' mine, squallin' and dirty and hongry—" He wiped his forehead.

She rose quickly.

"You kin make out cookin', cain't you, Lant?"

"Shore kin. Mebbe I'll git me enough bacon for oncet."

Sylvester stood up, relieved.

"Come eat with us, Lant," he said, "if you git lonesome or hongry 'fore your Ma gits back."

"Don't you worry 'bout him," Piety called from her bedroom. "He'll go down to Zeke's and set on the back-stoop and Kezzy'll sneak him out a hull half a lard cake."

"Uh-huh!" the man laughed. "That's likely where my Cleve goes when he comes home with his belly done a'ready full."

"Kezzy spoils all two of 'em. And Lulu wonderin' where the flour and sugar goes to."

She came out with a change of clothing in a clean flour sack and fumbled on the mantel for her snuff-box.

"I'm gone," she said to Lant. "Don't you starve my cats nor my chickens."

He watched after her down the lane, crooking his neck, as long as a water-turkey's. He had grown like jimson-weed in the past year. He was stretched out almost to his full raw-boned length. His body was a jointed pole for the support of his big red-haired head. He called Red and Black from under the house, laid them on their sides in the sun and picked off their fleas. The dogs groaned with pleasure.

Red was Lant's favourite. He was a strange dog. His nature was for night hunting. He had lain in the yard all day, napping, opening one eye, friendly enough, at the cats and chickens. The youngest kitten had played around him; had chased small grey lizards across his paws; had slept with him in the afternoon sunlight, warming its back against him. Now the dog seemed to watch the progress of the sun across the sky.

Lant ate a cold supper and fed the dogs. Black lay down again. Red yawned, shook himself, stretched. When the sun dropped behind the ledge, he walked stiff-legged to the slat-fence, wormed himself through a gap and began his rounds. He followed the first track he picked up. Usually a 'possum, a 'coon, a wild cat or a skunk had passed close to the fence since daylight. Tonight when he put his nose to the tainted earth, the prey proved to be one of Piety's kittens. It leaped ahead of him and made a persimmon tree in the clearing. The bark slipped. Red was on it. He gave one prodigious shake of his head. He strode off, superbly indifferent that the same dead kitten had lain in the sun that day against his ruddy belly. Lant followed him and buried the kitten under the persimmon. Red, on his way to the hammock, rolled his eye at him.

"You better be proud Ma never seed you ketch that un," Lant called after him.

He spent the evening oiling his traps to put them away for the spring and summer. The trapping season was ended. He had done well, especially with 'coon hides. He had made enough to live on, with a few dollars left over; for three years there had been no more talk of school. He was almost a man, he thought, and the danger from that source was over.

In the morning he rolled up his last bundle of hides to take to Eureka for the itinerant fur buyer. He re-strung his grandfather's banjo and tuned it to a pitch that suited him. Towards noon he went to the kitchen and looked from the cold range to the cupboard and back again. He went whistling down the road to Kezzy.

She came to the back door with red rims around her eyes.

"Lant," she said, "I'm feered ain't none of 'em goin' to make it."

He had not been concerned with his ailing kin. Because Kezzy was distressed, he became leaden. He was not even hungry any more.

"Ary thing I kin do?" he asked.

She shook her dark head. At eighteen, she had unplaited the smooth braids and coiled them loosely at the nape of her white neck. He missed seeing them shake when she moved her head.

"Jest come down ever' day to see," she said. "You'll belong to go for he'p if things goes the way I figger they're goin'."

She did not offer him dinner and he went home and cooked an unpalatable corn pone. In the late afternoon he took Red and Black and went hunting in the scrub. His whole family faded from his mind.

In the morning Zeke was again a widower, for Lulu was dead. Through the rest of the week the others died who had been stricken; Martha and two small girls, and Thaddeus Lantry. Piety thought that it was strange her grief for them should be so thin. Perhaps death could only do great damage once. After the pain of Lantry's going, sorrow for these others was a harmless shadow. She saw them buried under the blackjacks; saw the Lantry settlement dissolve out of the scrub within a few short weeks.

She half expected that Zeke or Sylvester Jacklin would marry Thad's widow, Nellie. If Kezzy would stay and keep house for him, Zeke said, he could get along without a wife.

"Take a heap more'n you, Zeke, to drive me outen the scrub," the girl said.

Nellie and her children moved back across the river. Sylvester Jacklin moved back too. On the first of June he married a woman with children of her own who would have nothing to do with his motherless brood. Nellie took his girls to raise with her own. Piety agreed to take Cleve, a lazy fellow of eighteen, until he should find steady work. She came away from the family meeting at Abner Lantry's house in the piney-woods to tell Lant, waiting with the rowboat, what she had done. He frowned.

"We'll be feedin' the scaper longer'n you figger on," he said. "What with Kezzy stayin' on in the scrub, and Cleve hatin' work the way he do, he won't find nothin' to do. You watch and see."

"You jest don't want nothin' around but a mess o' dogs," she said indignantly. "Cleve'll tote my stove-wood and he'p in the garden."

"Yes," he said, "and he'll set on the stoop and swop lies with you like ary woman."

They rowed across the river in silence. Half-way up the ledge to the clearing, Piety asked:

"You reckon Cleve's courtin' Kezzy?"

He said, "Cleve's jest natchelly the courtin' kind."

Cleve was to move his clothes over the following week. He would sleep in Lantry's bed in the front room. Piety spent a day sorting her bedding to find quilts for him. Her eyes burned and her neck ached. She emptied a shelf over her trunk to make a place for his belongings. The next morning she had a hard chill and could not get up. In the afternoon a high fever set in. Her back ached as though she would break in two in the bed. She had had malaria before, but it had not struck so viciously as this.

"I'll take me a leetle dose o' asafoetidy," she said to Lant. "You better take one, too, to clear your blood."

"I won't touch the stinkin' stuff," he said. "I been takin' my medicine."

"What you been takin'?"

"I've done carried a piece o' prickly ash in my shoe all spring to chew on."

"Did you make a soap and honey poultice for that risin' on your arm, like I tol' you yestiddy?"

"I made better'n that. I made a prickly-pear pad and its drawin' fine."

"You'll take them wild things," she complained, "and not doctor yourself fitten."

"You're down and I'm up, ain't I?"

The asafoetida, she admitted the next day, had not helped her. The rest of the week she took Black Draught and Pierce's Chill Tonic. The fever grew worse. Lant brought Kezzy to see her.

"Ma used to tie nine knots in a string," the girl told her, "and dip it in turpentine and wear it nine days around her waist, to cure the fever."

"I done that the first day I knowed 'twas chills and fever," the woman said. "I takened it off and had Lant dip it agin jest today."

"Maybe that's what's the matter," Kezzy said. "Ma never takened it off. The string keeps its strength a long time. When you take it off, it's that strong to where you can tie it around a tree and it'll give the tree chills and fever."

The girl bathed her and put a fresh sheet on the bed and a

clean quilt over her. She baked cornbread and biscuits and swept the house. Lant followed her about.

"If 'twas you, would you load Ma in the wagon and carry her to Doc?" he asked.

She stood in the bedroom doorway studying the sick woman.

"She ain't fitten to carry. You go tell Doc what ails her and leave him send her medicine."

Piety roused from her stupor.

"Lant needs medicine, too," she said. "He's got a humour in his blood and he'll eetch and eetch until he'll scratch his back agin a post like ary hog."

Kezzy said, " 'Pears to me like not havin' no fresh greens in so long is what ailded ever'body."

"Ol' Doctor Kezzy—" he taunted her. He reached for her hair. "Dog take it, since you put them braids up I cain't get me no handful to pull."

"Mebbe that's why I put 'em outen the way."

He walked with her to the gate.

"Cleve's movin' over Monday, ain't he?" she asked. "You and him come down to Zeke and me for your dinners. Don't you set up to the table and wait for your Ma to git outen the bed and cook for you. I declare, men-folks is a sight."

He left her and went to the river to row to Eureka. Doc Lorimer prescribed heavy doses of quinine and sent back as well a dose of his special liver-twister.

"This'll scrape that scrub sand out of her guts," Doc said. "Carry her down here when the fever leaves her."

In a week she was free of fever; weak and light-headed, but able to go in the rowboat to Lorimer's one-room office in Eureka. Lant joked outside with crazy Ramrod Simpson while she made her call. Old Doc wrapped up her medicines.

"How much do I owe you, Doc?"

"Nothin' but sixty cents for the quinine. Don't enough stuff go in these here other things to matter. My treatments ain't worth a cent when it comes to anybody I've doctored long as I have you. I know too much about you to charge you. I know your gizzard forrards and back." He handed her the package. "Take one of them big pills in the morning. I'm wormin' you for luck."

He walked with her towards the door.

"I mistrust the hookworm," he said, "where folks has got no outhouse. Modrun science," he said, lifting his snow-white eyebrows over his steel-rimmed spectacles, "modrun science figgers not havin' no outhouse has got somethin' to do with it."

Piety agreed with enthusiasm. Old Doc was deaf and she lifted her small voice.

"That's what I tells Lant," she said shrilly. "I keep a-tellin' him and a-tellin' him, but boy-like he's heedless. I've purely begged him to build us an outhouse, he's got the lumber, right there on the place he's got the lumber, and he won't go to the bother. I tell him I'm ashamed when the Wilsons and the Jacklins comes a-visitin', but what's shame to him?"

She had no strength. She was still faint and dizzy. Sitting idly in the breezeway through long afternoons of summer sun, she had a heightened perception of the changes that had swept across the Lantry settlement like a storm. She was conscious, as she had not been before, of the thinning out of the scrub of its human inhabitants. Her father, she thought, had lived not quite long enough. He had died with the noise of timbering in his ears; the sound of boats on the river; in the swamp the voices of men. Under the blackjacks he had no ears to prick up in gratitude for the new peace.

The fading away of human life was taking place all over the scrub. She remembered as a girl a settlement of English people and Yankees at Riverside. The Big Freeze of '95 had sent them scuttling away like rats, abandoning their homes and clearings. Stray settlers on the small scrub lakes had lost heart and moved away. The lumber company had taken the river cypress and had gone. Towards Riverside men had boxed the long-leaf yellow pine; had sent out rosin and turpentine, leaving the great trees to rot before their time. A small mill at Cedar Landing had sawed out most of the swamp cedar. Turpentine still and cedar mill now lay abandoned. Men had reached into the scrub and along its boundaries, had snatched what they could get and had gone away, uneasy in that vast indifferent peace; for a man was nothing, crawling ant-like among the myrtle bushes under the pines. Now they were gone, it was as though they had never been. The silence of the scrub was primordial. The wood-thrush crying across it might have been the first bird in the world—or the last.

It seemed to Piety that human habitation kept a house standing. Through the summer she saw Thad's and Martha's empty cabins sag a little at the corners, the roofs begin to cave in like battered hats. The rain pipes rusted through, so that the cisterns went stagnant, then dry. Oak snakes took up residence along the beams. The hammock crept in from one side and the scrub from the other. Wild grape vines began to lace themselves up the trellises where coral vines had been, and seedling pine trees sprang up between the steps. She saw with a strange clarity that it did not matter. Even Lantry did not matter, for her son walked long and brown across the clearing. The dead were the dead and the living were the living. The growing uncertainties of a daily existence absorbed her.

Cleve moved in with his small bundle of belongings. He was a quiet fellow and often sat so long without moving that Lant and Piety sometimes forgot at first that he was there. He was inert and pasty, with a round full face. His mother's sandy colouring had come to him still further faded. His hair was fine and light like corntassels. He had pale sulky eyes. Sometimes he grinned broadly and exposed his gums.

He helped Piety with the small chores of the place; talked cosily with her on the stoop, bringing gossip from across the river. Lant was away a great deal, gone like a lean red cat into swamp and hammock and scrub. She enjoyed the company of the older youth. She could not understand Lant's vague hostility to his cousin.

"If 'twas a 'coon with one toe gone, I'd takened in," she said to her son, "you'd jest think it was perfeckly fine."

XIII

THE SCRUB lay parching under an August sun. The wire-grass was brown and dry. The scrub pines quivered in the heat, their taproots pushing desperately lower for a water that was not there. The desiccated needles gave forth an aromatic scent as acrid as though they were being broiled. The sand underfoot was slippery, like fine glass. Even the gallberry bushes writhed and shrivelled, and blueberries dried on their stems.

Lant and Cleve trudged across the open rough. The boys and dogs were on the trail of a wild cat that had eluded them. It had killed chickens in the very yard. A week ago it had gotten away with a new-born pig. Whenever Lant had set the dogs after it, it had taken to the swamp and gotten away. This time its tracks had led directly into the scrub.

They were on the second afternoon of the hunt. They carried guns, ammunition, matches, jerked venison and cornmeal to last them several days. Lant intended to run down the cat if it took the rest of the summer. A creature that stole from the yard and got safely away was a challenge that could not go unnoticed. The big cat had struck out across the very heart of the scrub. It must be headed for the bay-head flats, miles away.

Heat waves shimmered before their eyes, blinding them, mingling with the smart of their sweat. The scrub palmettos, tearing at their overalls, rattled like thick dry paper. They were barefooted and sharp dead limbs scratched their feet and the baking yellow sand seared the soles. Now and then they shifted their guns from one blistered shoulder to the other. The dogs, Red and Black, no more than kept ahead of them, sniffing languidly at the wild-cat trail. Their tongues lolled scarlet. Their sides heaved. Cleve was ready to go back.

Lant said, "I be dogged if I do. I'll not have that scoundrel chompin' on my chickens. You go back if you want to."

Cleve said, blinking his eyes, "I don't crave to backtrack alone."

"Come on, then."

They had spent the previous night not far from home, for they thought the dogs had treed the cat just after nightfall. It was in a tall pine and they decided to wait for daylight to cut it down. When dawn came, the black-masked face of a raccoon had peered at them from the pine boughs. They had beaten the dogs for misleading them.

Cleve said, "Mought o' caught up with him if they'd had some sense."

Lant reminded him that they could have gone no farther in the night without a moon. The trail was a little stale, for the cat had travelled all night. It was hard to follow in any case on the bone-dry sand. The sun reached down long tongues of yellow heat and licked up the scent of the cat-tracks. The dogs were without sufficient water, for there were no creeks, no ponds, no lakes, no sink-holes, for a ten-mile radius.

At sunset they were still in the scrub. The area had gone un-burned for many years and the close-crowded pines were tall. To the north the boys made out an island of long-leaf pine. This indicated water. They made for it and found a small spring-fed pond. It was bordered with cattails and pink marsh mallows. From among the water-hyacinths, blue cranes flew up slowly. The dogs went belly-deep in the good water, and Lant and Cleve lay flat to lap with them.

The dogs were glad to rest, and lay quietly. Cleve lay on his back, his arms under his head, while Lant sat with cocked gun, waiting for fox-squirrels. He was sure they would be fox-squirrels. "They're piney-woods jessies," he told his cousin. The sun had been so hot that the squirrels were not anxious to feed. As the sun dropped below the pines there came a chattering and two fox-squirrels scurried down a near-by pine trunk.

Lant brought down the first one in motion. The second leaped to an adjacent pine, then flattened itself on the far side of the trunk. The bushy black tail flickered in plain sight. Lant moved a little to the side and dropped it. One was as large as a pole-cat, and as glossy-black. It was a castrated male. Lant wondered how the old males knew enough to wound the young ones, in their fierce squirrel battles, to their own advantage. The second squirrel was tawny gold, with a black tail and black-striped back and black velvet face-mask. It was a female with new young, for the breasts were full, and when he dressed it, the under-side showed a net-work of milk-filled glands.

Lant was sorry to have killed her. The skinned body looked like a naked baby with helpless arms. He cut it in pieces, thinking of the young squirrels in the nest, their bright eyes peering into the sunset, their small whiskered mouths thirsty for milk, sweet with acorn and pine. He baked hoe-cakes of meal and water on a split slab of fresh green oak and roasted the pieces of squirrel on a stick over the coals. Cleve had watched his face idly as he dressed the squirrels. When Lant chose pieces from the large male, Cleve guessed the reason. He reached over and pawed at the assortment.

"Gimme one o' them belly pieces from the ol' mammy," he said slyly. "Them leetle titties tastes pertickler good."

Lant took a thigh deliberately from the same animal and ate it savagely, tearing the strands apart with sharp teeth. Red and Black snapped over the bones. Cleve snickered.

The sand-gnats were troublesome and mosquitoes were plenti-ful. They turned the cook-fire into a smudge, and one or the other roused at intervals during the night to throw on a handful of leaves to keep the smoke going. The pines were black above them, and stirred constantly as though restless. Until daylight the frogs shrilled and the pond-birds croaked and called and beat their wings. As the east grew light, small birds of the scrub, silent through the day, trilled and twittered. The wrens and jorees were noisiest, until woodpeckers and flickers began to drum. There were few song-birds. The scrub was too vast, too lonely, too deso-late, for song. Only the solitary note of the thrush sounded, infinitely sweet and sad and forgotten.

The boys made their breakfast on cold hoe-cake and venison. They picked up the cat-trail, which went around the pond. They passed soon after sunrise through an open stretch of grass and scattered yellow pine. A heavy dew had made the scent stronger. They decided that cat-fur, brushing against the grass, was as odorous to the dogs as the track of the pads, just as quail feathers carried more scent than the feet. Black took a north-easterly cut, threw up his nose and bayed. The cat had rested this time, too.

High noon found them out of the open and into the almost impenetrable east scrub. The pines crowded one another, myrtle and sparkleberry bushes filled the gaps, thorny vines laced back and forth, and wherever an inch of sunlight came through, sawpalmettos sent up their jagged-toothed fronds. The dogs could not get through. Their ears and tails were bloody. Lant called them in and told Cleve to stay in one spot while he looked for a way out. He believed they were not far from the river, which, across the north boundary of the scrub, ran from west to east. He thought, above the pervasive pine, that he smelled swamp and river-bottom. He cut widely to the west. The scrub grew open again. A yellow-hammer flew ahead of him down the aisles of pine. The scrub was clearing. Instead of the cathedral half-light, as though the sun came down from high small windows, the space ahead was bright. Lant stepped suddenly out of the scrub and was on a dim wagon road. Ahead was a low stretch of gallberry flats and beyond, a growth of small bay trees, "the bay."

The precipitousness with which the scrub stopped always astonished Lant. It rolled, a great ocean of scrawny pine, with boundaries sharper than any sea. There were no pine breakers, feeling out an alien soil. It was there, the scrub, immense, aloof and proud, standing on its own ground, making its own conditions, like no other. When it ended, it ended, more implacably than a life, for there was something in a life that went on—a memory—a related life—a union with the earth, producing new growths and new lives. The scrub made no unions. The two swift rivers bounded it; a fringe of hammock, of swamp; as here, a strip of gallberry flats and bay-head flats; within, it was inviolable.

It was uninhabited. Where there was true scrub, there would never be human habitation. It pleased the boy that he may have crossed where no man had ever crossed before. It pleased him, that he would come up on no clearing, no cabin, no clatter of human voices. Here and there in the vast area was a lake, breedingplace for alligators and for strange white birds. There was always a settlement on one of these; sometimes one or two low cabins; sometimes a small community of a dozen souls. Even from these, with their spot of moisture, the scrub drew away, dry and disdainful. With humankind, which must have water, it had no concern. Old man Paine came the closest of any one to living in the scrub. His clearing was on a high pine island, but even so, there was a pond at the foot of the slope.

Lant would have been glad to have the old man with him now. If the wild cat had rested the night before, as the actions of the dogs indicated, it must be headed for the flats. Paine would know. Lant followed the road, boggy even after the summer's heat. If there were cat tracks, he could not be sure they belonged to the one they trailed. They were all too weary to pick up a fresh cat. His heart jumped. Ahead of him, coming from the scrub, were tracks so recent that fine particles of dirt were at this moment crumbling from the edges. He went back within calling distance of Cleve and set on the dogs.

They bounded forward eagerly. Black bayed, but Red was silent, intent, not on the chase, but on the kill. The tracks went down the faint, over-grown road a quarter of a mile, then swung into the scrub again. Evidently the wild cat, too, had no taste for the flats. Fresh scent of bear or panther might have turned him. Then there was the sharp staccato barking of Black, and the rumbling that was Red going in head-first, and he knew the cat had turned to face them.

The boys ran towards the fracas. They had trailed and camped burning days and nights for this moment. Black, as was his custom, had the cat at bay. The creature was large, its flat vicious head twice the width of either dog's. The striped and mottled body, crouched at the base of a pine, was a trigger-quick tumult of fury. The nose was wrinkled, the cat lips bared over dagger teeth. For every sortie Black could make, there was a lightning thrust of a lifted paw.

Then Red was in. He dove in head foremost, blind to pain. He clamped his jaws together on the tawny throat. His grip was not deep enough. He had not caught the jugular vein. The cat threw itself on its back, slashing down with its hind feet to rip open the dog's belly. Red knew the trick. He swayed his body to the side and eased his hold. The cat turned and sunk his fore claws behind the dog's ears. Slowly, inexorably, against the dog's desperate bracing, it drew his face close. Cleve danced madly around them.

"Lookit! Lookit!" He slapped his thighs in delight. "He's a-pullin' ol' Red to him like they was goin' to kiss!"

Lant was tense. Black, shrieking on the outskirts, watched him for a sign. The cat was twice the weight of Red, but the dog liked to do his killing alone. Blood streamed from his ears, but he resisted still. With a sinuous twist the cat achieved the last inch and sunk his teeth in the dog's soft nose. Lant snapped his fingers.

"Git him, Black."

The smaller dog went in. His jaws met through the nape of the thick cat-neck. There was the sound of teeth on bone. As the cat relaxed, Red broke free. When he took the soft throat this time, it was forever his.

The boys watched quietly as the dogs finished the wild cat. The hide was too torn to be worth the skinning and they left the animal lying where it died. They took the narrow road west again between scrub and gallberry. Black was hurt a little, but Red was well-mangled. Both dogs were often crippled for several days after a cat-fight. It did not impair their zest for the hunt. They always killed their cat, and they were always ready, with half-healed wounds, to go back for more. Red whimpered and sat down in the road. One ear was ripped half away, his nose was swollen, a triangular flap hung from one thigh where the big cat had used his slashing hind claws. The dog had bled much. He was in pain and exhausted. Lant slung him across his shoulders, as he carried a deer, holding each set of legs in either hand. The red bristles scratched the back of his neck and the dog's heat mingled with his own. Sweat streamed from under his hanging forelock.

The boys wanted to make for the river, running parallel with the river, half a mile away across the flats. It was an impenetrable half-mile and they did not dare attempt it. The ground beneath the gallberries was boggy. The bay-head flats, where a few of the bay-trees bloomed late and in deceptive sweetness, were thick and swampy, the haunts of bear and panther. They were afraid to cross them with fresh blood on the dogs. Cleve stared uneasily across the desolate stretch. The flats made the scrub itself seem civilised. The sun beat down the open road, too high overhead for the scrub on their left to cast the slightest cooling shadow. The hotter the sun, the more aromatic the pines. Lant drew the sweet warm spice into his nostrils and hitched the drooping dog higher. They stopped every few hundred yards to rest.

Lant said, "You tote him a ways, Cleve."

"I ain't goin' to tote no damn dog."

"All right, mister. You ain't got it to do. You're jest plain sorry, that's what you are. Try an' git to go huntin' with me agin, jest try."

"Don't know as I keer to try. Hit ain't pleasured me too much, no-ways."

Walking on angrily, Lant missed the trail he had intended to take. When he found that he had passed it, he decided to head on farther for the old Riverside Settlement. He had not been here before. His grandfather had told him that it was deserted but it amazed him to find the wilderness where he had pictured prosperity. The Big Freeze of '95 had wiped out the strangers' orange plantings, Lantry had said. All their money had been in grove. They knew no other way to make a living, and almost overnight they had packed up and gone away.

Here and there a good two-story house was standing, intact with all its cypress fencing. Here a house had been torn down by lumbermen or hunters to make a camp on the river. Forest fire had come through in irrational streaks and wiped out most of them. Brick chimneys stood, gaunt monuments to fire. Sometimes one stretch of fence had burned, and not another. The settlement was desolate. Only crepe myrtle survived, and oleander, planted by men and yet somehow indigenous. They bloomed pink and white across the abandoned clearings. Lant stared at the waste he had long thought of as a city.

"Dogged if I couldn't of made a livin' on that good land."

He marvelled that men should have owned cleared acres and good houses, and then, afraid of going hungry, should have hurried away. Perhaps it was not hunger that frightened them. Perhaps, like Lantry, they did not belong here. It might be that adversity was only the last straw in the burden of a wider desolation. The scrub had defeated them. The boy was glad they had gone. He hated these vanished people and pitied them.

He knew that an old landing should be here. The scrub had closed in on both sides of an old road and he looked to his right for a trail that should lead to the river. He found a dim track, tangled with wild pea-vines, and turned to follow it. The pea-vines were a mass of pale lavender bloom. It occurred to him that the few flowers of the scrub were bright gold, yellow as the strong sunlight which reached them through a break in the pines; or, like the wild peas, were this dim shade of orchid, washed thin and fragile by the shadows. The sea-myrtle, its leaves the same grey-green as his mother's sage plants, bore in winter puffed clusters of sweet lavender bloom. The rosemary flowered in a stouter purple.

The track he was following led, as he surmised it must, to an old river landing. A wooden runway went across the black muck, ending in a platform at the edge of the swamp. The platform overlooked the river. It ran here dark and swift. The boys sat on the landing, hanging their feet in the red-brown river water. Lant bathed both dogs. Red was refreshed and tottered to the shallow junction of swamp and river, cooling his slashed flanks. He lapped as though he would never get enough. The water tasted musty from long running at the feet of oak and magnolia and cypress, their leaves dropping perpetually in humid decay.

In the afternoon, the sun behind the scrub, so that the entire width of the river was in shadow, a freight boat came puffing up from Palatka. The boys hailed the captain, who recognised them. The season had been dry and the river edge was too shallow for the boat to warp in close to the landing. Zeke Lantry was on board. He had been to Palatka to buy Kezzy a new cook-stove. He called to the boys to wade to the boat. It reversed its engine, so that the sweep of the river current brought it towards them as they plunged, holding their guns high over their heads. The dogs followed. Red hesitated an instant midway and turned again for shore. Lant dropped back into the water to encourage him.

The dog swam to meet him and they came side by side to the boat-rail. Zeke pulled them in.

The boat crew gave the boys tobacco. The men sat on the shallow decks and asked questions about the cat-fight. They liked fighting dogs. They offered Red and Black scraps of food left in their dinner buckets. Red was too exhausted to want food. He patted his tail in thanks and turned his head away. Cleve bragged about Black.

"I mean, he hilt that big ol' wild cat to the bay. Hit were a turrible rumpus."

Lant spat loftily. " 'Twa'n't no more of a fight than they gin'rally gits into," he said.

The river men told of all the cat-fights they had seen. They talked of panthers and of bears. Most of them knew no more than the fringe of the scrub. They were vaguely afraid of it.

"Don't you come up on a heap o' rattlesnakes?"

Cleve said swaggeringly, "A mighty heap."

But Lant said, "Sho, they ain't bothersome. I mind me one time not seein' 'em skeert me more'n seein' 'em. I walked into a fern-brake and the ferns was jest now springin' back where somethin' had goed thu 'em. Plumb in the centre was two broke-off snake rattles. One had eighteen rattles and 'tother had twenty. I never did come up with the rattlers had jest done fought there. And not knowin' where they was at, skeert me worse'n seein' the snakes theirselves."

They asked him, "Don't you fellers git losted in the scrub?"

Cleve did not answer. He could not keep his directions half a mile from home.

Lant said, "I ain't been losted yit."

"What you go by? You always know where north lies?"

"I don't pay no pertickler attention to north. They's landmarks for them knows 'em. Jar Hill and Hog-pen Stand and Buzzard's Roost and Buckskin Parairie and sich as that. When the sun's shinin', I go by the sun, and the moon's good he'p when it's showin'. If they ain't no sun, and it cloudy or drizzlin', the wind's the best way to tell. Times, it blows from the river, times, from the scrub—don't matter which-a-way, long as you keeps track of it.

If it changes, you belong to notice the change. And if they ain't no sun nor wind nor moon, the trees theirselves is a good sign."

"How's that?"

"Why," he was impatient with their ignorance, "the '71 storm done bended the tall pine trees towards the southwest."

An old man nodded.

"I mind me. The big storm from the north-east. Hit blowed for three days and hit rained and purely loosened the roots."

"That's the one. That's how I tell."

The captain had been a river man all his life.

"I could watch the sun and moon and wind," he said, "and still get lost in that place. I've got no taste for such lonesome country. And dry. I like a place where I can get water to drink. And whiskey, too."

Zeke said, "I never heerd o' nobody in the scrub goin' short o' whiskey."

They laughed.

"That were when you was makin' it, Zeke. You shouldn't of quit."

"You mighty right. I shouldn't never of quit."

The river had made its right-angled turn. The freight boat was moving due south. Towards sunset it swung past the entrance to Taylor's Dread. Zeke nudged Lant and jerked his head in its direction. The boy nodded.

"I remember, a'right." He grinned at his uncle. " 'Member them hogs the day we all come down?" He lowered his voice. "I been trappin' Ma some wild hogs been actin' jest like unto that. I reckon hit's one o' the Poseys has got him a outfit 'bout a mile down the swamp. Them hogs is so wild you cain't come up on 'em lessen they're staggerin' drunk. Ma's been rarin' for some more hogs—the 'gators keeps 'em cleaned out so bad—and I been pennin' 'em up when they come by from eatin' Posey's mash. I got five a'ready, come by too drunk to see."

"You're shore they're wild, now?"

"Ain't nary one branded."

"A'right. Don't want you raisin' stock the way Ab raise it."

Lant frowned.

"I don't believe them things about Uncle Ab."

Zeke laughed.

"You've thought a heap of him since he gave you them dogs. Ol' Bull-bat's all right, I reckon. He jest looks out for hisself."

"Bull-bat?"

"I hears folks call him and his old lady, 'Bull-bat and Whip-poor-will.' Jest somethin' about them."

Lant laughed.

"Sort o' pussle-gutted, eh?"

The boat was to tie up at the old company camp south of Otter Landing. The river was in total darkness. The boys were drowsy. When the boat docked they were the first ashore. The dogs followed with lowered heads. They cut up the slope and walked silently home.

Lant clicked the gate-latch and scuffled up the path to the cabin. Red and Black crawled underneath and began to lick noisily on their wounds. Cleve went to the smokehouse.

"That you, Lant?"

Piety was waiting for him in the dark. The small figure in its light print dress wavered to the doorway.

"I figgered you boys was gone a'most too long."

"We was all right. We ain't no young uns. Leastways, I ain't. Cleve's a sorry piece."

"What's the matter with Cleve?"

"Oh—jest sorry."

"Well," she prodded him, "did you come up with your wild cat?"

"We come up with him. He won't never be no deader'n he is now."

"Is the dogs tore up?"

"They're tore up right smart."

Her pulse pounded in her ears, hearing his voice close in the yard again.

"Where's Cleve?"

"Puttin' his snout in your wine."

"What you doin' out there in the yard?"

"Lookin' at where these sons o' bitches is diggin' outen the hog-pen."

"Hit's that male hog," she said fervently. "He's like to drove me crazy and you and Cleve not here to nail him in good. I was feered he'd git pen-sick, shut up so long, but he's jest a-rarin'.'"

"Yes, and the skew-tailed bastard'll go on a-rarin' 'til he gits the pen tore up. And oncet he do git loose, you've seed the last of him. He'll be off like a jug handle."

He joined her in the breezeway.

"I don't know as I want no more wild hogs," she said.

"I told you they wa'n't easy penned."

She tried to see his face in the hot night. He was sweaty and his eyes and high cheekbones glistened. The smell of him was different from that of other boys and men. There was a scent she thought she would always recognise. It was an earthy musk, like an animal that bedded in dry leaves. Its pungency was threaded with something sweet and compounded, as though pine needles had been crushed with swamp muck and fish scales and blueberries. There was perhaps as well an odour that lingered on him from her own body, a mark by which a female might always know her young.

She asked, "You boys or the dogs want supper?"

"We all hongry. You got ary thing good?"

She said defensively, "How'd I know when you was comin' back? You goes off on them j'ants and stays off and stays off. I cooked yestiddy and I had it to throw out. Me and the cats don't eat as much as you and Cleve and the dogs. Nothin' don't keep and the days so warm. I ain't cooked today."

He was prowling through the wire-screened kitchen safe. He turned with his mouth full.

"You got biscuit puddin'. That's good, ain't it?"

"I forgot I had biscuit puddin'."

Cleve came to the house, wiping his mouth. He too hunted through the kitchen safe.

Lant went to the edge of the breezeway and threw a handful

of cornbread under the house for the dogs. Piety's tom-cat, greeting him, reared against him, clawing with pleasure. He shook his leg free.

"Git! Git! You ol' jib-cat——"

The animal persisted in its attentions.

"Git now! I'll beat your butt!"

"Lant," the woman shrilled indignantly, "if that ain't a pretty way to talk!"

The boy used the language of the Florida backwoods. It was not objectionable to Piety, for it was used by most men and many women without offensive intent. She had often heard "son of a bitch" spoken by her father and brothers with an amount of tenderness. "Bastard" as an epithet was more casual than obscene. Here she drew the line.

"Big as you be," she threatened him, "I'll take a bresh to you!"

XIV

DAYLIGHT in September was coming noticeably later. Piety wakened in the greyness with a feeling of hurry. She had been getting up all summer at five o'clock. Now it was six when she went to the kitchen to build her fire for breakfast. She put on grits to cook and decided it was time to start the coffee pot with fresh grounds. She had added to the old ones for a week, and Lant was particular. She was measuring coffee by the window in the dim light when she heard Red rumble faintly in the yard and Kezzy spoke to him. The girl came quietly in the back door.

The woman said, "You stirrin' mighty early, Kezzy."

"Lant said the mockin' birds was gittin' the grapes so fast I'd best come right quick. Zeke goed acrost the river yestiddy, lookin' for work. He ain't back yit. You know how 'tis when you're alone in a house all night. You ain't afeered, but you wakens soon of a mornin', listenin', somehow."

"I know. Seems to me the hoot-owls and me puts in the night together, when Lant's off. It's a sight better with Cleve here."

"I think it's fine the pore feller kin be here. They're both good boys. They ain't up yit, I s'pose."

She tiptoed across the breezeway and peered in. Cleve lay on his back on Lantry's small bed in the front room. His mouth was wide open in his round face. The door to Lant's bedroom was ajar. She looked through the crack.

"They're a pretty pair," she said. "I declare, Aunt Py-tee, come look at this young un o' your'n."

The woman joined her at the door. The quilt over the sleeping youth was an old one. It was worn threadbare and Lant was enmeshed in it. His knotty legs were pushed through the rents and his long brown arms were flung wide at his sides.

Kezzy said, "Dogged if he don't look like a crab in a net."

Her voice wakened him and he raised up, pushing his red forelock out of his eyes.

"What the devil. Mess o' women peekin' in a man's room."

Cleve roused in the front room and sat up in bed.

"Hey, Kezzy," he said drowsily.

He watched her with pale sleepy eyes.

He said, drawling, "Kezzy, come git right plumb in the bed with me, or git out so's I kin git up."

She laughed.

"I'll git out."

The women went back to the kitchen. Kezzy sat on a stool and tended the fire.

"Aunt Py-tee, is all your quilts in the fix that one o' Lant's is in?"

"They're all mighty nigh as bad. I got fifteen belonged to Ma. The summer ones, like that un, is holes and nothin' else. My big winter ones is purely ravelled along the edges."

"You better leave me he'p you cover 'em. You got ary piecin' done?"

"I got me a few kivers pieced. They're the Lighthouse and the Log Cabin patterns."

"Them's pretty."

"And I got a heap o' scraps cut and basted, Turkey red calico. I got a idee I'd like to make a quilt for ol' Doc Lorimer outen that

Turkey red, with white. I'd like to use the pattern o' the Right
Hand o' Fellowship."

"I'll he'p you do that thing. You got plenty rain water? We'll
set in and wash all the quilts is to be covered."

She went outside and began to carry water from the cistern to
the tubs. The boys came to the kitchen to their breakfast and
Cleve sat down and began to fill his plate. Lant went to the side
of the house to speak to Red and Black. The dogs came to meet
him. Their cat-wounds had healed in clean welts. They wagged
ingratiating tails.

"You 'bout ready for another cat-hunt," he said.

Piety brought out an armful of quilts and piled them in the
tubs and went to her breakfast. Lant ate hurriedly and reached
for his cap.

"Where you goin' today?" the woman demanded. "You been
huntin' all week. You ain't been home scarcely long enough to
warm the bed, and now you're gone agin."

"I got to go look up Uncle Ab's cattle. He won't likely drive
'em up 'til cooler weather, but I got to know where-all they're at."

"You got a yearlin' comin' to you this time, ain't you? You takin'
the dogs?"

"I reckon they're plenty fitten. You goin' with me, Cleve?"

The older boy hesitated. Lant turned in the doorway.

"You better stay and he'p the women-folks," he said.

Cleve did not answer.

Lant said, "Wrop me up some biscuits, Ma."

He shouldered his gun and called the dogs. He looked around
the corner to speak to Kezzy. She was standing in a washtub,
tramping the suds into the quilts with her bare feet. She threw
back her head and laughed when she saw him. He stood watching
her. She was full-grown, deep-breasted and heavily built. Her
black eyebrows met over a firm nose. Her thick smooth hair had
shaken loose and hung black against the white of her skin, brushed
about the mouth and ears with a fine down. Her eyes were large
and sweet like blackberries in the sun. Lant felt warm and
friendly.

He said, "You do a good day's work for Ma. That's what I'm payin' you wages for," and went away with the dogs.

Piety and Kezzy had eight quilts ready for the line by high noon. Cleve had tagged at their heels all morning. They put him at work at the last wringing. He helped to carry the heavy pieces to the clothes line. He was amiable and joked with them. They had used most of Piety's home-made soap on the quilts and before they went into the house for dinner they wet down a bed of hardwood ashes over loose boards. In three days Piety would be able to filter the drippings through broom-straw and use the resulting liquid lye with her collected meat fats to make a hardy yellow soap.

After dinner Kezzy stretched herself flat on the floor of the breezeway to rest and dry out in the September sun. She was wet through with soap-suds and sweat. She clasped her hands under her head and closed her eyes. Cleve sprawled beside her and drew his finger slowly along the line of her chin. She paid no attention to him and drowsed a little. Piety sat near them, rocking, her deep lids low over her eyes, one hand half over her mouth. Her lips moved a little, savouring the sweetness of her after-dinner snuff.

"I never thought to ask you did you want a leetle snuff, Kezzy."

"I wouldn't keer for it, Aunt Py-tee." The girl's voice was thick and sleepy. "I someways never could like it."

"Gimme a mite," Cleve said. "I'm out of t'baccy. Seems like I'm always out." He sighed. "I shore wisht I could find me a piece o' work."

Kezzy said, "You ain't tried for a month, have you?"

"No use tryin'. They's nothin' this time o' yare."

"Zeke's figgerin' on turpentinin' if he cain't git nothin' else."

"Chippin' boxes—I know. He's welcome. That's nigger work."

"You're no better'n Zeke," she said quietly.

Piety said, "Leave him be, Kezzy. Cleve's jest more'n welcome here. He pays his way, totin' wood and sich."

"He eats the weight o' the stove-wood," she said.

He grinned and dropped a few grains of sand on her throat.

"You'd starve me if you had it to do, wouldn't you, Kezzy?"

She sat up, smiling a little.

"Now you got me hongry agin," she said. "I'm goin' to go eat scuppernong grapes if they kill me."

"It's nearly last chance," Piety said.

The three went to the south field. Lant had built a new arbour and the vine covered a space sixty feet by thirty. A stem the size of a man's arm coiled up from the sand, bursting at the top into an immense expanse of lace-like leaves and branches. The grapes grew singly, as big as hog plums, and the colour of old gold. They stood in the fretted shade and ate from the vine.

"They don't taste half as sweet, time you bring 'em in the house," Kezzy said.

In mid-afternoon Lant found them still eating scuppernongs, popping them languidly into their mouths. He was frowning. He pushed under the arbour.

"Cleve," he asked, "when you was acrost the river last, did you hear ary thing about the Alabamy feller was contractin' for the Moody homestead up above Uncle Thad's old place?"

"No more'n he were contractin'."

Kezzy said, "Zeke said the deal was about to go thu. What's the matter?"

"The scaper's moved in and dogged if he ain't fenced in about two square mile o' worthless scrub."

"Fenced it in!"

Cleve and the women looked at him, gaping.

"You heerd me right. I come up on Ab's cattle towards Cedar Landing. They're pore as snakes, and their tongues hangin' out for water. Me and the dogs drove 'em a ways and they turned back agin us. Here, bless Katy, I finds me a three-strand barbed wire fence, cuttin' 'em off from the ol' run to the river. They hadn't found 'em a new way around. I drove 'em to the swamp near Uncle Thad's place and they was about give out."

Piety said, "Well, I do know. What you fixin' to do?"

"I'm goin' to Uncle Ab right now."

Cleve was all good nature.

He said, "I'll row you, Lant. You been walkin' all day."

Kezzy laughed.

"Look at 'em, Aunt Py-tee, pleased as spring roosters 'cause they's signs of a fuss. Cleve's the worst."

"I b'lieve he is. I b'lieve Cleve do love a ruckus a mite more'n Lant."

"Pertickler if it's the other feller fussin'," Cleve said.

The cousins went eagerly across the clearing and through the hammock to cross the river. They found Abner Lantry at his farm. Lant reported the presence in the scrub of the Alabaman and his fence. Abner, big and ruddy, cursed smoothly in a casual voice. When he stopped to spit, Lant asked, "What you fixin' to do? Move the cattle?"

"Hell, no. If he don't do what's right, move the man."

He stroked his chin.

"Zeke said he'd be by here this evenin' 'fore he goes back acrost to the scrub. I'll git aholt o' Syl Jacklin and Luke Saunders—they got cattle that side the river."

Lant asked, "Mus' I go git the Half-breed? He's got a mess o' cattle and hogs thu there."

Half-breed Tine lived in a shack above Riverside. He was believed to have Negro blood. He was known to be a hog-thief.

Abner said, "I don't want nobody like that into it. I aim to talk sense to this Alabamy feller and fix things civilised."

"Where you want Cleve and me to meet you, Uncle Ab?"

"Le's see. 'Bout a hour after sun-up we'd best meet at Zeke's."

They nodded, lifting their hands in parting.

Abner said after them, "Much obliged, boys."

They reached the cabin after sunset. Piety had supper waiting for them. Cleve rose from the table, picking his teeth.

"What time did Kezzy go, Aunt Py-tee?"

" 'Bout a half hour to sun. If you're goin' down there, tell her to come stay with me agin tomorrer if Zeke's fixin' to git into the row. You goin' down too, Lant?"

He stretched his long legs under the table and yawned.

"Not me. I want a piece o' sleep too bad. I done walked a good twenty mile today."

Lant, lean and brown at sixteen, looked as old as his cousin at eighteen; perhaps because Cleve's round face stayed boyish.

Watching the older boy walk off towards Kezzy in the dusk, Piety thought that it was like watching the development of cockerels in successive hatchings of chickens.

XV

TWELVE MEN from the piney-woods met at Zeke Lantry's place and walked down the scrub road to the Moody homestead. Lant walked in front with Abner and Zeke. Red and Black trailed him. Cleve dropped back to talk with Lem Posey. The lean faces of the men were taciturn under broad-brimmed black slouch hats. They were unarmed, their hands hanging open at their sides. Only the stillness of the faces was ominous. They went through the Alabaman's gate and into his yard. Debris lay about where he had begun to enlarge the old Moody house.

The new owner walked out and Abner said courteously, "My name's Lantry, and these here men is my friends and kin-folks."

The stranger said, "What you want? I'm busy."

Abner asked, "Is it you done fenced in consid'able scrub?"

"I've fenced in the land I've paid for."

Abner pulled his lip.

"Don't matter what you've paid for, Mister. All of us has home-stidded or paid for our land, and we never had nary cattle fence amongst us. We fences our yards and the fields we're croppin' and sich as that. But now stock has always been free to come and go in these parts, both sides o' the river. Your stock is welcome to go acrost my land and the land of all these here men. But, Mister, we aim for our stock to go acrost yours."

"You're wasting your time if that's what you're here about."

"That's what we're here about."

"Well, you just go on about your business."

Abner's thick neck swelled and turned crimson.

"Mister, we're here peaceable, but if you aim to act that-a-way, you'll jest natchelly find your fences cut."

The Alabaman was a bully. He made sure they had no guns before he reached for his own, standing on his porch.

"You damn Crackers get going," he said. "You keep off my land and keep your stock off."

Abner asked quietly, "You want trouble?"

"Yes, I want trouble, if that's all you know."

He shot deliberately over their heads. Three or four ducked instinctively and Red and Black turned tail and ran out of the yard. He shot again, this time to one side. Abner moved swiftly, so that the stranger did not see what he was doing. From the carpenter tools scattered about, incident to the building, he picked up a ten-penny nail and a hammer. He turned his back on the rifle and walked to the gate. The others half-turned to follow. A massive live-oak stood by the gate-post. The hoary Spanish moss, festooned almost to the ground, stirred as Abner moved to it. With a few sharp blows he drove the nail an inch or so into the tree. The men crowded after him, their eyes on the Alabaman, who came too, but warily, afraid of being rushed. Abner pointed to the spike.

"Mister," he said, "when that ten-penny nail is done drove in that oak-tree plumb to the head—you be gone from here."

He closed one eye leisurely, squinting out of the other.

"I mean, long gone," he said.

They moved off down the road. The Alabaman gaped after them. They went silently as far as Zeke's place, then sat down to talk. There was little to say.

Syl Jacklin asked, "How long you studyin' to give him to git?"

" 'Bout a week."

"You want somebody should slip up and drive the spike 'bout a half inch or inch a day, eh?"

"That's right."

"You want we should all take turns?"

Abner's eye fell on Lant and Cleve. He looked, calculating, from one to the other. Cleve stooped and began to pick sand-spurs from the hems of his pincheck trousers. Lant grinned at Abner and the man grinned back at him.

Abner said, "How 'bout it, Lant?"

Lant said, "You-all best leave me do it. I'm right here. I ain't workin' until trappin' begins, jest messin' around, huntin' deer and sich, sellin' the saddles when I kin."

Syl Jacklin asked, "What you gittin' for 'em?"

"Dime or so a pound. Wisht I'd been huntin' when them passenger boats was on the river. They quit runnin' 'bout the time I commenced huntin' reg'lar. Them scapers paid forty cents a pound."

Syl said, "That were good money."

Lant said, "I make sufficient now. Ma don't complain."

There was a silence.

Zeke said uneasily, "Don't seem right, lettin' a young feller take the risk."

Syl said, "That's right. That bastard'll cut down on ary thing he see move."

Lant spat contemptuously.

"He cain't hit me. I kin move faster amongst them pines than he kin watch me."

Abner nodded.

"They's no special risk. Leave the boy do it."

They agreed.

Zeke said, "But now if they's much shootin', somebody else got to git into it."

They nodded and began to break up to go home. Lant started down the road with Cleve. He turned to Abner, moving towards the river.

"Uncle Ab!"

"What you want?"

"What you fixin' to do time I git the spike drove in and the feller ain't gone?"

Abner laughed, shaking his ponderous chest.

"How come you askin' sich triflin' questions?"

He said softly, watching the grave young face, "Fixin' to git jest a leetle rougher, son."

Lant brightened. He would have felt foolish slipping up to drive in a spike that meant nothing.

The Alabaman ignored the ten-penny nail for a day or two; or was not aware that it had sunk deeper. It was undisturbed the first two times Lant slipped up to the gate, just after dusk, and gave it a measured blow. The third time when he came, it had been pulled out. He had considered this possibility, for he would have done the same. He replaced it with another that he carried for the purpose. On the fourth night he made out the figure of the man sitting beside the gate. The glimmering of the late twilight struck the gun barrel in the watcher's hands. Lant squatted noiselessly on his haunches to wait. He could outwait a squirrel hiding in a palmetto; a snake in a hole; a catamount in a tree; he was in no hurry now.

Until midnight there was no sound except a vague restlessness from the stranger. He shifted his position occasionally. He was sitting on a chair or box. Once it scraped against the wooden gate. Now and then he coughed softly or cleared his throat. Lant could not see him move, but at last he heard him stir; heard the even crunch that was the sound of a man's feet walking on sand. He let the sound no more than fade, to run to the tree, for if the man was smart, this was a ruse, and he would return in an instant. The nail was there. He struck it lightly, his hammer-head muffled this time with the shirt he had taken off to wrap around it. He ran on soundless bare feet down the road. It was like fishing for a bass that struck and got away. It was good sport to keep after him.

At breakfast he said to Piety and Cleve, "This ruckus is mighty good fun. I b'lieve I'm obliged to drive that nail a mite slower."

Cleve said, "I'll spell you off, Lant."

"You shore won't. You lost your chancet when you didn't speak up to Uncle Ab."

The next two nights the Alabaman kept vigil all night long directly under the live-oak. He was in position when the boy arrived; so still that Lant checked himself only in time from walking up on him. He had to stop in his tracks, much closer than he cared to be in case an accident gave him away. He made up his mind that if ants stung him, or a small animal startled him, or a snake crossed his feet, he would not stir.

The Alabaman sat almost as quiet. There was a time towards

morning when Lant was afraid that he would not know if the man dropped to sleep. But as the first grey light appeared in the east, he heard a heavy sighing under the live-oak that must, he thought, be slumber. That too might be a trick. He waited. In a little while there came an unmistakable snore. Lant crept in, struck the spike over the sleeper's head and was gone without awakening him.

The next night he did not fare so well. The watcher must have been on the alert most of the day, expecting this time a daylight visit, but he was at his post at dark. Lant was able to choose a safer position from a distance. He did not dare come in so close again. He had seen tracks over a wide radius where the man had hunted him. This time the Alabaman, exhausted, fell asleep a little earlier. Keyed to a high pitch, his sleep was light and restless, for when Lant, hearing him snore, moved in and sunk the nail to its head, some sound registered.

There was the frenzied "Eh, eh, eh!" of a man startled from a nightmare slumber, and the figure started up under the boy's withdrawn arm. Lant was off like a deer, but he was seen. A rifle bullet whined over him, snipping off a small limb. The man was shooting high, but Lant ran madly to get out of range. He slowed down only when he was opposite Zeke's clearing. The night was black, and hearing the hoot-owls cry, and rabbits stirring in the hammock, he knew the south moon was under him.

The direct encounter unnerved the Alabaman; or he was already at the end of his tether. The next day he packed his household goods in his wagon and drove across on the ferry at the Springs, his face drawn and ugly. He was not seen again, and Lant took down the fencing and wound it into rolls. Abner gave him a yearling and told him to keep the fencing. The big red man laughed deeply.

"Them Alabamy fellers is got no chitlin's," he said. He waggled a portentous finger at the youth. "Now you see, son, how nice it be to settle things peaceable and civilised."

XVI

THE FIRST October nor'easter blew in grey gusts across the scrub. Beyond the immediate beating of rain against the Lantry cabin, there sounded a low roar that was the movement of pine trees in the wind. The small east windows rattled in loose frames, and a sudden spurt of water, hissing against the panes, dripped in around the edges. The night was raw and after supper Piety built a small fire on the hearth in the front room and drew her rocker close to it. The orange light flickered against the rough walls and up into the high rafters. When a pine-knot crackled, and the sap burned like bubbling fat, the wind and rain seemed to move farther away.

Cleve lay on his stomach in front of the hearth, studying the almanac. Lant sat in a corner, picking idly at his banjo.

Cleve said, "We better be changin' them two boars, Aunt Py-tee, if you aim to make fitten barrows outen 'em in time to butcher on the first cold."

"We're some late now," she said. "See what the zondike signs is for this week."

"That's what I'm lookin' for now. No, 'twon't do. Hit comes right on Scorpion."

" 'Twon't do," she agreed. "That's in the Secrets. They'd bleed to death."

He traced the calendar days with his forefinger.

"The knees or legs or feet is best," she said.

"Here's the Goat—here's the Water-man." His finger rested. "Here you are, Aunt Py-tee. Monday-week the sign's the Two Fishes."

"Monday-week, Lant," she repeated. "You remember, now."

He nodded and began a tune on the banjo. He loved it as Lantry had done. He played with his grandfather's fervour, but he had his mother's peculiar timelessness. He picked out the tune before he began to sing. He played tied up in knots, his long legs intertwined, his bony elbows at right angles, his crane's neck looped in a passionate absorption over the instrument.

> *"Somebody stole my ol' 'coon dog—*
> *Wish they'd bring him back.*
> *He'd chase the big hogs over the fence,*
> *The little ones thu the crack."*

Cleve said, turning the pages of the almanac, "Way I heerd that, 'twere about a feller 'stead of a dog, and it said, 'He'd chase the big girls over the fence, the little ones thu the crack.'"

Lant threw back his head and patted his foot in rhythm with his tune. He sang in a high nasal minor, his forelock dangling over his closed eyes.

> *"Raccoon is a cunnin' thing—*
> *Travels in the dark.*
> *Don't know what trouble is,*
> *'Til he hears ol' Ranger bark."*

Piety's turtle-lidded eyes blinked at him as he played. She watched him with a half-smile. He began a tune for which he knew no words. She reached up to the mantel for the mail-order catalogue. She turned the pages with a luxurious slowness, seeing articles on every page it would be pleasant to have. Kezzy called it "the wish book," she recalled. She had plenty of underwear and towels, made of flour and sugar sacking, but she needed unbleached muslin for sheets.

Her eyesight troubled her and she hitched her rocker closer to the fire, so that the light wavered across the book. She strained her eyes to make out the description under a picture of a bargain bundle of remnants.

"Neat small prints in blue and grey and brown. 10 yards for 79c."

She was so small that very little material made her a dress. She sewed laboriously by hand, making her dresses after the pattern she had used for ten years. She put together a sleeve pattern, long and full, gathered into a band at the wrist; a waist pattern that came to the throat, with a turned-back collar and buttoned down the front; and a skirt-pattern, long and full. The bargain bundle was just what she wanted. It would make dresses for a year or two. She needed shoes. She went barefooted often about the house, but for farm and garden work she needed to be heavily shod. She turned to the pictures of boys' shoes and thumbed the page that showed a pair, high and thick-soled and sturdy, at $1.69. She laid down the catalogue and drew a salt sack from behind the clock on the mantel. She turned the handful of loose silver into her lap and counted it slowly, moving her lips. Lant slid the banjo across the floor and came to her side. He squatted on his heels by her chair. He reached a bony hand into the change and clawed it over.

"That all we got, Ma?"

"That's all. I declare, it don't last."

"It shore won't last us 'til trappin' money comes in."

Cleve looked up from the almanac, flushing. His full lips quivered.

He said in a low voice, "I better go."

Piety said quickly, "You hush, Cleve. I reckon Marthy's boy's jest plumb welcome to what we got, long as we got it."

He laid one cheek against the almanac and threw one arm over his face. His voice came, whining.

"Ma wouldn't of wanted I should dis-furnish you-all."

Piety and Lant exchanged startled glances.

Lant said anxiously, "Cleve, we didn't mean nothin', talkin' about the money."

"You shore did. You was throwin' off on me."

"We wasn't nothin' o' the sort. I ain't brought in a penny myself since early summer. We always gits to figgerin' this time o' year."

"I better go. You got no way to git money 'fore trappin' time."

Piety said, "Cleve, I cain't bear you should talk that-a-way. We'll jest all go hongry together, if need be."

Lant said sharply, "Ain't nobody goin' to go hongry."

He began to walk up and down the room, his hands in his pockets, his chin sunk on his chest.

Piety thought, "He ain't old enough to be worryin' about things the way Pa done."

His shadow followed him, leaping from wall to wall as he turned, twice as long as he, twice as gangling. He paced so for half an hour. His concentration lightened. The red-brown eyes snapped.

"They's as good cypress logs sunk in the creek and along the old landin's on the river," he said, "as them timberin' scapers ever rafted."

Piety brought her small, work-twisted hand over her mouth in the familiar gesture.

"I heerd you say that a yare ago," she nodded. She added thoughtfully, "Hit'd be a pain to git it out."

" 'Twould," he agreed, "but cash money is cash money. Cypress is still worth twelve dollars a thousand."

"You ain't got the strength for it," she said. "Nor Cleve ain't got the strength to he'p you."

Cleve sat up. He sniffled self-consciously.

Lant said, "I don't aim for Cleve to he'p me. Way I sees it is this. We belong to have us a good fall garden."

"Hit had orter be in now," Piety said. "Worryin' about you and that Alabamy feller put the work outen my mind."

"The ground had orter be ploughed and bedded up right now," he agreed. "The sweet pertaters had orter be dug on the next full moon. There's hogs to be butchered on the full moon, if it's cold. If you'll take in and do my portion o' sich work, Cleve, I kin git at them sunken logs. I aim to git me ol' Ramrod Simpson to he'p me raise 'em and raft 'em down to Palatka. He's been loggin' it alone since the cypress company quit the river. That-a-way we'll have garden stuff and pork and cash money all comin' in 'bout the same time. Then hit'll be time to trap agin. You and me kin trap together, Cleve."

Cleve studied his fingers. He absorbed their anxiety with satisfaction.

"A'right," he said. He grinned.

"Ol' Ramrod Simpson! He's crazy, Lant," he reminded him.

"The pore ol' feller's cold-out crazy," Lant agreed, "but he's strong as ary bull and he makes a mighty clever raft."

Piety put away the salt sack of silver and Cleve began to turn the pages of the almanac.

Lant asked, "Ma, were Ramrod always crazy?"

She chuckled.

"Long as I've knowed him," she said, "but ol' Granny Jacklin used to say he wa'n't no crazier'n no other boy, 'til the preacher baptized him in the river."

Cleve said, "I've always figgered a feller was crazy to git baptised, but I never figgered a baptisin' 'd make you crazy."

" 'Twa'n't the baptisin' itself. The preacher were jest visitin' and he hadn't never baptised in the Ocklawaha. Granny says she tol' him to watch for the hole, but he got to prayin' and didn't pay no mind to where he were leadin' Ramrod. First thing he knowed, he were in to his neck, and when he dipped Ramrod he like to drowned him. He scratched for land and cracked pore Ramrod's head on a rock, haulin' him out. Granny says he wa'n't never right agin. Now I won't tell it for fact. That's jest Granny's tale."

"Hit sound likely," Lant said. "Must be some reason he hate Jesus Christ the way he do." The boy stretched out his neck and imitated Ramrod's high rusty voice and cleft palate. " 'Dod damn ol' Desus Chwist!' "

Cleve guffawed with him and Piety's small frame shook.

"That's him, a'right," she said. "Now Lant, you be keerful. You cusses bad enough 'thout takin' on none o' Ramrod's."

They went to bed smiling about Ramrod.

In the morning the nor'easter still blew. Lant and Cleve spent the day indoors, their heads together over Lant's assortment of traps. Sitting cross-legged on the floor, the dark red head against the round light one, it seemed to Piety they lost the look of men that often startled her. Because they seemed suddenly young, she went to the kitchen and made them a pan of syrup candy. They filled their mouths and chewed and argued amiably through the afternoon. Cleve's pasty face was smug.

The storm cleared on the third day. The early October air was crisp and clear, and the fronds of palmettos glittered against the sharp blue of the sky. The change had brought a suggestion of frost, so that the persimmon trees in the clearing were bronzed, and the fruit stood out like small orange lanterns. Cleve hitched Piety's old mule to the turn-plough. He whistled, puckering his mouth in his round face.

Lant said, "I'm gone," and went past the persimmons on the trail to the river landing. It was eleven o'clock when he reached Eureka. He went to the store to ask Ramrod Simpson's whereabouts and found the man himself in its dark, odorous interior, buying dried navy beans.

"Hey, Lant," he said.

"Howdy, Ramrod. I want to see you when you git done your business."

"I'm done now."

Lem Posey came in the store. He jerked his thumb at Ramrod.

He said over his shoulder to Lant, "He buys whatever's cheapest —black-eyed peas, beans, anything. Today it's navy beans." He lifted his voice, although Ramrod was not deaf. He winked at Lant. "How'd you come out with those black-eyed peas you bought in the spring, Ramrod?"

The man rubbed a large knotty hand over his thin-stranded white hair. He turned pale-blue puzzled eyes on Lem. His Adam's apple worked up and down in his cylinder neck.

"I've done tol' you, Lem," he protested in a high thin squeak. "Awy time awybody's in the sto' you ask me 'bout dem peas. I want you should wemembeh and not ask me no mo'. It this-a-way," he turned to Lant, "I bought me fifty pound o' seed peas and I planted half. 'Toteh half I put in lard pails and kept 'em to took and eat. That's all."

"Did the cooking peas last you until the seed peas grew?" Lem prodded him.

"No, they divv out 'fore the peas tome up. You wemembeh hit were mighty dwy all spwing. Nothin' didn't gwow like it belonged to."

"Did you go hungry, Ramrod, 'til the peas you'd planted, made?"

"I teep tellin' you, I neveh went hongwy. The peas in the gwound wa'n't even spwouted and I dest dug me up fo'-five wows and washed 'em in the wiver and I done et 'em."

Lem turned his back and slapped his leg in a soundless mirth. The storekeeper chuckled. Lant frowned.

"I hope I ain't never put to it as clost as that," he said.

"What you want o' me, Lant?" Ramrod asked.

"I'll walk with you a piece," he said. He disliked Lem. "I'll not have him makin' fun o' me for workin' with Ramrod," he thought.

Ramrod shared his dislike. When they were part-way down the trail that led along the river to his small pine shack, the man burst out, "I don' see how ol' Desus Chwist tould let away woman hatch and waise such a son-od-a-bitch!"

Lant guffawed. He slapped Ramrod on the shoulder.

"Don't you never let nary man tell you you're crazy," he said.

Ramrod turned to the youth with a swift mildness.

"You tome home and eat wi' me. I dot dood beans to took."

"Ramrod, you cain't cook that kind for dinner today. You has to soak 'em all night and boil the devil outen 'em the next mornin'."

"I tell you a secwet. I put a 'poonful lye—Giant Lye—in the pot, and hit took dem beans soft as gwits by noon."

"Don't never tell that to Lem Posey," Lant cautioned him.

"Not me. Hit's a secwet."

Lant wondered uneasily if he were bargaining for more than he could handle. Another look at Ramrod's hands, hanging like great rooted stumps at the ends of powerful arms, reassured him.

"You jest the man I want, Ramrod," he said. "Is your loggin' to where you kin leave it for a whiles?"

"I dot me enough logs to make one section," he said. "I kin leave 'em in the bushes if ol' Desus Chwist don't find 'em."

"How about you takin' a few weeks with me to raise them good cypress logs is sunk in the swamps and near the landin's, where the Comp'ny goed off and left 'em?"

"You and me waise 'em and waft 'em?"

"Raft 'em to Palatka, was my idee. We'd belong to cut enough floaters to carry the sinkers and then crib-raft 'em."

Ramrod was excited. He stuffed his bag of navy beans inside his shirt and insisted on turning back and rowing down-stream with the boy to look the ground over. As Lant cut through a channel to one of the shallow swamp creeks, the man hung far over the side of the rowboat to peer into the brown clear water for cut logs.

"Yonde' one!"

Wild-rose brambles caught at his white hair, but the insane pale eyes kept to their searching. He pointed out another.

Lant thought, "He ain't so crazy he don't know good solid cypress."

He agreed to Lant's suggestions for the raising. A pair of improvised scows with a windlass and a pair of log tongs would do the trick. Lant had much of the equipment among his grandfather's oddments. By the time they had swung in and out of half a dozen creeks that paralleled the river, locating large sound logs and laying their plans, the sun had dropped behind the westerly bank. The river began to steam faintly as the chill night air came down.

"You're obliged to come spend the night to the house," Lant said.

Ramrod shook his head vigorously. Between his cleft palate and his excitement, he made Lant understand that he was nervous in a strange house. He had matches and would build a fire at the edge of Otter Landing. As for food, he had had breakfast, and one meal a day sufficed him. He wanted to be up to start the work well before day. He laid a confidential hand on Lant's arm.

"I dest bed up in leaves on the gwound like a 'possum beddin' in a twee," he said.

XVII

THE RAFT lay at Otter Landing under the fog of early morning. It was tethered at both ends. The river current swirled under it and it tugged at its moorings. The ten thirty-foot sections, joined flexibly, stirred and rippled like the vertebræ of a great snake. The fog filled the river from bank to bank; only the palmettos shook their heads free from its chill dankness. Ramrod was waiting at the edge of the water. He sat motionless on his heels, his arms between his legs, his hands resting ape-like on the ground.

Lant saw him from the last bend of the hammock trail. The

low-hanging mist rested over the man's head and the white hair was dissolved in it. The outline of the crib-raft showed beyond. The boy hurried his pace. He laid his hand on Ramrod's shoulder. The old man started and brought his gaze to him from a far distance.

They moved to the raft without speaking. Most of the supplies had been loaded the evening before. Lant placed the last box in the rowboat tied for towing behind the last section. He unfastened the line that held the end of the raft in to the bank. Ramrod loosed the line that held the first section and jumped quickly to the oar-bench. Lant walked the three hundred feet of raft to the head and pushed his jam-hook against a cypress at the water's edge. The head swung slowly away from the bank. A quiver of movement passed from one section to another; the wing pieces swung, pair by pair. Ramrod bent to the sweep. The current took the raft and delivered it into the long grip of the river. Lant shivered with delight.

In the fog the movement was scarcely perceptible. The boy thought anxiously that they had started too early. The sun had been about to break over the scrub as he had left the house. Now he saw that inch by inch the fog lifted. The water rushed visibly past the shore. The river was straight for several hundred yards. When they reached the first curve, the banks were clear of mist for a foot in height. Ramrod swung the thirty-foot ash pole on its pivot and the head of the raft took the bend neatly. The sections followed docilely. Within the cribs the great cypress logs lay loosely penned, pinned only at the heads.

Ramrod dropped to the oar-bench and motioned Lant beside him. He placed the boy's hands on the long sweep; held his vast ones over them. Lant felt the river lick at the tip of the pole. Ahead, the fog seemed impenetrable. It lifted just ahead of them, then closed again behind. The river, deep and swift and narrow, wound tortuously. It flowed to the north, but curved sometimes east, sometimes west, and straightened out again. As it turned towards the east, shafts of sunlight split the fog. The mist rolled on itself; billowed and disintegrated. The thin morning sun broke through, tearing the last shreds from the river-pinks and asters.

It lay in warm bands across the boy's shoulders, chilled by the November dawn.

He was amazed at Ramrod's silence. The old man had been feverishly garrulous through the weeks in which they raised logs from mud and creek-beds and made up the raft. He had sometimes let go of the windlass rope when a log was half hoisted, waving his hands to tell some mad grievance. Now he sat in an oblivious peace, his pale eyes calm and watchful. He hummed a little in a whining minor.

Lant knew the river by heart for a few miles below his own landing. Shingle Landing, Mud-Bottom Springs, Saw-Grass, Indian Bluff, where he had found the old 45-70 bullet, as big as his thumb, from the Indian wars—he passed them as he would pass folk he knew. Today their faces were a little strange, as though they showed an unsuspected lack of friendliness. The steep east bank was a wall to be avoided, and every bend a menace. Where the river current whirled under low-hanging boughs, or rushed against the shore before it took itself about a curve, the raft too whirled and rushed. Where the sweep was insufficient to steer, Lant used the jam-hook to keep the head out of the wood.

Ramrod had prepared the boy for passing the Lady Slipper. The turn was sharper than a right angle, and as they approached, the river debris that floated with them picked up speed. If the raft were not snubbed, it would pile up at the turn. Lant's heart pounded. He walked the raft back to the rowboat, untied it, passed along the side of the raft and received from Ramrod one end of a long rope. He rowed to the convex bank to the east and as the head of the raft drew opposite, made half a dozen turns of the rope about a stout cypress. The rope tightened and sang. The cypress quivered. The raft-head swung slowly around the bend. Lant released the rope slowly, lying back against it as it slipped through his hands. The sections rounded the bend.

"Just like a ol' snake movin'," he thought.

The current returned from it frenzied rush against the far bank and settled again into its steady four miles an hour. The raft swayed a little and settled with it. Ramrod pulled in the trailing rope-end. Lant caught up in the rowboat, fastened it to the rear and boarded the raft. Ramrod nodded. The boy felt strong and experienced.

He remarked wisely, "The Lady Slipper's a perfeck scoundrel."

The sun was high. The river was red and gold and bronze, for the sweet gums and hickories and maples were in full autumn colour. The cyress needles had turned to the deep-red of Lant's hair. The river water, stained by cypress and magnolia, dissolved the colour in its clear brownness. Scarlet berries were thick on the swamp laurel. They were reflected in the calmer water along the shore, as though they grew staunchly below the surface.

Towards Hog-Thief Creek the river straightened for a distance. The sun was directly overhead. Ramrod put the sweep in the boy's hands. He had only to flutter it now and then, as a fish-eagle soaring lifts one wing. The man stretched his arms and legs. He went back to the supplies and brought forward a tin lard pail Piety had packed with ready-cooked food. He set it on the boy's knees and took the sweep from him. Lant opened the pail and took out biscuits and cornbread from the top. Underneath were fried squirrel and white bacon. To one side was a bottle of Abner Lantry's new cane syrup. Ramrod watched the bucket a little cross-eyed, like a hungry dog. He hitched close on the oar-bench. Lant divided the food in equal portions. They ate while the raft drifted, handling itself. There was more than they could eat in the one meal. Lant left his uneaten share in the bucket. Ramrod turned pieces of squirrel meat over in his hands, and put them regretfully in his pockets. They dipped river water in their hands and drank deeply. The water was cold and had a clean taste of brown leaves.

The stream broadened to nearly three hundred feet. A few rare white oaks grew close to the water's edge. The raft passed close and Lant could see the large acorns. The afternoon sun was strong. It moulded the jimson-weed into towers of red and gold. The next time Lant rowed to shore to snub the rafthead, woodbine trailed across him as he passed under overhanging ash saplings. Their touch was reassuring. The vines were as they had always been. The banks were unchanged, after all. The job of snubbing went smoothly and the raft took the bend like a string of well-handled horses. The boy lost the feeling of uneasiness that had struck him in the chill morning. The river was safe and he could handle it.

Ramrod gave him the sweep on every straight reach. Towards sunset the bends grew frequent and the man took over the steering again. Lant drew his long legs into the circle of his arms. He was suddenly exhausted. He closed his eyes for a moment.

He wakened with the river lapping under him, the tethered raft rocking gently. Ramrod had tied it up around a curve where the current was deflected and slow. The rear was moored on the near side of the bend and the head on the far. The sections made two sides of a triangle around the bend. The sun was gone and the river lay in shadow. The bank beside him was black. Live-oaks and magnolias in a patch of hammock loomed monstrous. He looked up. Ramrod stood over him, his hands hanging at his sides. Lant sat up sharply.

He asked, "What we stopped for? I thought you figgered we'd drift both night and day."

The man said, "You 'bout divv out. I been pushin' you. You belong to west. We dest camp tonight."

Lant frowned. He was ashamed of going to sleep.

Ramrod said, "You dot to det used to this. You young." He waved one hand at Lant's long legs. "You gwowin'."

He pushed his hand through his tufted white hair. His eyes stared across the dark water. He shook his head, trying to clear it of its confusion. He reached across his madness into a far past. He groped in a torment of remembering.

"I been a boy," he said.

The raft was under way before sunrise. There was less fog than the morning before. The weather was turning warmer. The river past Orange Springs Ferry was not so familiar. It turned sharply here and flowed almost due east along the north boundary of the scrub. Ramrod pointed out trails to the water's edge that the boy had not known existed. Black Hawk Cut-off, the Needle's Eye and the Galloping Reaches—these began to be strange.

The south bank flattened. There was more swamp and less hammock. The river-pinks grew in dense masses, piled as high as

small trees. There were fewer live-oaks and maples; more bul-
rushes and willows. At Turkey-foot Landing a child in a ragged
dress watched them pass. They lifted their hands to her and called
"Hey!" but she put half her hand in her mouth and did not
answer. Rounding the next bend Lant looked back. She stood
without moving, gazing after them from under shaggy hair.

The days went faster for the boy because the north bank was
new. They drifted day and night. He took turns with Ramrod
at napping in the day-time. The weather turned warm, the current
slowed, the river was sun-shot and sleepy. The afternoons were
hot. Blue-johns flapped languidly ahead and vultures did not
stir from their roosts. The river edge was a bronze mirror.

There came a time in mid-afternoon when all life seemed suspended. The river flowed interminably but as though without
advance. The boy thought that he had been always in this still,
liquid place. There was no change. There was no memory and
no imagining. The young male restlessness that had begun to stir
along his bones was quiet. If Piety and Cleve and Kezzy were
really persons, instead of names, they lay drowned behind him.
Nothing existed but the brown, clear water, flowing in one spot
forever. Ramrod sat hunched at the oar-bench; lunatic, insensate;
silent at the sweep. The water lettuce whirled slowly around and
around, like dancers waltzing in their sleep. Lant watched until
he drowsed with it; around and around and around.

In the night-time he was sharply aware of movement. Ramrod
insisted that the river current was faster at night. They had
waited for full moon for the trip and the river was as plain as by
day. Lant liked the swirling progress in the moonlight between the dark banks. He felt the same drowsy excitement as
when he played his grandfather's banjo. He could see water-
turkeys and limpkins roosting high in the cypresses. Wood-ducks
lifted from the coves with a wild rush of wings and herons, disturbed at their slumber, flew ahead of the raft, snow-white in
the silver brightness. Owls quavered from the shore. He breathed
sparingly, listening to the river sucking at the raft, smelling the
rank sweetness of the swamps.

On the straight reaches Ramrod seemed to nap at the oar-bench, rousing instinctively when the head of the raft swung too close to shore. Lant lay on his back, his arms under his head, the soles of his bare feet against the smoothness of cypress, and watched the stars and the sailing moon. The trees, the clumps of tall tufted river-grass, the shadowy banks, went by in the night like things remembered in a dream. The river flowed, a dream between dreams, and they were all one, the boy and the river and the banks.

He was conscious of lying immobile, borne resistlessly between two motions. The river moved under him and the sky slipped over him. Out of the sky appeared the sun and the moon, the stars and the wind, and they had something to do with the earth. They made day and night and they made feed-time, when the deer and rabbits stirred at the swamp edge, the fish jumped in the river and the owls hooted in the hammock. These things, he thought, were concerned with the earth even when they were invisible.

Dead River and the Narrows; the Blue Boar and the Blue Sow; Bill Blount's Honey and Turpentine Creek; the raft passed them in the moonlight. They went by the old Riverside Landing by daylight. Looking up the shallow bank, Lant saw pine saplings massed against the sky. He recognised the east scrub, where he and Cleve and Red and Black had run down the wild cat. He wondered if Red would keep everybody out of the yard while he was away. The dogs were showing their age. Even Black, he thought, was getting cranky.

The familiar points of the scrub's boundaries were increasingly strange from the river; the Winding Blades, the Devil's Salad Patch; Davenport, the last landing on the river; he would scarcely have known them. The sun was setting. The palms reached up tousled heads and caught the glow, red-gold among their fronds. The spider lilies were ivory washed with thin gold. Red hibiscus and the wild Blazing Star flamed richly. Almost without warning the river ended. Beyond, the broad St. John's moved sluggishly northward to the sea, and there were pale orchid water hyacinths on both sides of the raft.

They tied up to wait for daylight and cooked supper on shore. In the darkness before moonrise there came sounds from a camp of

Negro fishermen, a mile away across the greater river. The blacks were singing. Lant thought that he had never heard such sweetness; dark and rich and flowing, like the river through the swamp. In the morning they picked up a tow-boat for the thirty miles down the St. John's to the lumber mills at Palatka.

XVIII

CLEVE AND PIETY were at supper when Lant returned from his raft-trip. He grinned at them from the doorway and tossed his grandfather's old leather wallet on the kitchen table in front of his mother. She opened it and took her eyes from him a moment to make a rough count of the bills.

Cleve said, "Lemme see."

Piety said, "Hit do pay mighty good."

Lant dropped down beside her and poked his grimy fingers in her plate. He dipped a piece of sweet potato in the bacon gravy and gulped it down.

"Dog take it," he said, "I'm hongry. These is the first white man's rations I've seed."

"Now you tell me," she said, "how'd you cook and manage?"

"You git me filled up, you'll be more like to hear what I got to tell."

He ate from her plate while she heaped another for him.

"I got no pie nor puddin'," she said. "I wa'n't expectin' you."

Cleve said sulkily between mouthfuls, "If I'd knowed we was waitin' on Lant to git pie and puddin' on the table, I'd of goed to Kezzy for it."

Piety said anxiously, "I ain't meant to be scarce with sich as that, Cleve." She turned to Lant. "We been workin' mighty hard. We got two hundred pounds o' meat smokin', and half the sweet pertaters dug before the moon begun to wane."

Cleve said belligerently, "I got 'coon hides salted, most enough to bring as much money as you got."

Lant reached for a pork spare-rib.

"We 'bout to make us a livin', dogged if we ain't."

The fire in the kitchen range was deeply comforting. He sat on the bench beside it while Piety washed the dishes.

"Put me on a kettle o' water time you're done, Ma. It'll take water hot enough to scald a hog to get the stink off me."

"Well, you smell all right to me," she said. "I ain't felt too easy, and you on that river."

"I reckon you figger it'll pay to go ahead with the rest o' them logs," Cleve said.

"You mighty right."

"That raftin's a man's work," Piety said doubtfully. "Now you tell me about the cookin'."

"The first night and the last un, we done tied up the raft to the bank and cooked on shore. 'Tother times we cooked oncet a day on the raft."

"Didn't the water git to the fire?"

"The logs sticks up consid'able."

"Didn't the fire burn the logs?"

"No. We piled water lettuce and wet river trash on top and made the fire on top o' that."

"Well, I do know."

Cleve asked, "How'd you git home agin?"

"Rowin' and towin'. We got a tow part-way up the St. John's and up the Ocklawaha from Riverside to Orange Springs. We rowed home from the Ferry."

It was agreed that he would make two more trips with Ramrod while Cleve trapped. He would be through in time to trap, too, before spring. It was hard to think of the trapping and the farm work and the garden. He felt unsteady on his feet, as though the earth were liquid. His mind moved forward to February and March and April, but the core of his body still drifted on the river.

He made the last rafting trip in January. The wind was blowing out of a grey north when they set out. The uneasiness of atmosphere infected Ramrod. He was awkward and nervous and chattered constantly. He let go of the sweep to wave his hands. Lant took it from him.

He asked, "What-all ails you, Ramrod?"

The man burst out unintelligibly. Lant made out at last that Jesus Christ was after him again. Ramrod shrilled in his thin falsetto, "Dod damn ol' Desus Chwist!" The boy was disturbed.

He thought, "I'm like to have a hell of a twist with him."

He did not have Ramrod's sure hand on the sweep. He went cold at the narrow margin by which he was keeping the raft head out of the wood. Ramrod dropped to his haunches on the raft, swaying from side to side. Towards the first bad curve, where the raft must be snubbed, Lant reached back and shook the man by the shoulder.

"You got to take the sweep while I git to the bank," he shouted. "If you don't hold the sweep ol' Jesus'll shore git the raft."

Ramrod's dull eyes cleared. He leaped to his feet and seized the long oar in a frenzy.

"Snub it, boy! Snub it! We dest fool ol' Desus!"

Lant considered tying up the raft at the nearest bend and abandoning the trip. But he had seen Ramrod come harmlessly out of his frenzies.

He thought, "I be dogged if I'll quit."

At Indian Bluff it began to rain. Large drops fell singly like exhausted bird-shot. Then they came rapidly, like rats running across a roof. Long before they reached Orange Springs Ferry the rain was falling in sheets, a little slant-wise across the stream.

He asked Ramrod, "You think it'll clare tomorrer?"

The man was a good weather prophet when he was calm.

He said blankly, "Sho."

The rain stopped at sun-down long enough for them to dry out by a smoky fire on the raft. The night was gusty, with spatters of rain that moved swiftly away. Ramrod held faithfully to the sweep. The boy napped on and off through the night. He thought, "I better get my sleep while Ramrod's quiet." In the morning it was plain that a three-day nor'easter had set in. They were drenched. The wind beat at them through the rain and flattened their clothes against their bones. Lant's forelock dripped between his eyes and Ramrod's thin white hair lay like wet fur. The man was excited again and Lant took the raft from him and persuaded him to sleep through the afternoon. He was calmer when Lant opened a lard pail of cooked food for supper. He talked coherently. Yet it seemed to the boy that the man quivered with the tautness of a snubbing rope when the raft strained against it. Darkness came without a visible sunset. The wet greyness of banks and river turned black. Wind and rain made a sudden tumult.

He shouted, "Ramrod, we got to tie up."

The man began to dance up and down with thin crooked legs. "Teep on! Teep on! Ol' Desus waitin' yondeh by the bank!"

Lant thought despairingly, "Just as good to keep going and be done with it." If the raft piled up, at least the nightmare would be ended.

Straining his eyes ahead, he found after a time a luminosity in the very rain, so that the banks showed dark against it. Ramrod's sight seemed sharper than his own. Again and again the man laid his hand on the boy's arm and pointed to an impending shore line. Lant could hear the pines and cypresses threshing their tops. The wind whipped the palmettos and they stirred with the roar of a heavy surf. Suddenly Ramrod began to hum. The sound was high and whining and vibrant. It picked its way in thin threads of madness among the harmonies of the wind. The boy felt the hair rise on the back of his neck.

Towards midnight a distant thunder and lightning moved close. The river was illuminated in broad flashes. The storm seemed to be making up-stream. Lightning struck a hundred yards ahead. Then it struck a pine on the right bank so close that splinters fell on the raft. The pine blazed a moment before the rain extinguished it. Ramrod braced his feet wide apart and threw back his head. Water streamed down his neck. He shook his fist at the sky.

"Shoot some'eres else, Dod damn you," he shrilled. "You a-missin' me!"

The wind was high the next day but the rain came in intermittent squalls. In a lull, Ramrod leaned over the frame of the crib for a drink of water. Lant heard him exclaim and turned. He was in time to see the upper plate of the man's false teeth eddying down through the dark water. Ramrod dissolved in frenzy.

"Ol' Desus Chwist done it! Ol' Desus Chwist have stole my teef!"

Lant shouted, "For God's sake, Ramrod, don't git off this raft!"

Gibbering, the man was clambering in the rowboat and casting loose the line. He picked up the oars and rowed with powerful strokes back to the spot of the accident. He leaned half out of the boat to peer into the water. Straight ahead was the Double S Cut-off. River debris and part of an old raft lay heaped at the far side of the turn.

Lant thought, "I just got to pile up, is all."

The current picked up. He felt a stir along the line of logs. They would pile up, one on the other, with the power of elephants. Ramrod was rowing up-stream again. Lant ran the length of the sections and picked up the snubbing rope fastened at the end. He gauged the increase in current and his distance from the left bank. He dropped into the river and struck out with the knotted end of the line in his teeth. He swam like an otter. Close to the bank a clump of elder boughs brushed the water. He slid under them, feeling for bottom with his naked feet. It was not there. There was, instead, a terrifying world of water, and he could neither see nor breathe. The raft tail, swinging, had tightened on the line. The knot had brought him up short; pulled him under. He held on, fighting for the top. In his panic he thought, this was the way a trout felt on a line.

He could let go. It was all hopeless. Come to the top and let the raft pile to blazes. In an instant more he would burst wide open. The raft swung again. The line slacked and he shot clear. The air was a thick red. He could not see the stump on shore. He felt its staunchness and passed his line around it; once, twice; half a dozen times. He dropped slowly forward across it and felt the tightness of the hemp under his lean belly. He opened his eyes with Ramrod standing over him, twisting his hands. Lant wanted to curse, but he was too tired to open his mouth.

Ramrod said, "Minute I done lef' you, ol' Desus Chwist slip up on you. I won't leave you no mo'."

Lant sat up. His sight cleared. He spat river water. The mocrings held, he noticed. The head of the raft was in mid-stream, but the rear tugged futilely, like a 'possum caught by the tail. Ramrod lifted the boy to his feet and bent anxiously to wring the water from the torn legs of his overalls. He would take the boat, he said, and snub the raft head at the right bank. When his line was fast, Lant could free the end and get aboard. The man's mind worked clearly. He was mild and chastened. He went at his job with a painful concentration.

The skies cleared and the wind blew cold on the fourth day. They dried out in the raw sunshine. Lant thought he would never be warm again. Because the weather had been threatening, he had brought an extra supply of cooked food. It was all gone. He laid a fire on a pile of rubbish on the raft and opened the twenty-pound lard pail for meal to fry cornbread. The cover had been ajar through the storm and the supplies were ruined. Meal and coffee and sugar were inextricably blended, wet and rank and moulded. Only the grits in a separate tin can were dry and usable. He boiled a cupful. They ate unsalted grits for dinner in silence.

Lant took his light rifle from under the oak-bench and wiped off the moisture. He watched the banks sharply for a shot. The ducks were in safe coves and the squirrels would not stir in the high wind. A 'possum, come to the river's edge to drink, would be acceptable meat. Ramrod waved wildly towards a water-turkey in a cypress. Lant shook his head.

"They ain't fitten," he said.

Limpkin would have to be the dish. The brown spotted cranes were plentiful and were an easy shot. The man and boy ate limpkin boiled with grits three times a day the rest of the way to Palatka. Lant felt unhappily that the river had betrayed him. It was a bad matter when there was treachery in familiar things.

Piety was startled the day that he walked in from the scrub road at noon. He was gaunt and tattered and there were hollows under his eyes.

She asked, "Why you comin' in from the road?"

"'Cause the rowboat sprung a leak at Davenport."

"You and the ol' man walked all that way?"

"We walked it."

"Whyn't you bring the pore ol' feller in?"

"Ain't no gittin' him under a roof."

He fished the wallet from his shirt and handed it to her.

"They cut the price this time. I ain't sorry it's the end o' the cypress. If I got to starve to death, I'd like to starve to death rested."

He went into his bedroom and took off his overalls and dropped into bed. Piety worked quietly through the afternoon while he slept. She was glad he was through with rafting. She had no fear for him from the scrub. He could travel on foot from one end to the other and no danger, whether of rattler or panther or bear, was quicker than he. No storm could confuse him; no darkness cause him to lose his way. But all the time he was on the river, she thought of him. She thought of him borne helpless on a strong flowing thing.

She cooked an early hearty supper and when she heard him stir shortly before sunset, she sent Red and Black into the house to him. She heard the old dogs whining with ecstasy, patting their tails on the floor of his room. He bathed and put on clean clothes and sat by the hearth fire in the front room in the late winter afternoon and told her of the trip and the storm and Ramrod's madness. She sat rocking gently, watching him as though the sight of him fed a hunger.

He asked, "Where's Cleve?"

"He goed acrost the river to see about work. He says he's got to have work, when the trappin's done. He figgered he could git him a job cuttin' ties. And board with Abner."

"Gittin' right peert, ain't he?"

She laughed.

"I reckon he's got a reason."

She left him and went to the kitchen. She called him.

"Supper's done."

He sat down at the kitchen table. She brought out from the oven a large bird, roasted to a golden brown, exuding a stuffing odorous of sage and onion. He dropped the steel knife and fork with a clatter.

"Ma, what's that?"

"Limpkin," she said proudly. "Cleve caught it accidental in a trap."

"Git me somethin' else quick. I've got a bait o' them squallin' fellers. I've et 'em to where they was purely squallin' in my belly. I got no more use for 'em except to hear 'em holler when the cold's done or a rain's a-comin'."

After supper he said, "I better go on down to Uncle Zeke's to see kin I quarrel with Kezzy. She seed me go by this mornin', but I was too give out to stop."

He had scarcely gone, she thought, before he was back. The breezeway was still lighted by the bright west. He was scowling and scuffling the sand ahead of him with his feet.

"Wa'n't Kezzy there?"

He spat across the steps in disgust.

"Oh, yes. Her and Cleve too. Great God!"

"Now what's the matter?" she asked impatiently.

"Nothin', if it suits Kezzy. Cleve's courtin'—I reckon you'd call it courtin'. He had his damn nose in the back of her neck like a cat chompin' on a rat."

The woman chuckled.

"You shore Kezzy didn't need no he'p?"

"I figgered at first she were tryin' to git loose." He spat again. "Kezzy's strong as Cleve. She could of pitched him outen the yard if she'd took the notion. I come off before they seed me."

He brushed past her, into the front room. His face startled her. She followed him.

She said hesitantly, "Hit's hard for me to think you're so near growed."

She braced her small frame and came out with the question bluntly.

"Lant! You want Kezzy?"

A hot flush darkened his face in the twilight.

"Hell," he said, "I don't want no damn girl."

XIX

A SLOW BREEZE stirred across the April night. The moon-light washed through the clearing in waves of warm silver. Kezzy sat with Piety and Lant on the front stoop.

She said, "I kin smell the white oleander bloomin' by the gate."

Piety said, "Things is mighty sweet on a warm night. I kin smell ploughed ground back yonder."

"How's the new mule?" Kezzy asked.

"He ain't as smart as the old un," Piety said, "but likely he ain't learned my ways. Lant, don't you shoot that gun in the night this-a-way."

"I ain't fixin' to shoot. I'm jest sightin' it."

He lifted his new 30-30 Winchester rifle to his shoulder; down and up again. It had an ivory sight that caught the moonlight. He laid the gun across his sharp knees and drew an appraising hand along its smooth length.

"I kin knock hell outen a deer with this, most as far as I kin see him."

Kezzy asked, "What were the matter with your old gun?"

"Nary thing," Piety said. "He jest had the money when him and Cleve divided after their trappin' and he couldn't git to the catalogue quick enough."

"You done the same thing with the mule," he argued. "He'd done been eatin' his head off and doin' no work, but when you put him to the plough the one day and he dropped dead in the traces, you takened on like 'twas me was dead."

He nudged Kezzy and waited for his mother's wrath.

"The gun and the mule wa'n't the same thing," she shrilled. "I uses a mule to make us rations. Your ol' gun were plenty good. You kin shoot with a old-style gun, but you shore cain't plough with a dead mule."

"Ne' mind, Ma," he said, "you got the new mule and I got the gun."

"That's jest about all we got, too. I declare, Kezzy, seems jest lately like him and Cleve has done swopped natures. Cleve workin' for Ab acrost the river, and Lant a-settin' and puttin' out the last o' the cash money for a rifle. And the house full o' guns," she added.

"Ma, you jest gittin' cranky. Listen!"

In the near-by hammock a whip-poor-will sounded his tumultuous cry, tearing the still night.

"That's jest the feller I been waitin' for," he said.

Piety said uncertainly, "If you been waitin' on somethin', why'n't you say?"

" 'Cause I perfeckly enjoys tormentin' you," he said.

Kezzy slapped at her legs.

"I don't know what the first whip-poor-will mean to you, Lant, but dogged if it don't mean the first skeeters to me."

She stood up.

"I got to be goin'. Zeke'll think I'm spendin' the night. Ary one keer to walk the road with me?"

Piety said, "We'll both go. Seem like we're wakeful, first warm weather."

They strolled together the half-mile of scrub road to Zeke's land. Kezzy walked between Lant and Piety, linking her arms in theirs. The sand road showed brighter by moonlight than by sun. A squirrel ran across in front of them. From the river there came the roar of a bull alligator.

Lant said, "I figgered you belonged to stick your snout outen the water 'bout now. Beller, you scaper, go on and beller. Ma, you got so short o' patience—how many 'gators have you heerd?"

"That's the first."

"Uh-huh. And how did you reckon I'd go 'gatorin', when they wa'n't no 'gators out?"

"If you was aimin' to 'gator," she said indignantly, "you should have said."

" 'Twouldn't hurry the 'gators none to say."

Kezzy said, "I been wonderin' if 'twa'n't about time for 'em. I been wonderin', too, why 'tis they don't never come out 'til the nights gits warm."

"Because spring and summer's their matin' season. And matin' season, hit's jest the nature of the creeters to pop up."

She laughed and looked up into his face.

"Now listen who's talkin' about matin'. What do you know 'bout 'gators matin'?"

"I know all about it," he said earnestly.

Piety said, "You've seed their nests on top o' tussocks, ain't you, Kezzy?"

"Lant dug into one oncet to show me. Down near the Dread. Sixteen eggs, wa'n't it, Lant? And them all covered with the biggest mess o' rotten leaves and river trash. When Lant put my hand down in to feel, it were hot as if a settin' hen had jest left the nest. Lant, what you fixin' to hunt 'em for? You after the live uns or the hides?"

"The hides o' big uns and very small uns alive."

"What they worth?"

"Four and a half for seven-foot hides and over. A quarter apiece for small live uns."

"If the price holds up."

"You mighty right. Trouble with this country, the word goes out they's money in a thing, and the hull mess lays in and works that thing. They got the price o' skins down to where winter trappin' don't scarcely pay."

They stopped at Zeke's gate.

Kezzy said, "Much obliged for bringin' me home. Aunt Py-tee, if this long-coupled young un o' yours needs he'p pullin' out 'gator teeth, leave me know."

The bull 'gator roared again as Lant and Piety walked home together. The boy was preoccupied and did not notice that his long double-jointed stride was taking him ahead of her. He missed her and looked back to see her floundering in the sand. He waited for her and took her hand in his.

"Pore Py-tee," he said, "gittin' so old and slow she has to git drug along."

He pulled her behind him.

"Like towin' a extry rowboat," he said.

She laughed. She was surprised to find the walking now so comfortable.

The next day was warm. Humming-birds darted at the coral honeysuckle on the fence.

Piety said, "The June-birds is early."

Lant spent the morning putting his 'gatoring equipment in order. He cleaned and filled his bull's-eye lantern that had replaced the fire-pan for night-hunting, loaded his new rifle and sharpened the point of his harpoon. He longed to be on the river, but the alligators were too wary to be hunted in the day-time. A boat slipping down the current could come almost within gunshot of the creatures sunning on logs or mud-bathing in a 'gator wallow, but at the crucial instant they slid into the water.

He ate his supper at five o'clock in order to be on the creeks with the first dark. He went down the hammock ledge with the sinking sun and sat in the boat at the swamp landing until the dark vegetation, the cypresses and the water had absorbed the last of the twilight. He poled silently out of the swamp and into Catfish Creek. Such a night should bring out the old male that had been stripping his bass and catfish lines.

The boat moved without sound. Now and then the pole made a gurgling as it dipped, as though a bass had leaped. Rounding a sharp turn in the creek, the low-hanging boughs of a blue bay scraped the gunwhales. The rustling was no more than the brushing of boughs across a floating log.

Ahead of him the creek narrowed to little more than the boat's width. The circle of light from the bull's-eye lantern in the bow, covered the water. To the right, low under a bank, appeared the tell-tale twin glow of a 'gator's eyes. They shone unblinking like red-hot coals. He poled towards them and they were gone. He was sure the 'gator had not submerged. He backed up to his original position. The twin coals met his light. Six inches of movement in any direction wiped them out. He was too far for a shot, he thought, but when he next flashed the red eyes, he fired. There was a muffled thumping. He approached cautiously. A five-foot 'gator lay dying inside a hollow log. He was disappointed in the animal's size. Above his regret surged a joy in the new rifle. He ran his hand down the barrel, faintly warm from the shot.

"I jest figgered you belonged to be a killin' thing," he said.

When the creature stopped thrashing about, he dragged it into the boat. He was anxious to be moving along and paid it no further attention. A few minutes later the boat was a tumult of motion. The 'gator had come to its senses and was snapping its jaws and flailing the boat with its scorpion-quick tail. Lant lifted his feet out of its way and exchanged pole for rifle. He dared not shoot indiscriminately for fear of sinking the boat. When, in the blackness, he made out the head against the side as the 'gator reared to go overboard, he fired again. It sank back.

"I'd forgot you bastards was that hard to kill," he told it. "Next time I bring my cane-knife," he added to himself.

He followed the network of false channels that honey-combed the swamp between mainland and river. He knew a 'gator cave where False Catfish all but met the river. He swung towards it. Over the deep pool he called up the young alligators by grunting, imitating their sound. They swarmed up from the cave, milling like minnows. He scooped them in with his hands. A broad nose lifted itself. The female had risen to fight. Lant pushed the flat head under with his harpoon.

"Git down there, damn you, and send me up your babies."

He scooped in a handful more, and the female charged the boat. He heard the jaws meet near the side and the powerful tail churned the water. She was something under the desired seven feet and he decided to pass up the shot. The greatest danger in 'gatoring was from infuriated females. He poled rapidly away.

The young alligators swarmed in the boat. The sides were high and they reared helplessly. One lay across his feet. He could not see in the blackness behind the lantern, but he felt the lift of the small thing's breathing. In the main channel of the creek again he was aware of a faint luminosity. The moon had risen. He might as well go home. The lantern light was no match for the silver translucence that washed through the swamp.

At the swamp landing he dragged the grown 'gator on shore to skin by daylight. He turned his lantern on the young ones in the boat. They lay clustered and motionless, blinking evil eyes. He picked them up with a hand closed over their jaws and dropped them one by one into a live-box, counting as he dropped. There were ten. Piety heard him whistling jubilantly, tramping up the ledge and across the clearing.

Through the summer the 'gatoring proved more profitable than the winter's trapping. Lant met Cleve at Kezzy's in June and suggested that his cousin join him. Cleve shook his pale head and grinned, showing his gums.

"Don't you fret about me and the 'gatorin'," he said. "Wilsons and Saunders has wanted I should go with 'em. Not me."

" 'Tain't no risk to it."

"Don't tell me. How come Nub-footed Turner lost half his foot if they ain't no risk?"

"He were jest keerless."

"I might git keerless, too. I'm ridin' range for Uncle Ab and savin' a dollar-two a week. I aim to keep away from 'gators right on."

Towards the end of the summer the larger saurians were seldom seen. The females prepared for the September hatching of the eggs, laid in the spring, and hunted winter quarters. They were already holing up here and there in deep watery caves in swamp and river-bed. They had been decimated by the spring and summer hunting. The remaining adults added an acquired wariness to an instinctive one.

Lant poled into the main current of the river for his last night's hunt of the season. He had never seen an alligator at the mouth of Taylor's Dread. He was not expecting to shine a pair of eyes there. The double coals caught him unawares. They shone so wide apart he could not believe what he saw. He sculled quickly and noiselessly across the river and lifted his rifle. His ivory sight glinted between the twin fixed fires. He followed his shot immediately with the harpoon. He poled the boat forward madly.

"Bless Katy," he said to himself, "I got me the granddaddy o' the hull bunch."

The 'gator was rolling with the harpoon. The line twisted in his hands so fast it burned them. But the great creature was dying.

Its struggles grew spasmodic. It lunged and lifted itself on the muddy bank. It whipped its tail and was still. Lant leaned over the side of the boat. The head and jaws, flat on the mud, were three feet in length. He dragged at the forefeet and shoulders and chopped twice through the backbone with his machete-like cane-knife.

"I'll not have you comin' to life in the boat," he promised it. "I aim to have you dead good."

He thought at times he would never be able to get the animal in the boat alone. The mud-bank was level with the gunwhales of the boat. He tugged and pulled at the great carcass. He lit a cigarette and rested. His strength at seventeen was manlike, but it came in explosions and exhausted itself. He pulled again. He felt his muscles quiver and refuse to hold. He cursed. He rested and tried again.

"You stinkin' bastard, I'll not leave go——"

He sobbed and held on. A few inches at a time, he heaved the body across the gunwhales and into the boat. The big bull was all of twenty feet. The tail hung over the end. He paddled up the river, home. He left the 'gator in the boat, mooring it high among cypress knees. He stumbled through the dark hammock; panting, into his bed.

In the morning he went for Zeke to help him handle the carcass. Kezzy and Piety followed. They sat on their heels in the swamp and watched the skinning and trimming.

Lant said, "Kezzy, I'll make you a pencil-holder like mine outen this feller's skull. See where them ivory tushes comes from the bottom jaw and thu them openin's in the top? Them openin's, and the eye-sockets, time the bone's cleaned and bleached, makes purely handy pockets for pencils and files and sich."

"I'd jest be mighty proud to have it."

The belly of the beast was bulging and Lant began to cut it open to see what it contained. Frogs, fish and cooters he had found the usual fare; with, in the larger animals, deer and hog meat. Most of them had lighter'd knots in their stomachs. Piety edged in close.

"Ma wants to see kin she find one o' them missin' hogs o' hers," Lant said.

Zeke said, "He's jest about the feller to git 'em, too, comin' to the water's edge to drink."

The stomach fell open. It held much meat and an astonishing assortment of undigested antiquities; wood and bones and a recognisable shoe.

Lant said, "It's a pity Cleve ain't here. He'd swear that shoe belonged to Nub-footed Turner."

Kezzy poked about the saurian's head. She discovered two of the six musk spots, exuding a pungent matter like the yolk of an egg.

"Why you reckon he have that musk, Lant?" she asked.

"I dunno," he said, "lest it is to make him stink like a damn alligator."

XX

PIETY AND KEZZY leaned over the edge of the hog-run on an afternoon in a late November. Kezzy was waiting for Lant to come back from a trip to the Eureka post-office.

Piety said, "He's expectin' a catalogue will give the new fur prices. He says he's got a idee this'll be the last winter they'll be a livin' trappin'."

"Prices pore, eh?"

"Prices nothin' extry and the varmints ain't too plentiful now, neither. The men's been trappin' both sides the river so long they 'bout to git 'em cleaned out. Lant says hit'll be a good thing if they ain't a livin' in it for a whiles. Folkses'll quit trappin' and the creeters'll git a chancet to breed agin. The same with the 'gatorin'."

"He do figger things out, don't he? He's got a good head on him for sich a young feller."

"He's nineteen," Piety said.

"Cleve and me's twenty-one. Seem now like we're standin' still and Lant's ketchin' up to us."

Piety said, "I ain't standin' still. A day's ploughin' near puts me in the bed."

"You'd ought to quit sich work. Leave Lant do it."

"He do the heavy part, when I kin ketch him before he's gone to the woods or river. He says the land ain't worth foolin' with no more."

"You know he's right, Aunt Py-tee. You cain't make you no money-crop on fields has been worked as long as these. How long's it been?"

" 'Bout thirty-five years."

The young woman leaned over the run and scratched a sow's back with a corn-cob.

"Aunt Py-tee," she said, "Cleve's takin' on somethin' turrible for me to marry him."

Piety said, "I like Cleve."

Kezzy said, "The pore feller's worked right faithful, tryin' to save a leetle somethin'."

The hogs grunted at the trough, guzzling in the table scraps and dishwater.

Kezzy said tenderly, "They do love slop."

She leaned her round arms on the fence-top and looked out over the scrub.

"I got two things agin it," she said. "I hates to leave Zeke. He's been a good ol' thing." The black eyes clouded. "And don't seem like I kin bear to leave the scrub."

Piety said, "Cleve's doin' nothin' he cain't quit. Why don't he come back and farm and raise hogs and sich and you and Zeke and him all live together?"

"Him and Zeke don't someways git along."

"I don't blame you then. 'Tain't no pleasure to live where folkses is quarrellin'."

She could not help being glad that something was keeping Kezzy in the scrub.

Kezzy said, "A nigger woman to Ft. McCoy done tole me if you burns your onion skins in the stove it'll keep quarrellin' outen the house. Sho, I burnt me the biggest mess, and Zeke like to run Cleve off the place that very day."

She hesitated.

She said, "Aunt Py-tee, I reckon you're proud Lant ain't brought hisself home a wife yit."

The older woman pondered.

"No," she said, "I'll be proud to see him marry. I gits lonesome, Kezzy. He ain't to the house much."

"I reckon you do git lonesome."

"But not him. I declare, Kezzy, he don't know what 'tis to be lonesome."

Kezzy said, "But he's a lonely kind of a feller, too."

"He's lonely, in a way o' speakin'. He goes off by hisself, huntin'. Or sets studyin'."

Kezzy said, "I reckon Cleve and me had orter been takin' him to the breakdowns with us. Gittin' him a girl to make him more sociable, mebbe. You reckon he'd like a girl?"

Her eyes were fixed on the pine-tops across the road. Above them an opaque moon, nearly full, rode thin against the blue of the late afternoon.

Piety put her hand over her mouth, searching her memory.

"Last time I said ary thing—what was it he said—said he didn't want no damn girl. That was it."

Kezzy did not speak. After a minute the woman looked at her curiously. The girl was trembling.

Piety asked, "You cold, Kezzy?"

The girl pressed her lips tightly together. She drew a deep breath. She closed her eyes.

She said in a strained voice, "I reckon so."

She turned abruptly to the hogs.

"I thought that pieded sow found six pigs. She ain't got but three."

"She did." Piety ruffled with enthusiasm. Her small voice grew high. "She found six pigs and lost three in the scrub. Jest lost 'em. Or else the Half-breed got 'em. My boars strays so fur into the scrub he's been trappin' 'em and changin' their marks. One come home with a fresh mark in his ear. A perfeckly fresh mark! I know that's where my ol' male hog goed to."

Kezzy said, "Your barrows is nice and fat. You butcherin' on this moon?"

"We got to let it go. Next week'd jest suit us, but the moon'll be wanin' then."

"No use to butcher on a wanin' moon. The meat jest shrivels in the fryin' pan. Quare, the way the moon do things, ain't it?"

"Hit's quare about the meat shrinkin'. 'Tain't so quare about the crops. Plantin' root crops, like onions and 'taters, when the nights is dark, makes sense. Plantin' top crops between new moon and full, that makes sense. The moon draws the leaves outen the ground, same as the sun."

"Hit don't make sense makin' soap on the full moon nor pickin' sage leaves," Kezzy said. "Pickin' sage leaves reminds me—you got to give me some more plants. Them others died, and I toted water and toted water."

"Sage plants is mighty pertickler. My ma used to say the tech o' some people were poison to 'em. A woman-person, special, belongs to be keerful. A woman in the family way'll kill sage, techin' it."

Kezzy burst out laughing.

"Now Aunt Py-tee, that wa'n't my trouble."

"I'm jest tellin' you. Kezzy, they's somethin' quare to ever'thing. Bill Lewis says now persimmon trees grows from grub-worms."

"They don't no sich thing. They grows from persimmon seeds."

"That's what I always figgered."

She wanted to do justice to Bill Lewis.

"But mebbe now he knows."

The two leaned over the fence, the small thin woman and the big-boned young one, the greying head close to the smooth black one. Lant saw them before they heard his tread.

"Cain't you two talk about nothin' but hogs?" he called.

They turned. Kezzy was taken unawares by his height each time she saw him. Until the past year he had been little taller than she. Now he was stretched out as long, Piety said, as his grandfather. He was double-jointed and gangling. His hands and feet hung like attached false pieces outside his Sunday suit, bought two years before with money from his rafting. Kezzy's eyes softened at the sight of him. She caught her lip between her teeth.

She said lightly, "Hogs is jest about it, Mister. We been talkin' about you."

He guffawed and reached across his mother to pull at the girl's sleek hair.

"Come on in the house," he invited her, "if you're visitin'. It's cold. I like to froze to death comin' down the river."

"What about hides?" she asked.

"Nothin' extry."

"Did you see Cleve at Eureka?"

"I seed him comin' in from Uncle Ab's. He said tell you he'd be over soon in the mornin' to he'p you and Zeke with the beef butcherin'."

"That's what I come to see you about, Lant. How 'bout you goin' with us in the mornin' to find the cattle? If them scapers ain't jest this side the Ferry, I won't know where to look for 'em. Zeke nor Cleve neither one cain't track no better'n a jay-bird."

"Hit mought take a sweet pertater pie to toll me away from my traps."

"Leave me go on home then and make you one. You got the biggest belly for sich a gank-gutted creeter."

"Ma won't make me no 'tater pie. Somebody got to do it."

"I'll have your pie. If Cleve don't show up so hongry he cleans out the house."

Lant and Cleve, Zeke and Kezzy set out before daylight to find Zeke's herd. They rode in Zeke's spring wagon, drawn by Lant's grey mule. Red and Black followed under the wheels. The cattle had been last seen in the scrub between Orange Springs Ferry and Cedar Landing. In mid-morning they located them far beyond, near Riverside. Lant offered to drive them in but Kezzy refused.

"You-all go on," she said, "and leave me the dogs and Lant's rifle, and I'll cut the cattle in towards home the very easiest. They drive good for me, you know that, Zeke."

Cleve said, "If you won't leave Lant drive 'em, I'll stay with you, Kezzy."

"I don't want you."

He grinned at her.

"You skeert o' me, Kezzy?"

"No, I ain't skeert o' you. You or no man," she said hotly. "You'll find it out, does we r'aly marry."

Zeke said, "Best leave Lant bring 'em in."

She said, "Lant's got his traps to visit. He'll have the half of 'em empty now, and him so late. You-all go on now. Me and the cattle'll be in ahead of you."

The animals were already grazing towards the south-west, pulling off the ripening palmetto berries from the low stalks. Kezzy had brought home the herd half a dozen times. She would be all right, and she liked to have her way. The men left her, laughing at her. They watched her strike out firmly in a diagonal line across the scrub.

Zeke said, "She shore is a sight. Jest like her Aunt Annie. Jest like her."

The men reached home in early afternoon. The day wore on to sunset. Lant had gone on to his traps. Cleve had stopped off with Zeke. Kezzy and the herd were not within hearing at dusk. Soon after dark the cattle came in. Zeke and Cleve heard them in the swamp, stamping and lowing. Kezzy did not come. At midnight Lant and Piety were awakened. Cleve was calling from the yard.

"Lant! Aunt Py-tee! Git up! Kezzy's lost in the scrub."

Lant drew on overalls over his undersuit and did not stop for a shirt. Piety could not find her drawers in the dark and dressed herself in her muslin shift and the soiled dress of the day. She felt her way to the kitchen and groped for a plate of cold cornbread and chicken to take with her. She joined Lant.

She said, "I kin find your Pa's compass in the trunk."

"I don't need no compass." He hesitated. "Better git it."

He lit a kerosene lamp and held it while she lifted the round lid of the small trunk at the foot of her bed. She lifted aside Lant's banjo, her treasures of a white tablecloth, her hat, and small personal trifles that had belonged to her father and her husband.

"Here 'tis."

She handed him Willy's compass.

Cleve called, "Ain't you comin'?"

"We're done. We're comin'."

The three walked down the dark road together. Piety scolded both of them all the way. She broke out freshly when Zeke met them at the gate.

"None of you had no business leavin' her. She don't know the scrub good enough to strike through alone."

Zeke said, "I thought she done so, Py-tee, or I wouldn't of left her."

Cleve said, "I wanted to stay, but she wouldn't have it. I wouldn't of been no good to her. I don't know north from south, time the sky cloud over."

Lant said, "I was the one to stay."

His mouth was white. He could picture, as they could not, the immensity of the scrub, rolling mile on mile without water or human habitation. Kezzy could wander in circles, as lost folk did, until she dropped.

He asked, "Ary one know, did she have matches?"

No one knew.

Piety said, "She'll git the pneumony, if she's got no fire tonight."

Zeke was nervous and helpless. The drake's-tails in his neck trembled as he breathed. Piety went into Kezzy's kitchen, started a fire in the wood range and cooked hot food. Cleve wandered in and she put him at wrapping food in two parcels; a large one for themselves and a smaller one for Kezzy. He filled a quart Mason jar with water. Piety wrapped it in a flour-sacking towel, thinking that if they found Kezzy hurt, it would do to tear up for bandages. Lant came to hurry her. They sat in the kitchen by the light of a lamp and ate a quick meal.

There was nothing to do but take the road again to the spot where Kezzy had first struck into the scrub. Every quarter of a mile Lant blew a long blast on his hunting horn. There was never any answer. Once Cleve thought he heard a cry and they stopped the wagon to listen. Lant blew again and again, but they heard nothing more. Then, far in the distance, they heard a wailing scream come out of the darkness.

Cleve said breathlessly, "Panther!"

Lant said in irritation, "Them things is cowards. They ain't never attacked nothin' but leetle ol' young uns."

But they were uneasy. They thought of the panther all the way. Piety remarked miles later, "Them things cries jest like a crazy woman," and Zeke said at once, "Ain't it so!"

At daylight they reached the spot where they had left Kezzy. The tramped hoof-marks of the cattle were here and where they straightened out again in single and double file, Kezzy's square foot-prints were discernible among them. The sun rose in a thin red streak and was immediately dissolved in grey. A mist sifted through the air, fine and sharp as myriads of broken needle points.

Lant said, "I don't keer for this ol' otter-drizzle."

Cleve asked, "Why not?"

Lant glared at him.

"My God, if it comes on to rain, hit'll wash out Kezzy's tracks and they'll be no trailin' of her at all."

He strode into the scrub, following the foot-prints, his head swinging from side to side on his long neck.

He called back, "Ma, you drive the wagon towards home agin. Rale slow now."

"I want to come," she shrilled defiantly.

"Come on, then. Somebody drive back, so's I'll know about where to come up with the wagon."

"I'll go on with the wagon, Py-tee," Zeke offered, "if you wants to foller. I'm all of a tremble, no sleep and all. I ain't good as you for this scrub travellin'."

She set out after Lant and Cleve. The scrub oaks were higher than her head, so that the twigs caught her hair and the acorns scratched her lifted arms. She pushed through doggedly. Her long skirt wrapped around her legs. It caught in the vines and bushes. She would have pinned it about her waist, as she sometimes did in a wet field, except that it gave some protection against the barbed edges of the scrub palmettos.

As they continued the trail, it became plain that the cattle had cut widely to the east and south before turning towards the river. Lant began to shoot every few minutes. As the reverberations died away through the close-crowded pines, all three stood still to listen. When they had worked their way three or four miles into the scrub, they came on Kezzy's camp-fire. It had been put out with sand and a wisp of smoke still wavered from it. Lant touched it with his toe.

He said excitedly, "She ain't been long gone from here."

Lant shot, and Kezzy's rifle answered them. They shouted and she shouted back. They came to her grinning broadly with a sudden lightness of mind. She was sound and fresh. Her dark eyes seemed new-opened from sleep.

"You scapers," she laughed, "come a-lookin' for me! You got water?"

Cleve handed her the quart jar and she drank half of it, then held the jar at an angle so that Red and Black might lap their share. The old dogs bounded against Lant.

Cleve said, "You be biggety agin, Miss Kezzy. When did you know you was lost?"

"Lost?" She looked at him, astonished. "I wa'n't losted. I seed I couldn't foller the cattle in before night, so I figgered it was better to spend the night a-sleepin' than a-travellin'. I slep' back yonder, agin a pine tree. I had me a good fire and me and the dogs bunched up together."

Cleve did not believe her.

"Nobody couldn't sleep, out here in the scrub alone," he said.

"Jest 'cause you see scare-boogers," she taunted him, "don't mean nothin'. They's nary thing here to harm a body."

"All right," he said angrily, "if you wa'n't losted, where's the river at?"

She pointed.

"Yonder 'tis. You cut right acrost yonder, you'll come out on the road about Thad Lantry's ol' place. Ain't that right, Lant?"

The boy said, "That's right."

Cleve said sullenly, "We-all wasted our time, then, settin' up for you and comin' out to hunt you 'fore crack o' day."

The girl said gently, "I'm plumb sorry you-all set up for me. I figgered shore you'd know what hilt me back. Did I worry you, Cleve?"

"You worried me."

She linked her arm in his and handed him the rifle to carry.

"Don't you never worry about me agin," she said. "I ain't the kind needs worryin' over."

Piety said stoutly, "You worried me, too. We was all worried. I been losted in the scrub, Kezzy, and I know what 'tis."

"You been losted?"

"I mean. I kin tell my way purty good when the sun shines. But now come a cloudy day, I'm losted. This were a cloudy day, and I goed into the scrub to pull acorns for the hogs. I got my apron full and when I turned around I couldn't tell north from south nor east from west. I feared to wander, so I jest set there. I knowed when Lant found dinner missin' and me gone too, he'd hunt me."

Kezzy laughed.

"What was she doin' when you found her, Lant?"

He slapped his mother's thin shoulder and chuckled.

"She were jest a-settin' there, lookin' big-eyed and skeert, like a leetle ol' scrooch-owl on a limb in the day-time."

They were all in high spirits, but they stopped talking and hurried their pace as best they could through the undergrowth. They wanted to cut off Zeke and the wagon as soon as possible. Here and there the match-thin crowded pines gave way to a stretch of open scrub, with large pines and a smooth floor. They could make as good time across it as on a road.

Lant said over his shoulder, "Here's the kind of a place I like to ketch me a big buck in."

Cleve said amiably, "Me too."

Lant explained to Kezzy, "A buck'll make for sich as this, for he cain't go it thu the low thick bush the way a doe kin. He's got them horns to look out for."

They caught up with the wagon near Thad's deserted clearing. Kezzy was the only one who was not tired. They jogged drowsily down the road, eating the food from the paper parcels.

Kezzy repeated, with her mouth full of biscuit, "I shore would of made it on in last night if I'd studied you'd of took on about it."

Cleve said, "Aunt Py-tee, don't it jest show she'd orter marry me and quit sich foolishness?"

Zeke said drily, "You cain't do nothin' with her now—don't never figger you kin do more with a woman when you git her. You kin gentle a wild hog and a raccoon and a 'possum and a wild horse. I even knowed a feller had a rattlesnake in a barrel. He claimed hit knowed him and wouldn't strike. But don't git nary idee you kin gentle a woman has got no mind to be gentled."

Kezzy said, "You-all talk like I was a pole-cat in a pen."

"I'll say it to your face, Kezzy," Piety said loyally, "you're per-feckly clever and a man couldn't git him no better wife."

The girl said gravely, "I would be good to a man, Aunt Py-tee."

They were at Zeke's clearing.

"I'm fixin' to git me a piece o' sleep," he said, "now I know Kezzy ain't to bury. But you-all come in, if you will."

"No," Piety said, "my hogs and chickens ain't been fed and they'll be a-rarin'. How 'bout you goin' on home with me and stayin' all night, Kezzy?"

"If Zeke's fixin' to sleep, I jest as good to go visitin'."

"You take the wagon, then," Zeke said.

Piety asked politely, "How 'bout you, Cleve? You come go, too."

"I cain't git along thouten my sleep," he said. "I'll go on in with Zeke and lay down. Mought be we'll butcher soon in the mornin', one o' them beeves give us all the trouble. Time Kezzy gits back tomorrer, she kin begin to fry down meat."

Zeke and Cleve waved to them from the door as the wagon creaked down the road.

"Save me the liver," Piety called back to Zeke.

Kezzy asked, "Kin I go with you to your traps, Lant?"

"Shore kin, if you'll promise to pick out all the pole-cats."

"They cain't smell no worse dead than alive."

"Nary a mite, but the fun begin when they ain't dead good."

"Don't you let him git you into no mess, Kezzy," Piety told her.

Kezzy unhitched the mule and led it to the shed while Lant backed the wagon against the fence. Red and Black dropped down in the sun. Piety went into the house. A large yellow cat bounded from under the steps, greeting her with loud yodels. The woman called across the yard.

"The cat's back agin!"

"The ring-tailed bastard always do come back," Lant said. "Dogged if I'd give him yard-room, the way he goes off. Clear to Eureka," he explained to Kezzy.

"Pore feller," she said. "Have to go so fur to do his courtin'."

Lant said impudently, " 'Tain't no further than Cleve come to court you."

"Shut your mouth!"

She cuffed his big ears and he guffawed.

Piety took the cat in her thin arms. She talked to him in a high mincing tone that he understood. He closed his green eyes in ecstasy and butted his head against her ribs.

She called, "Must I cook before you go off?"

"You cook, and you and that yaller jay-bird go ahead and eat. Me and Kezzy'll eat when we comes in. Longer I waits, the more 'coons'll be gnawed out."

He went ahead down the narrow trail that led across the clearing and down the hammock ledge to the swamp. He carried his cane-knife, as big as a machete. Wherever a thorny vine or new-sprouted sapling was in the way, he slashed at it as he walked, keeping the trail open.

The first half dozen of his traps had been empty. Now they approached what Cleve called "Lant's 'possum log," for he could almost count on a daily trapping here of one of the rat-tailed creatures. This time it held a small white cat. Other traps yielded a skunk, three 'possums, a weasel and at the swamp edge, an otter. There were no 'coons, but a toe in a trap here and a mass of skin and fur there, indicated that two at least had followed their custom of gnawing themselves out. A 'coon had been known to gnaw off his foot to get away.

Lant said, "They're hard to git. But now if you kin trap you a female in heat, and rub the hide acrost your traps, you kin ketch all the ol' male 'coons in the county."

The otter was worth more than all the other hides together. It would stretch to six feet when it was drawn over a board to cure.

Lant said, "I figgered he belonged to visit that slide last night. Otters slides on the four quarters o' the moon. But it takes a mighty good trap to hold one. If they're jest caught by the skin, they'll twist their bodies and draw theirselves outen the trap. A otter kin turn over in his own hide."

The trick in trapping in general, he explained earnestly to Kezzy, was to know the paths by which the animals came and went; and to set the traps, well concealed, without leaving any more human scent than possible.

"You don't want to stomp around a trap," he said.

Otters could best be trapped at their slides; 'coons on their trails leading from one half-dried swamp puddle to another, where they fished for crawfish and minnows.

"A 'coon's hell for fishin'," he told her.

Kezzy carried a handful of the limp dead bodies. The smell of fur and of musk was strong. They figured Lant's profits.

He said, "The comp'nies ain't payin' near so much for hides this year. Seem like ever'body's trappin'. 'Cordin' to the new law, you cain't trap but three months. Don't look this time like you kin make enough to last you."

"That's what Aunt Py-tee was tellin' me last evenin'. What'll you do for a livin' if the prices fails you?"

He scowled.

"It's got me worried up. You cain't raise you no money-crop on this land no more. It's wore out. The 'gatorin's give out. Time folks quits a while, they'll likely be a livin' in it agin. They ain't a thousand feet o' big cypress left in the swamp. Time you and Cleve has young uns and they has young uns, they'll be big cypress agin. Them trees is slow-growin'." He pointed to an old stump. "If you was old as that stump, Kezzy, I mean you'd do a piece o' rememberin'."

He had reset his traps and they walked rapidly back along the trail through the swamp. They were hungry. The autumn air was cool in the shade of the hammock. They struck up the bluff and came out into the warm sunlight that yellowed the field back of the cabin. Blue smoke curled from the kitchen chimney. Piety would have dinner hot and waiting for them.

Lant said, "I ain't broke it to Ma, but if hides keeps droppin' off, all I kin see to do is to take her to Palatka and git me a job in the saw-mill." Sweat broke out on his forehead at the thought. "We cain't jest set here and starve."

"Is wages good?"

"They pays a dollar and a quarter a day. They works you five and a half days. You got rent to pay and you got no way o' raisin' hogs and corn and sich. You got to buy grease and meal and meat and all them things. But I ain't give up yit. I've always had a idee, if a place suits you, you kin make a livin' there somehow."

"I hope you right." She added wistfully, "Wisht Cleve liked the scrub the way you and me do. I some kind o' love it."

He skinned his catch in the shade of a live-oak near the smoke-house. He tacked the hides, fur side down, against the walls. During the cool dry winter weather they cured quickly and rolled, salted bundles were ready every week to mail away or to take to the itinerant buyer at Eureka. Kezzy put the dinner on the table and Piety went into the yard and built a fire under the black iron wash-pot. Kezzy put her smooth black head out of the kitchen window.

"What you fixin' to do, Aunt Py-tee?"

"Cook the varmints for the chickens."

"Tell Lant if he gits a 'possum nice and fat, cheat the chickens and I'll take it home for Zeke."

"I'll tell him."

The animal bodies, short-legged and red, like new-born babies, cooked in the pot. The ants climbed the smoke-house walls to feast on the scraps of meat and fat clinging to the hides. Lant and Kezzy and Piety sat at the kitchen table, neat under checked oil-cloth, and ate their dinner zestfully. The food was hard come by and its taste was sweet. It was doubly fine because the meal was late. Kezzy licked the bacon gravy from her fingers.

"Them sweet pertaters eats good," she said.

"Ma'd have a fit if she couldn't raise her a bed o' 'taters," Lant said. "She keeps 'em bakin' in the oven all day."

He poured cane syrup on his soda biscuit and then sprinkled sugar over the top. Kezzy laid down her knife.

"Well, I do know. Look at that boy put white sugar on his syrup."

Piety laughed. She made a sign to Kezzy over Lant's head. The girl nodded. When Lant, finishing ahead of them, left the table and went to the yard, Piety looked after him until he was out of hearing. She lowered her voice to a half whisper.

"I marked him for white sugar," she confided. "He cain't he'p hisself. When I was carryin' him, we had nothin' but brown sugar. Willy—that was my husband—Willy was goin' to Orange Springs and I said to him, 'Willy, I've took the biggest notion for some white sugar. Fetch me back a half a pound, for I'd some kind of enjoy it.' He comes back and he hands me the sack and he says, 'Here's your white sugar, Py-tee.' I opens the sack. Kezzy, the sugar were brown. I says, 'Willy, the sugar's brown.' When I said it, I could feel the young un turn over inside me. You see I marked him. Willy felt awful bad about it."

"You marked him for white sugar, a'right. He cain't he'p it."

They sat long at table.

Kezzy said slowly, "Anyways, if I marry Cleve and leave the scrub, I still got the river."

Piety said, "You kin come visit me in the scrub ary time."

"I shore will do that thing, Aunt Py-tee."

At twilight they stirred themselves and the women washed the dishes.

Kezzy said, "I want a big plate o' dinner for the dogs. They was mighty faithful comp'ny last night."

Lant sat drowsily, his big feet propped on the apron of the glowing kitchen stove.

"Must I make a fire in 'tother room?" he asked.

"This is good enough, ain't it, Kezzy? You say."

"This is plenty good. A range seem to warm you better'n a hearth fire."

Lant's red-brown eyes were cloudy. The lids drooped. The

broken night's sleep had drained his gaunt growing body. But he was never too weary to play the banjo. He brought it from the trunk and tuned it lazily while the oak coals snapped and burned red in the range. There was no other light. The yellow cat came in and jumped with a throaty cry into Piety's ginghamed lap. He kneaded his paws and buried his head against her. She stroked him.

"He's the biggest crazy for me," she said apologetically.

Their delight was mutual.

"You'd orter be out ketchin' rabbits 'stead o' settin' coiled up so," she said to him sternly.

For answer he settled deeper in her lap and purred in a vast rumble, blinking his eyes foolishly.

"When he comes back from them j'ants," she said, "it's rub and purr, rub and purr, until I cain't git nothin' done, for him."

"The ring-tailed bastard's no good," Lant said.

He laid his ear against the banjo keys and turned them.

"When I'm sick in bed with the fever," the woman said, "he's perfeckly worried. He'll come to the bed and cry."

"He's hongry," Lant said, "is all ails him."

Kezzy said, "I'll bet Lant do a fine piece o' cookin' when you're sick."

"He'll cook," Piety said, "but he'll strow the grease until it's a day with the corn-shucks scrub when I git outen the bed."

Lant closed his eyes and sang. He tapped his foot on the floor and picked the strings of Lantry's banjo.

> *"If I had a scolding wife*
> *I'd switch her sure's you're born.*
> *I'd carry her down to Richmond town*
> *And trade her off for corn."*

He threw back his head. His long neck vibrated. He beat time with his feet so that the room shook.

> *"Git along down, git along down,*
> *Git along down to Richmond town*
> *To lay my t'baccy down."*

Piety said, "Pa sang that."

He drooped his sleepy head over the banjo. He played "Billy in the Low Ground" and "High Sheriff" and "Bluejay Died with the Whooping Cough." He picked idle chords and wondered if he needed to wash his feet before he went to bed. The bed would be cold and clean. The sheet underneath would be slippery, like thin ice. The corn-shucks mattress had a nest hollowed out that fitted his body. The pile of quilts over him would be as warm as goose feathers.

The fire in the range died to embers. The wind whistled along the roof-tree. Piety and the girl were silent. Their faces were white and small in the darkness. They were warm and drowsy and well-fed. When the belly was full, and three sat cozily in a warm kitchen, and good beds waited, there was nothing more to be asked for, Piety thought, or had. She did not notice that Kezzy's black lashes were wet with tears.

XXI

ON CHRISTMAS DAY Zeke Lantry went across the river to a gathering of Jacklins and Wilsons. Kezzy came down the road to spend the holiday with Piety. Cleve had come over the day before. He and Lant had roosted a flock of wild turkeys at dark. At daylight on Christmas they had gone to the swamp. Cleve was a poor shot and missed the birds entirely. Lant brought down the old gobbler and a young hen. They brought them home for Piety and Kezzy to dress and stuff and roast and went away again for a day's deer-hunting.

The birds smoked, golden-brown, in the centre of the white tablecloth when Lant and Cleve came in at sunset. Piety brought out a blue glass bottle of her scuppernong wine. It was white and sparkling. A tumblerful apiece made them flushed and talkative. Kezzy's black eyes shone and the white skin of her cheeks was touched with a faint colour.

"Don't let me git so drunk I cain't fight for my share o' the turkey," she said.

Piety said, "There's enough nobody won't have to quarrel about it."

They ate with zest and sat talking after the meal was done. Towards dark they heard a hail at the rear gate.

Piety said, "That sounds like Zeke."

Lant called, "We're too full to come to the door. Come in."

A double set of steps sounded, somehow furtively, on the floor of the breezeway. Zeke opened the kitchen door sparingly and crowded through, drawing a tall gaunt woman behind him. He was tremulous in his excitement.

"Who's got a better Christmas present than mine?" he asked. "I goed to the frolic and I got me a wife."

The woman parted her mouth and flashed a gold tooth. The mouth snapped shut again. The four at the table stared and did not move or speak. Piety stirred at last.

"Won't you set down to the table and eat?" she asked dubiously.

The woman looked over the table.

"We've et," she said.

She brought a cold hard glance to rest on the younger woman. "You Kezzy?"

The girl stood up.

"I'm Kezzy. Pleased to meet you."

The woman inclined her head.

"Pleased to meet you." She turned to Zeke. "Let's git goin'."

Zeke backed out of the door.

"We jest stopped to give you the news," he said. "Come see us, Py-tee. See you later, Kezzy."

They were gone.

Cleve muttered, "God A'mighty."

Kezzy stood numb and bewildered.

"You'd of thought Zeke would of told me," she said.

Lant said, "He were drunk, ain't that about it?"

She shook her head.

"He's been sort o' hintin' at it. He's a big ol' tease—I never took it serious."

Cleve began to whistle and stopped to grin.

"Looks to me like this about settles your business and mine, Miss biggety Kezzy," he said.

She smiled a little.

"We'll see."

Cleve took her home at bed-time.

Two weeks later Cleve and Kezzy together stopped at the house. They found Piety alone. Kezzy had a bulging suit-box under her arm and Cleve carried a worn handbag. Kezzy laid down the box and held the older woman close in her strong arms.

Piety said, "Don't seem like I kin hardly stand it to see you go."

Kezzy said, "I'll come see you. Zeke's the one's in trouble, Aunt Py-tee."

"I reckon so. I knowed that were a mean woman when I laid eyes on her."

The girl laughed shortly.

"She thinks Zeke's got money hid out. I seed her goin' thu my boxes, scairt I was makin' off with it. Hell won't begin to tear loose 'til she finds Zeke ain't scarcely makin' a livin'."

"Did Abner let you have that ten-acre farm out his way?"

"He were mighty nice about it. He come down on the rent to suit what Cleve had saved up. Better come go to Eureka with us, Aunt Py-tee, and see do a justice o' the peace do as good a job as a preacher."

"I got no way to git back, or I'd shore go. That Ab's team you got there, Cleve?"

"That's Uncle Ab's. How much money you think a man kin save? I was feered I'd have to cut Kezzy a weddin' ring outen a sardine can 'til I found they wa'n't as high as I figgered."

She walked down the lane with them to the gate.

"You better wait 'til Lant gits in from the swamp," she said. "He'll feel bad not to see you."

Kezzy said, "You jest tell him good-bye."

Piety waved after the wagon as far as she could see it and Kezzy waved back.

Zeke and his new wife kept to their house. Lant went to Eureka no oftener than once a month and brought back through the spring no more news of Cleve and Kezzy than that they were farming part of the ten acres and were getting along. Piety urged Lant to take her across the river to see them.

He said, "I got no time for visitin' right now."

By the middle of May she had decided to row the river herself. But in a mid-afternoon, trudging across the clearing from the swamp garden, she saw with her failing sight a figure in the breezeway, and shaded her eyes to make sure that it was Kezzy.

"You quit stealin' my peaches," she called delightedly.

She laid her soft wrinkled cheek against that of the young woman.

"I knowed somebody were comin'," she said, "for the rooster crowed in the day-time. I jest hoped it were you."

Kezzy said, "I figgered you'd be comin' along soon. I could see you'd done been gone 'most all day."

"How'd you know?"

"I could see where-all the chickens had tromped out all your tracks. It takes chickens 'bout all the day to cover the hull yard."

"You and Lant is perfect sights for keepin' up with tracks."

"I like to know who-all's come and who-all's gone."

"That's what Lant says. He'll come in and he'll say, 'Zeke come thu the hammock 'bout a hour 'fore sun and goed back about dusk-dark.' Or he'll say, 'Next time you go for fat-wood you take the gun and crack down on the Half-breed. He's been huntin' your hogs in the scrub today.' Lant's a sight that-a-way."

"Where's the scaper now?"

"He's off down the river some'eres. I cain't keep up with him. We fished the creeks this mornin' and took dinner with us. He put me out at the swamp landin' and goed back. I don't know where. I been workin' the low garden."

"I been worried to death about you-all, Aunt Py-tee. Did he go to Palatka?"

"Yes, and to Jacksonville too. There wa'n't no job to be had."

"I'm mighty sorry, Aunt Py-tee."

"Well, he ain't. I don't know as he hunted him a job too hard. He says if 'twa'n't for me, he'd rather starve in the scrub than eat light bread in sich places."

She looked intently at the girl.

"Kezzy, he acts quare. He's up to somethin'."

"Is?"

"He brought back somethin' on the river boat. It passed by at dark and Zeke heerd Lant totin' somethin'."

"Zeke's always hearin' things. Don't you pay him no mind. Lant knows what he's doin'."

Kezzy frowned. Cleve had failed to care properly for his spring crops and he would probably lose them, but she was more concerned for Lant and his mother than for herself. As long ago as November, when she had gone with him to his traps, she had seen a desperation in his eyes, as of a young bull penned up and fretted for too long a time. She sat in the breezeway and listened to the mocking-birds and stroked the grizzled head of old Red. Black had died soon after she had left the scrub, Piety told her.

They heard the front gate click. Zeke came to the breezeway. He stopped short at sight of Kezzy. His mouth quivered and his drake's-tails fluttered in his neck. She went to him and put an arm across his slight shoulders.

"I jest got a good will to quarrel with you," she said. "I didn't dast come to you, but I figgered you'd slip off and come to see me."

He looked long at her with unhappy pale eyes.

"Py-tee," he said, "ain't the sight of her jest meat and drink?"

They sat side by side on the steps and Piety rocked near them. Kezzy asked, "Has your old lady found all that money yit?"

He shuddered. His blue eyes were watery.

"I'm gittin' my just deserts," he said. "I should of left well enough alone. You and I were mighty comf'table, Kezzy. But I got to studyin', how a woman in the house ain't a woman in the bed. But I see now, I should of left well enough alone."

He looked at her solemnly.

"You know I've always been fond of a leetle whiskey."

She nodded, smiling.

"Not enough to harm, but jest a leetle snort." He lowered his voice confidentially. "Now I have to keep me a jug hid out in the bushes. Then the Lord he'p me do she smell it."

Kezzy said, "You come to see me, and I'll try to have you a pint you kin set and enjoy decent."

He watched her wistfully.

"I feel like I done drove you out. Kin you forgive me, Kezzy?"

She laughed easily.

"I had it in my mind to marry Cleve right on," she said. "Don't you take no blame for nothin' I do, no time."

He rose to go.

"I'm jest unlucky with my women," he said.

When he had gone, Piety said, "He shore is unlucky. When he buried your Ma, Syl Jacklin said he couldn't figger what-all a rabbity leetle feller like Zeke could do to his women to wear 'em down to the grave."

Kezzy smiled.

"He's got one now, Aunt Py-tee," she said, "he shore won't be lucky enough to lose."

Lant came in for supper at sunset. Kezzy hailed him across the yard. He grinned broadly. He tossed a dead limpkin at her.

"I seed your boat," he said. "This speckled bastard were settin' on a limb. I knowed you liked 'em."

"I'll carry him home like he was a gold piece I'd won to the Fair."

"Don't do that, for God's sake. You and me both'll go to the jail-house."

"Don't you belong to shoot limpkins?"

"It's agin the law."

"Well, I want to know, what ain't agin the law!"

"That's what I say!" Piety agreed.

The youth was excited. He walked back and forth through the cabin, taking down his guns from their nails, unrolling a bear-skin, whetting his knife on a soap-stone. He sat restlessly at table and picked and chose among the dishes. When he had finished, he took his banjo from the trunk but laid it down again without more than tuning it. Darkness took over the cabin and he sat rocking violently in a hickory rocker, shuffling his long legs nervously.

"Them cities is a mess, Kezzy," he told her. "I got losted in Jacksonville, dogged if I didn't. I was to the saw-mill oncet with Uncle Ab and I took my bearin's by a big ol' oak tree jest goin' into town. Then we made a turn by a yard where they was a boat upside down. Bless Katy, 'tother day, they'd done cut down the oak tree and I never did find me no rowboat in a yard."

She laughed.

"You been used to trees stayin' where you kin find 'em."

"I wouldn't live in a place where they wa'n't no landmarks. It all looked alike."

He jumped up.

"Wait 'til I fix us somethin' for some fun."

He disappeared in the kitchen. After a few minutes he came back and sat down.

"Tell her what 'tis," Piety said.

"She'll hear direckly. You-all be still."

They sat in silence for half an hour. There was a small explosion and the squeal of a mouse. Lant guffawed and Piety chuckled.

"Got him," he said.

He lit a kerosene lamp and showed Kezzy his patent mouse trap. He had rigged up a miniature cannon, loaded with lead from buckshot shells, and attached it to a small storage battery. The mouse, stepping on a platform after the bait, completed a circuit, fired the cannon and received a diminutive pellet in his breast. The mouse lay dead.

Kezzy said, laughing, "You crazy! Whatever put sich a idee in your head, makin' mice shoot theirselves!"

"The winter evenin's gits kind o' long. Hit jest gives Ma and me somethin' to set and listen to." He whispered in her ear. "I'm 'bout to git me somethin' else to listen to."

"Tell me," she whispered back.

"You be patient. I'll tell you when the time come."

Piety called, "You noticin' the moon? The buck'll soon be in the sweet pertaters. You said you'd try agin tonight."

"I'm a-noticin'. Kezzy, let's you and me go 'bout moondown and kill us the scoundrel been usin' in the 'tater field."

She hesitated.

"I ain't been feelin' too good, Lant."

"It'll do you good. You're gittin' fat."

"That's jest why. I'm startin' me a young un, if you want to know. Long as you're so nosey 'bout the way I look. Well," she conceded, "they say if you put a pointer bitch in the woods, and her carryin' pups, they make the finest bird dogs ever. Jest born with huntin' sense. Mebbe it'll work the same way with a person."

"Kezzy, if it's a litter, save me one. Ma'd love a young un to raise."

"If it's a litter," she said, "you kin have the hull bunch."

It was good to have Kezzy prowling around with him again. They set out across the yard and Piety called after them.

"I'll wait up for you. If I hears you shoot, I'll come with knives and pans."

Kezzy said, "This is agin the law too, eh?"

"You mighty right. Out o' season and fire-huntin', too. 'Tain't like it was a ways back."

"I reckon not. I ain't hunted much."

Lant said, "They was more game in the scrub when they wa'n't no laws, than they is now, with 'em."

She watched his tense lean back with an affectionate amusement. She followed close on his heels, for when she dropped behind, the focussing flashlight fastened to his head shone too far ahead, and she stepped on noisy limbs and stuck the barbs of prickly pear in her ankles. He walked quickly across the open clearing through the broom sage, past the scuppernong vine, speaking in hoarse whispers. When he reached the fence that joined the hammock he put his fingers to his lips and motioned her to caution. He slipped over the fence like an eel and turned to help her climb it without noise. The low palmettos stood flat under the arc of his flashlight. The hammock was flat. The broom sage was a golden wash. There was no roundness anywhere except the barrel of his gun, smooth as a black snake under the steady light.

His body stiffened. His jerking awkwardness disappeared. He moved now in slow-motion, one position flowing liquidly into another. He held his Winchester rifle in his left hand. He used his right arm for balance, laying it on the air ahead of him, as though he grasped an invisible support. He lifted his right foot with a dancer's grace and laid it down toe first. If a palmetto frond was dry and crackling, or a dry twig met his foot, he withdrew it as though it swung on a pivot, and laid it down on another spot.

A yellow half-moon hung low between two palms. Kezzy thought the youth in front of her was like a great red cat in the night, stalking his prey. Long nights of hunting had turned his muscles to ribbons of flexibility. He flowed through the hammock, his head swinging from side to side like a snake's. He focussed his headlight on every clump of palmettos or curtain of low-hanging Spanish moss where a deer might stand. She could not move as he did. She thought that he was very patient to let her spoil his hunt, perhaps, with her clumsiness. She understood that he was hunting tonight as any young male animal would hunt; because he was restless, and his blood itched in his veins, so that he must scratch it against the moon and the wind and the darkness.

He was taking his present direction to keep down-wind of the deer. Instead of waiting for the buck to come to the potato patch, as he had been doing, Lant meant to meet him on the deer-run where he came through the hammock from the scrub. He took a stand under a low-limbed hickory where his light swept the deer-trail on both sides. He motioned Kezzy behind him. The moon turned to orange against the ledge and only the palm tops were visible. A hoot-owl cried over them. Suddenly there was a thin shrill squealing under a near-by oak and a sneezing in the dark. Lant cursed softly and Kezzy thought the deer had come and gone.

"Hammock rabbits," he whispered to her. "Them whistlin' bastards." In a moment he whispered again. "I'm feered no deer will come tonight. A rabbit's a kind of a witch. When the rabbits is feedin' and scaperin', it ginrally means no deer is out. When the deer is feedin', no rabbits is out but mebbe a ol' buck rabbit, and him keepin' mighty quiet."

Again and again Kezzy thought she heard hoof-beats in the distance. She realised that it was her own pulse pounding in her ears. When the buck came, she did not hear him. Lant put one hand behind him and tightened it on her arm to give her warning. He turned his light on the trail between the hammock and the broom-sage field. The buck came trotting through, his head high. The light caught his attention and he stopped short for an instant. His eyes and white throat shone. It seemed to Kezzy that he had time to run to the river, away forever, before Lant shot. But the one steel-jacketed bullet was all that was needed. The buck leaped forward, kicked a moment and straightened out. Lant ran to him, then stood with his head as high as the buck's had been. He listened. The game warden, Bill Mersey, lived ten miles away across the river, but it was reasonable to listen for him.

He said to Kezzy, "Let's drag him off in the hammock. Then we kin cool out do we hear ary one comin'. Ma'll be here direckly."

Piety came, floundering in the dark without a light, by the time they had the buck in the bushes. The single shot had indicated a kill to her, and she had left the house as soon as it was apparent there would not be another. She had with her two large dishpans and two heavy knives. She fussed and fumed about the danger from the warden when Lant went fire-hunting, but she was as anxious as he to have the meat in the house and the hungry caller out of the cow-pea or potato patch. Lant skinned the buck, looking for the bullet hole. It had passed through the centre of the chest to the heart.

He said, "I'm a mind to bury the hide along with the head and sich. That nosey Bill Mersey find a hide and head and chitlin's, he'll know good and well the deer didn't jest run off and leave 'em."

Kezzy said, "Roll it up for me, Lant. I'll take it home with me in the mornin'. I been wantin' a deerskin for the side o' the bed the worst way. I ain't afeered o' Bill. I kin ask him out of ary thing."

He cut the meat into pieces and piled as much in the pans as they would hold. He guessed the deer's weight at something over a hundred pounds. The scrub deer seldom weighed over a hundred and fifty. Piety and Kezzy each took a pan and he strung a strip of palmetto through the remaining pieces and slung them over his shoulder. He covered the refuse with woods debris.

"Now you git," he said. "If you hears ary sound, you stop dead in your tracks."

He switched off his flashlight and led the women to the house in darkness. They put the meat in the smoke-house and he double-barred the door.

"Tomorrow," he said, "I'll smoke hell outen it before Bill comes moseyin' around."

He had his pants and shoes off before the women had finished talking in Piety's bedroom. They heard him strike the bed and when they passed his room to wash their faces for the night, he was asleep.

In the morning he asked Kezzy to go to the river with him.

"I'm in a slow hurry," she said. " 'Tain't right to leave my ol' man Cleve too long."

They sat in silence while he paddled the rowboat through the swamp and down the river. She asked no questions. When he swung the boat under a clump of laurel and up a shallow creek, she looked at him.

"I reckon I know," she said.

"Wa'n't nothin' else to do, Kezzy."

"No, 'twa'n't," she agreed slowly, "and stay in the scrub."

"You remember the place?" he asked. "Taylor's Dread?"

"I don't know who'd remember better. Lest it's Zeke hisself. Do Zeke know?"

He nodded.

"Zeke told me jest what to start off with."

She smiled.

"The cute ol' scaper—never lettin' on to Aunt Py-tee——"

He landed in muck, a half-mile of tortuous travelling from the river. He led her in to the swampy heart of the island to the site of Zeke's old still. The freight he had brought with him from Jacksonville was two large squares of sheet copper. He had four barrels made from old staves and salvaged hoops. He had begun the cooker, utilizing Zeke's old bricks and rocks for the furnace. The girl listened quietly as he explained what further was to be done. She walked about examining the assembled materials.

"You got money to git you started?" she asked.

"I got no cash money left. I figgered the storekeeper to Eureka'd trust me for meal and sugar to git goin'."

"He's trustin' half a dozen on my side the river for the same thing. He's been mighty good to trust ever'body. You got plans for sellin' it?"

"Not special. They was hunters here all winter askin' where could they git whiskey. I figgered they'd come ask agin."

"Lant," she said, "how old you, boy? 'Bout twenty? You sure you know what-all you're doin'? I'd mighty hate to see you git into trouble. What'd your Ma do for a livin', and you in the jail-house?"

"What'll she do for a livin' if I don't git to makin' one? I don't aim to see the inside o' the jail-house. Nobody cain't slip up on me here. They's a risk, I know that. I'm jest natchelly countin' on nary snooper gittin' in to this lay-out."

"It's mighty well hid-out," she agreed. "Couldn't nobody but you find the way in here."

"Dogged if I know why I ain't thought of it before," he said. "I've always knowed they was a livin' makin' corn liquor. You've heerd Zeke say he shouldn't never of quit. He jest got skeert. I someways never thought about it before."

"You got it to think about now, son," she said drily.

They walked back to the boat. The channel reassured her as Lant poled out to the river again. There were a dozen blind leads and only one true entrance. Time and again the water was so shallow, or ran over so obstinate an obstruction, that any one would have turned back, refusing to believe there was an opening and an end.

"You're jest a wild enough scaper," she said, "to where it'll suit you perfect. It'd jest suit you, givin' a mess o' strangers the slip."

His enthusiasm mounted as she found fewer objections.

"I'm fixin' to make it clean and nice, Kezzy," he assured her earnestly, "plenty fitten to sell to ary man."

"Well," she said at last, "'tain't like it was somethin' wrong. 'Shinin's an honest trade. A man buys his meal and sugar and he pays for 'em and he takes 'em and makes somethin' other folks wants."

XXII

WISPS OF SMOKE wavered from the swamp below the clearing where Lant's whiskey still was working. The ash wood used for firing burned with a clear flame; only an occasional thread columned blue-white against the cobalt sky. Zeke saw it from his stoop and when his wife's back was turned, slipped away. Lant had moved the outfit up from Taylor's Dread the week before after an undisturbed year. Zeke had not visited him in the new location. If he had timed Lant's activities correctly, the first new batch of mash must be due to run. The smoke against the summer sky was encouraging. Zeke's jug was empty and he was thirsty.

As he cut through the hammock to the swamp, he whistled like a quail. He gave the mating call, which was out of season, for the young quail were lately hatched. An answering whistle came back and he struck openly along the creek. The outfit stood exposed to plain view. Yet nothing but the sheerest accident—such as hunters and dogs on the trail of a deer—would bring a stranger here.

Lant had built a wooden platform high over the slow-running creek. There was room for the rowboat to pass beneath for loading and unloading. On the platform stood a stout brick furnace; a box-like cooker of cypress and sheet copper; drums and barrels. He had driven four long ash saplings into the creek-bed at the four corners and made a canopy over the whole. Palmetto fronds formed a neat thatched roof. Lant squatted on his haunches in front of the furnace, stoking the fresh fire with small sticks of immaculate white ash.

He said, "Hey, Uncle Zeke," without turning.

Zeke said, "I'm about in time to he'p you run a charge, dogged if I ain't."

"I'll put you to work direckly, don't you worry about that."

Zeke peered into the cooker.

"How much do the pot hold?"

"The buck from two barrels. I only got one barrel dipped out. I'm somethin' late. I figgered I'd git my fire goin'. You kin finish dippin' from the other barrel. Don't you rile the buck."

Zeke said mildly, "You got no call to tell me how to handle mash, boy."

He investigated the barrels. The one Lant had just dipped out into the cooker, showed a loose sediment over a residue of close-packed cornmeal at the bottom. Two barrels of mash were midway in their fermentation. They seethed and bubbled. The hissing sounded like a thin batter being poured on a hot griddle. The cap had formed and the surfaces were covered with foam and small particles. The fourth barrel was the mate to the one Lant had emptied. The cap had settled. The liquid, with an alcoholic content of some twenty-proof, was clear.

Zeke said, "Jest about here is where a feller got to hurry. The buck goes flat in no time, and you jest as good to pitch the mash in the creek, for you'll git no more alcohol."

"You don't need to tell me about the beer goin' flat," Lant said. "That were my first mistake."

"Lettin' it stand too long, eh?"

"Lettin' it stand."

Zeke rinsed the bucket with creek water and dipped the strong sour liquid from the barrel into the cooker. The ash fire underneath reached a flaming climax of orange heat. Lant fed it again. The sheet copper shone, hot and clean. The buck in the cooker began to simmer. Lant stirred the blazing sticks to fierce coals. The liquid bubbled and made a complete turn-over, like soap-suds boiling. The pot was ready to cap.

Zeke helped him fit on the tight cypress cover. Its protruding copper pipe made an angled turn and joined the copper coils immersed in a barrel of cold water. Lant raked some of the fire from out the furnace. Zeke nodded.

"A low steady heat's the thing, all right, son," he approved.

The ash burned evenly. The cooker was vibrant with energy. Zeke dipped the bucket into the emptied barrels and mucked off the sediment, leaving the dense mass of meal intact at the bottom.

"Here's your bed," he said.

"Put a chinchy couple o' buckets o' fresh meal in each barrel, please sir, Uncle Zeke. That bag yonder."

The old man measured the cornmeal carefully.

"I got to have he'p with the sugar," he said. "I cain't git a hundred-pound sack this high and not waste it."

Lant left the fire and came to him. They lifted the bag together and shook the sugar in the barrels, fifty pounds to each. Zeke measured creek water with an affectionate slowness.

"Now a bucket-two o' hot buck from the pot, time your charge is run, and these here scapers'll go to work for you. Dog take it, Lant, this is a fine business. I shouldn't never of quit."

"You better start up agin. Go partners with me, if you say."

He shook his head.

"Hit's too late now. I jest ain't spry enough to run."

Lant laughed. The fire burned to slow coals. He sat by Zeke at the edge of the platform. They dangled their legs over the creek and spoke in a low monotone that carried no more than a few feet.

Lant said, "This is the least worrisome business I ever been into."

Zeke said, "I ain't talkin' about worry. When lightnin' strike, you got no time to worry." He sang softly, under his breath:

> "Raccoon is a cunnin' thing,
> Travels in the dark.
> Don't know what trouble is,
> 'Til he hears ol' Ranger bark."

He added, "Then he know."

Lant spat into the swamp.

"I jest don't figger them gov-mint 'Rangers' is goin' to bark up this creek," he said.

Zeke agreed. "Well, I reckon hit ain't likely. Floridy ain't never been too much bothered that-a-way. Take back when I were makin' it. Up to the time I had that pure accident, you never heerd tell o' no revenooers in these parts. 'Course, the law was different then. Whiskey-makin' was all right if you paid the tax. Half the folks I knew, used to make a leetle jest for theirselves. Sho, nobody paid no mind."

Lant moved across the platform to mend the fire. A slow procession of crystal drops passed out at the end of the copper spout. Where the sun struck, they flashed blue-white like diamonds. Lant touched his finger to the spout and tasted the warm liquid. He winced and held his lips open to the air to cool them.

"Take a fool to drink that first of it," he said. "It'd burn the guts outen you if it ever got past your throat."

Zeke went on with his ruminations.

"Now they've got the new law since the war," he said, "and nobody don't belong to make whiskey at all, no-way, no time, tax or no tax. And boy, don't you think them new kind o' revenooers ain't comin' into the state. And the county, too. But now, hit's one thing for them strangers to find a still in open blackjack. Or by a branch in the piney-woods. This here river is jest another matter."

Lant grinned.

"Them tryin' to find their way thu the swamps, eh? Sinkin' down in the muck—puttin' their ol' hands on a log and jest missin' a moccasin—I reckon it don't suit them Prohis too good."

Zeke said, "'Bout the only way they'd git to a feller 'round here'd be for somebody to turn him up. Ain't nobody fixin' to do that. All the Jacklins hates Lem Posey. Sharp Kinsley romps on Luke Saunders mighty nigh ever' time he crosses his tracks. Sho, Lem and Luke got no cause to fear they'll have their livin' interfered with. A man's livin' is somethin' it takes a mighty low-down white man to mess with."

Lant said, "Well, I don't mess up with nobody no-ways. I figger ain't nobody'll mess up with me."

"You'll keep outen a heap o' trouble," Zeke said, "mindin' your own business and keepin' to the scrub this-a-way. Hit's a scaper like Lem Posey'll git the law takin' notice, always whoopin' and sooeyin' and sic-a-boyin' the way he do."

They sat in silence.

Zeke asked, "How's ol' Red?"

Lant said, "He's been havin' more o' them fits. He seemed some better when I left the house this mornin'."

It made him unhappy to talk about Red and he began to hum

under his breath. The warm crystal stream dripped steadily from the coils. The scent of the distillate was rank and sweet.

Zeke said, "That's about fitten now."

Lant said, "Take a can and git you a drink."

The old man gulped half a cupful. Courage and discontent possessed him.

"I'm goin' on home," he announced, "and git my old woman told."

Lant was as well pleased to be alone. After Zeke's steps had faded away, he went to his favorite seat in an area he had cleared in the hammock above the creek. He sat with his back to a magnolia overlooking the platform; hunched; idle with the immobility of an animal. He liked the work, he reflected. He had liked it from the beginning. He would want to make corn liquor, he thought, if there wasn't a dollar in it. There was, in fact, a good living. His profits during the year ranged from four to ten dollars a week. Moonshining was more certain than farming; than trapping or 'gatoring.

He liked the smell of the sour mash and the heat of the copper. When he ran a charge at night, he liked the blue flame of the burning ash in the black of the night, and the orange glow on the sweet-gum leaves. Here he liked the intimacy with the hammock. Its life washed over him and he became a part of it. The scrub yonder sent its furred and feathered inhabitants past him to eat and drink, and he and the scrub were one.

He liked to know all there was to be known of every animal and bird and tree. At the Dread he had seen a wood-duck walk down with her puff-ball ducklings on her back, submerging in the cool creek water so that the young ones were floated gently on the new element. He had watched pole-cats with their young in single file. Black snakes had mated a few feet away. Since he had moved to the swamp below the clearing, he had seen a wild cat with her kittens, and half-grown fox-pups tumbling within a stone's throw of him, quarrelling over a rabbit.

Beyond the still he could glimpse his mother's swamp garden, where she grew collards and turnip-greens in the dampness the year around. Seeing a shadowy movement there, he crept close.

A pair of quail trailed by a new-hatched covey was feeding under the tall collards. They reached on tiptoe, turning their small heads this way and that, picking insects from the under-leaves. The cock kept up a running conversation, making small sweet sounds, to which the hen now and then responded. Lant swooped down and picked up half a dozen of the young in his square brown hand, each bird no bigger than his thumb. He said to the fluttering adult birds, "Hell, I ain't fixin' to harm 'em," held them a moment and let them go.

He thought he heard the sly dip of a paddle out on the river. He held his breath. Any untoward sound was the signal to stop and listen: the clatter of a squirrel along hickory limbs; the crackle of twigs in the swamp; an alarmed flight of duck or crane or water-turkey. Sounds from the river he dreaded most. From that way would come danger. Listening, his innate wariness was intensified. But the ripple he had heard was only the murmur of the river current. It breathed sometimes like a live thing.

The new buck was yielding the proper amount and quality of raw whiskey. Ten gallons averaged a hundred and twenty proof. He jugged it and ran into separate containers another eight gallons of low-wine that tested forty. The low-wine was sour-tasting and full of undesirable elements. He was tempted to mix some of it with the first-run whiskey, for he had an order for more than he could fill. Many 'shiners, he knew, drew a scant line between the two grades. He decided to follow his custom of adding the low-wine to the fresh buck when he ran his next charge; re-distilling it to extract the alcohol and leave behind the impurities.

He thought, "I'd not drink the stuff the way 'tis and I'll not sell it to no other man to drink."

He dipped out buckets of steaming buck from the cooker and added one to each of the two barrels of fresh-set mash to hurry fermentation. He planned always to set new mash at the time he ran a charge. Then the old bed of meal, which needed to be changed only every two months, was not wasted. Sometimes he was not paid on time for his whiskey and he was without cash for sugar. Then he must either ask the storekeeper for credit, which was distasteful, or let the old bed of meal spoil, and start all over again when he was in funds. The proportion of fifty pounds of sugar and thirty gallons of water to each fifty-gallon barrel was the same on any set-up. The waste was in the meal, for it took fifty pounds to start a barrel of mash all over again.

He puckered his lips and whistled soundlessly. He was pleased with the run; pleased with the new location. A summer rain had set in. He worked in comfort under the thatched roof. Silver sheets of rain slid musically down the palmettos. Beyond the platform limpkins walked stiff-legged in the downpour, searching the creek for snails.

He concealed the jugs of fresh liquor under adjacent low palmettos and went to the house in the rain. Piety was waiting on the breezeway. She wore a print dress the colour of her hair. He noticed her greyness, blending with the grey of the rain.

She said, "Hit'll soon fair off. Why didn't you wait? Seem to me you jest enjoy gittin' soaked to the hide."

He said, "Hit's the next best thing to goin' naked." He looked at her. "What's the matter, Ma?"

"You'll hate it," she said. "You'll jest perfeckly hate it. Red died while you was to the outfit."

His throat tightened.

He said, "He's out-lasted hisself. He should of died two-three years ago."

"I know you feel bad," she said.

His eyes burned. He set his teeth. She had not complained of Red in late years, for the dog had become gentler, but he said, "Well, I know you don't. I know you're jest proud he's gone. You'll have nothin' but them bastardly cats to feed."

She blinked at him. He turned and walked across the yard and into the smoke-house. She watched after him. Then she went into the kitchen and fired the range and baked a sweet-potato pie. She watched him at the supper table, but he seemed unconscious of the deep-lidded eyes fixed on his face. He was restless. He bent his head low over his plate, his forelock almost touching it. He ate his potato pie.

He said, " 'Tain't as good as Kezzy's."

He cut himself another piece.

He said, "I'm goin' some place tonight."

"Some place acrost the river?"

"I dunno."

"This is Friday. You like not to find Cleve and Kezzy to the house. She said two weeks ago they aimed to go to the next frolic."

"I ain't said nothin' about Cleve and Kezzy. I'm like to go to the damn frolic myself."

XXIII

THE GIRL was small; almost as small as Piety. The first time Lant swung her in the square-dance, he was astonished at her lightness. When he passed her again, he said to her, "Must be you don't weigh no more'n a full-growed field-lark." She looked at him gravely and dropped her eyes.

He danced fiercely, all arms and legs, like a jack-on-the-stick. His shaggy forelock dangled between his eyes. His blue shirt stuck to his back where the sweat had moistened it. He was lean and ugly and virile, and the girls cut their eyes at him and pushed him impudently. Lottie Hobkirk said, "Lant Jacklin, I jest as soon be swung by a pole, as you." He grinned in answer, amiably enough.

At the end of the set he saw the small light girl go to the long bench above the fiddlers' platform. The boy with her asked a question. She shook her head and the boy went outside where some of the young bloods were wrestling and tumbling. Lant walked to the bench. He discovered himself sitting by the girl as though he had walked there in his sleep. He had nothing to say and was sorry he had come. Her hands were folded in her lap. She looked straight ahead. When he saw that she was not looking at him, Lant turned furtively to watch her. He decided that he had thought of a field-lark because her hair was the tawny yellow of the bird's throat. It was drawn back over her ears and it looked soft and ruffled like feathers. Something about the pointed chin was like the neatness of a lark's bill. She looked frightened. He shuffled his feet.

He was conscious that someone had crossed the platform and was sitting on the other side of him. He turned quickly. Kezzy was looking at him curiously. He was relieved. She put a hand on his bony knee.

"Now I want to know what put it in your head to come to the frolic," she said. "Cleve and the baby and me come in the door jest now and I says to Cleve, 'Cleve, I wouldn't be no more surprised to see a cattymount settin' up there behind the fiddlers.' "

"Nobody but you kin dance and carry on, I reckon."

He tried to remember what had been in his mind when he left the scrub. The buff-headed girl left the bench and slipped along the wall to the far end of the dance hall. He was depressed again.

"I jest takened the notion to hear somebody's music besides my own." He remembered. "Red's done dead," he said.

"The pore ol' feller—" She sat silent a moment. "You didn't bring Ardis to the dance, then?"

"I didn't carry nobody."

"I figgered you was together until I noticed you wa'n't talkin' to her."

He craned his long neck to look down the room. Kerosene lamps flickered high on the walls and obscured the room beyond. He was aware that Kezzy was asking him a question. He turned blankly. She looked at him thoughtfully. She smiled a little. She rose and rested her hand an instant on his shoulder and went across the room where Cleve had turned the baby over to the older women. Mrs. Kinsley puffed to the platform.

"I got your quarter yet?" she asked cheerfully.

"You shore ain't. I was about figgerin' on dancin' free."

He was alone above the fiddlers. Old man Lonny Sours tuned up and tried out the melody. The next set was forming. The floor was crowded. Cleve and Kezzy stood hand in hand below him. Kezzy whistled quickly to catch his attention. She jerked her head towards the group of girls and women at the other end of the hall.

She whispered to him across the fiddlers, "She's got nobody with her, Lant."

The caller and his partner came in the door and took their places in the circle. Lant hurried from the bench and past the waiting dancers. The girl stood between two old women. He held out his hand to her and she put hers in it.

He said, "We got to hurry. We 'bout to git left."

He was conscious of her hand. He held it as carefully as he had held the young quail in the afternoon. The tune was "Sally Good Un." Its liveliness tempted him to gallop, but he tried to tone down his pace. Swinging her, the girl seemed fragile. He was afraid of snapping her to pieces. He breathed easily again when he passed and swung Kezzy. Her solidity was comforting. He heaved her towards him so that her feet flew up behind her. Her breasts were hard and full against him.

When the set was ended he took the girl's arm and led her to the bench. He leaned over and asked, "You want a dope?" She nodded. He whistled shrilly to the Kinsley boy and fished in his pocket for a dime for the two bottles of Coca-Cola. She sucked at her bottle slowly and daintily. He watched her steadily. She looked out over the room or down into her lap, tracing the pattern in her dress with one finger. Suddenly he imitated the distant chattering of a squirrel. One of the fiddlers turned to look and the girl opened her eyes wide and full at Lant. They were grey-blue, with long lashes. He laughed loudly.

"You better look at me," he said. "I been studyin', if I couldn't git you to look at me, how'd you know me agin?"

She said, "I know you. You're Lant Jacklin."

He said, "You got a tongue, too. I'd 'bout figgered I'd takened up with a dumbie."

She dropped her eyes. Girls usually tormented him, trying to make him talk. It delighted him to be tormenting her.

He said, "You keep on, you'll purty near tell me somethin'."

She said, "You live in the scrub."

He laughed and nodded.

"If they wa'n't so many folks around," he said, "I'd show you how a panther screams. It scares folks," he added, "if they ain't expectin' it."

Her eyes were wide again.

"Are there many panthers there?"

"Mighty few. They keeps to theirselves mostly, over in the bay-head flats. You ain't never been across the river?"

She shook her head.

He said eagerly, "How'd you like to come go huntin' with me, time the season opens?"

She said, "I've never shot a gun."

He said disconsolately, "Well—" He studied her. "You so small and light," he said, "I reckon you couldn't scarcely tote a gun." He remembered his mother, lifting a gun almost as long as her body. "You could too, by God," he said fervently. "Your shoulders is slopin' and narrer—you'd need a lot o' drop in a gun-stock. A .410 is what you want, or a .22 rifle, with a short stock and plenty o' drop."

She said, "I like to fish."

"I bet your wrist is good and limber for castin'."

"I don't mean casting. My father fishes that way. I mean, with a pole."

"Oh—nigger fishin'." He brightened. "That's the onliest way to ketch bait for set lines. It's a trick now, to ketch very small bream with them leetle pin hooks."

They fell silent. The sets were called and danced and ended; called and danced again. People were going home. He was amazed that the dance was over. The girl slid from the bench and went to the door.

She said to him over her shoulder, "Good-bye."

She disappeared into the darkness. Panic swept him. He jumped from the fiddlers' platform to the floor and followed after her. She had joined a group of women. He pulled at her sleeve.

He said hoarsely, "Ardis! How 'bout you comin' to the next frolic? I'm comin' if you'll come. You meet me here?"

She said, "Yes."

XXIV

THE SCRUB had fewer inhabitants than for fifty years. The stretch in front of the Lantry clearing that had been low-growing, with far vistas, was dense and dark with growth. Its pines, grey-trunked and scrawny, crowded close together. The entire region was again almost a virgin wilderness. Yet the law had come into the scrub and lay over it like a dark cloud.

Several years ago the government had taken over the greater bulk of it, unowned, uninhabited. Thousands of acres at its heart were now a game refuge, where no one might hunt or trap. Fire towers had been established here and there. There had been panic among the few inhabitants. Old man Paine, whose clearing lay in the new reservation, had died recently in a burst of frustration.

"I've killed me hun'erds o' deer in my time," he had told Lant sorrowfully, "and with my age upon me, the law says I got no right to take me a leetle piece o' venison to fill my pore ol' guts."

Even the piney-woods side of the river had felt uneasy, living so close to an unwelcome neighbour. They had pictured federal spies behind every clump of palmettos. They craved venison in August as they had never craved it before. There were still immense areas that might be hunted during the open season. But it had seemed at first, with one section shut off by invisible lines, as though there were no other section worth hunting. The deer had come to be called "gov'mint cows" and "gov'mint yearlin's."

It had become apparent, as the years passed quietly, that the government was as remote as ever. There were no lurking spies, no agents, no tangible evidence of the federal hawk circling in a clouded sky. There was nothing in the scrub, except game, that anyone wanted. The Southern spruce, or sand pine, was value-less, even to the government. The varmints came obligingly to the swamps to be trapped as before. The deer still came to the river to drink. If a man hunted carelessly on into what a small sign designated as a National Forest, there was no living creature to know.

The fire towers had proved harmless. Each held a lonely fellow who lived at the top and kept a watch for forest fires. The man in the Salt Springs tower was from Georgia. He invited Lant up to the top to look out over the rolling scrub and see his maps and implements. The government, he said, wanted only to keep away the devastating fires and to give the game a place for breeding. He played an old flute that had belonged to his grandfather in the War of the States. One night, down the narrow sandy Salt Springs road, Lant heard him high up above the trees, tootling eerily on his flute. The notes had dropped sweetly over the scrub, like the cries of a lost soul riding the sky.

Now in a dry November the heart of the scrub was burning. Since morning the smell of smoke had grown stronger. Lant was running a charge at his outfit. His nose twitched like a rabbit's. He uncapped the cooker and put out the fire in the brick furnace before he had run off the usual amount of low-wine. He added hot buck to the two new settings of mash. He had two demi-johns of whiskey and one of low-wine. He drove the corks in firmly and buried them in the soft black muck of the creek bed. He hurried to the house and joined his mother on the front stoop. They shaded their eyes against the round ball of sun, red and sick behind the greyness that was smoke in the east.

"The hell of it is," he said, "the gov'mint'll be here direckly."

Piety nodded. It was reasonable, she agreed, that the federal government would send men to put out fire on its own property. The danger was manifold. The wind was from the north-east. If it turned into the east, worse, into the south-east, the fire itself would sweep towards the river across the scrub and would lick up the Lantry clearing, broom sage, fences, shingled house and all. Yet it was men, not fire, he dreaded. There would be not only strange federal men swarming in the scrub, but sheriffs and their deputies, game wardens and the like. He minded a game warden the least. He could fool a warden any time. Bill Mersey had never bothered him.

"Jest the same, them boogers is all mixed up together," he said to Piety. "I got no question Bill carries what he sees to the Prohis, and the Prohis does the same for Bill."

He pictured the fire sweeping towards the river, and the fire and Bill Mersey and the high sheriff and the Prohis smoking out his still like a rabbit warren. Bill Mersey was Ardis' cousin. He had forgotten her all day. Ardis Mersey. She had lived in a town and gone to school and had come back to the piney-woods where her father had fallen heir to her grandfather's prosperous lands. It was incredible that she had been away and out of his mind all these years simply because he had not known her.

He had intended to row across the river after he ran his charge to tell her that the scrub was on fire and he could not take her that night to Abner Lantry's cane-grinding. In September he had let a setting of mash go flat because he had promised to go with her to a peanut-boiling.

He said to Piety, "My girl's like to think mighty hard of me, but I reckon I better git goin' acrost the scrub to see what that fire's a-doin'."

"You've been mighty faithful for about four months. She hadn't orter take it hard." She looked at him, still shading her eyes. "You call her your girl to her face?"

He shook his head.

"I'm feered I'll scare her. I got to sort o' slip up on her."

"Don't you be too sure about that." She laughed. "I've noticed it ain't hard to slip up on a girl if she's of a notion to be slipped up on."

He said, "She'd be off like a dove if I was to put my hand on her."

"Well, you'd orter know."

They stared into the murky east. Their eyes smarted. They heard voices across the clearing. Cleve and Kezzy and two Wilson men were coming through the rear gate. Kezzy's youngster was old enough to walk a little, but she carried him in her arms. The woman and three men pushed hurriedly through the sand. The men carried axes and spades.

Lant called, "You got news about the fire? I was jest about to git on the mule and go look for it."

One of the Wilsons said, "We got news, all right. South o' Lake Delancey the hull Big Scrub's a-burnin'. The fire warden to the Salt Springs tower jest now sent a boy ridin' hell-bent into Eureka for he'p. Ever'body's called out to he'p fight."

Lant said, "Cleve, you know where-all the harness is at. You go git it while I ketch the mule."

On his way across the yard he tolled his grandfather's farm bell to call in Zeke.

Kezzy said, "Aunt Py-tee, let's you and me load some jugs o' water in the wagon and what bread and meat you got cooked."

The men loaded axes and hoes and shovels. The women would go along and drive the wagon back again. By the time they were ready Zeke had arrived. He climbed in and they rattled down the road. A few miles to the south they turned left and took the Salt Springs road through the heart of the scrub. It was inches deep in shifting sand. The smoke grew more acrid. Cleve and the Wilsons talked excitedly. Piety and Lant and Zeke and Kezzy were silent, with drawn faces. The wind was still out of the north-east.

Cleve said, "You don't figger on fire in November."

But the summer had been dry, frost had come early, and the scrub was like tinder. The floor was carpeted with parched brown pine needles. Dead palmetto fronds were like oil-soaked paper. Old lighter'd knots and fallen pine limbs made a network of inflammability. Cars and wagons and men riding mules and horses were on the road, some going towards the fire; other cars and wagons had dropped their men and were going back for more. Lant turned the mule off the single-track road when he met a car, for wheels spun helplessly out of the deep ruts. To another wagon he gave half of the road. Hands lifted in passing but there was no friendly hailing. Faces were grave. Men who were not concerned, even for the endangered game, were coming away startled from that sea of flame.

The billowing smoke had been visible for the past five miles. Within a mile the fire was plain, leaping like red-tongued dogs after juicy bones of palmetto and oak and pine. The roar, overlaid with a sharp crackling, filled their ears above the thump of mule-hooves in the sand. Lant tied the mule in the scrub off the road and they walked in. Kezzy went with them. Piety sat in the wagon and held the baby. It was strange to have them go away and leave her. A brief time ago she would have been in it with the men.

Government fire-lines had been ploughed a few years before, but grass and weeds had grown over them and had dried in the drought. The fire had taken the first set of ditches like a runaway horse. Men were working far to the south, widening and clearing the fire-lines as yet unreached. Ahead, an open area lay in the path of the flames. Men were back-firing here, and beating out the fire of their own making with green palmetto fronds and pine saplings.

Newcomers joined Lant and Cleve and Zeke and the two Wilsons and they set to work as a unit, without orders. The fire-warden could be seen on a slight rise, directing the line of fight. Fire was familiar to men of the piney-woods and they needed scant instructions. The Florida woods burned every spring.

"Thanks to them turpentine men," Kezzy said, "burnin' out the brush so they kin git to their boxes, and not keerin' what happens to the rest o' the woods."

Zeke said, "Yes, and the cattle men has been as bad."

Kezzy said, "Well, I cain't see a mess like this un and not git into it."

She borrowed Lant's light axe and cut a sapling for herself. She worked beyond the Wilsons, beating out the fresh flames as they fired. The wind freshened and within an hour it was plain that most of the front would have to be abandoned. Across one corner a burned-over patch turned the fire, but the great body of it rolled in. The sound, so close, was terrifying. The green leaves of oak and myrtle and gallberry and palmetto exploded like fire-crackers. The floor of the scrub burned with a snake-like sizzling. The dry pine-tops burst into flame with a roar. Balls of fire leaped twenty feet at a jump.

Zeke shouted, "I never heerd no storm come thu the pines with sich a noise."

From a slight elevation to the south-west where they had retreated, the conflagration could be seen as a sweeping flood. It rolled in billows, the flaming surf of an infernal sea. Other groups joined them, waiting a moment to see which lines would hold, and where they must go at it again. Here and there the advance of the fire cast itself helplessly where there was no fresh fuel. Watching, they saw it leap, because of a slight shift of wind, or for no apparent reason at all, across an entire small area, or skirt around an island of slash or long-leaf pine.

Kezzy worked with the men until late in the afternoon. They were blackened with smoke and charcoal. Their eyes shone inflamed in dirty faces. They realized that Cleve had been missing for two or three hours. They walked in a body to the wagon for drinking water and to inquire after him. Beyond the wagon, under a myrtle bush, they saw the man, asleep. The Wilsons nodded to each other, their eyes narrowing.

Lant said to Zeke, "Go rout him out."

Eph Wilson said, "Hell, leave him go on in with the wagon, or go on sleepin'. He's no he'p, noways."

Kezzy turned scarlet under her dirt. Eph gulped.

"Excuse me, Kezzy. No offense."

"No offense," she agreed lightly. She added quickly, "He were 'coon huntin' all last night."

Eph said politely, "That so?"

Piety unwrapped the food she had brought. They turned from the wagon, wiping their mouths.

Lant said, "Kezzy, you quit now and go home with Ma."

She frowned.

"You'll starve your damn young un if you don't take keer of him."

Piety said anxiously, " 'Tain't right, Kezzy. You'll give him the colic, and you so hot and sweatin'."

Kezzy took the sleepy body from Piety. She laid her face against the silky head. A streak of black came off on the child's cheek.

"Gittin' you smuttied— Folkses'll think I had you puttin' out the fire." She said reluctantly, "I'll go on in. We'll come back if you don't git in soon."

Lant said, "If we cain't lick this soon, we jest as good to clare out and let her rip."

Zeke and the Wilsons started away.

Lant said, "Kezzy, you do somethin' for me? When you go home this evenin', git word to Ardis why I ain't comin'."

"She'll know," she said easily. "Bill Mersey was comin' over."

"She jest might not hear."

"Lant, I wasn't figgerin' on goin' home. I'll likely be drivin' the wagon back here after night-fall. You don't need to fret about Ardis not knowin'."

"All right."

He turned away, wiping the grime from his face. His back was dejected. She understood that he wanted the small yellow-headed girl to know—not that he would not come—but that he was sick at heart because he could not. She walked after him and pulled his sleeve.

"I'll row acrost soon's I git your Ma to the house and tell Ardis you're sorry," she said, and hurried to the wagon again.

He looked back in a moment. She was leaning over the snoring man under the myrtle bush. He heard her say desperately, "Cleve, for God's sake—" He felt guilty. Kezzy, with her breasts stretched hard and tight for her child, rowing across the river, smutty-faced and weary and damp with sweat, to take his casual word to the pale, bird-like girl who was afraid of him— He plunged into the thick of the fire-fighting. The warden was setting dynamite and it gave promise of checking the advance.

The fire continued through the night. Zeke Lantry's harridan, frightened, joined Piety and Kezzy and helped them cook food and make gallons of coffee. They put the coffee in Lant's demi-johns and wrapped the jugs in thick blankets of Spanish moss to keep them hot. Setting out towards the Salt Springs road a little before midnight, they could see the whole eastern sky ablaze. Miles away, a cloudy roar came to their ears, as though bull alligators battled and bellowed in the distance.

Fresh men arrived in the morning from farther settlements. The first day's fighters crawled away from the front of the fire, far advanced and inexorable, and fell on the pine-needled earth for an hour's rest. Towards noon the wind shifted and the sky clouded. In the early afternoon a light shower sprinkled its way across the burning scrub. At four o'clock rain fell in sheets. The red tongues flickered high against it. Steam began to rise in clouds and join the descending greyness.

Men laughed and shouted and corn whiskey appeared. They sat on their heels and joked suddenly. Stumps smouldered and tall trunks smoked, but the fire was done for. The Big Burn lay black and desolate, as it was to lie for years, with skeletons of trees reared against a sky that would seem here always of hot and dirty steel. The unburned patches stood anomalous, as though they had known a secret and evil magic to turn the flames.

Cars and wagons and horses and mules were all moving towards the river again. Cleve and Kezzy and the Wilsons had gone home in Abner Lantry's automobile. Piety waited on a side trail with the wagon. Lant and Zeke were among the last men to leave. Lant was light-hearted. He had seen almost no strangers; certainly no federal men. Turning down the dim side road he saw a small figure running past the pines. The blood beat against the top of his head.

He called, "Ardis!"

She was white with terror. She ran to him and sobbed breathlessly against his arm. He stroked her sleeve gently. Zeke shuffled his feet uncertainly a moment and hurried ahead of them.

Lant soothed her, "Easy, honey. Was you losted? What you doin' out here, anyway?"

She caught her breath and laughed a little.

"I came with Father and Cousin Bill, just to see. I saw some girls I knew, in a car down the road. When I came back, I couldn't find anyone."

"Why, honey," he said, "I seed Bill and your daddy drive by a half-hour ago. They must of figgered you'd gone on."

He pulled a handful of moss from a pine and wiped her eyes. She quieted.

"You'll take me home," she said.

Piety clambered down stiffly from the wagon to meet the girl.

"Zeke jest figgered you was Ardis," she said cordially. "You come set on the wagon-seat between Lant and me and keep warm."

Dusk fell before six o'clock and the scrub road was dark and winding. The wagon rattled and the mule jogged steadily and Zeke whistled behind them, hanging his feet over the tail-boards.

Piety said, "Wa'n't your Pa Thomas Mersey? Lant, I tol' you Ardis' Pa were the one I knowed. I went to school with Tom when I was a gal young un. The leetle I went, Tom Mersey were in the school when I was."

Ardis said, "We were all away a long time."

"That's what Lant said. You glad to be back?"

"Father's glad. I like it better now."

Lant felt her arm warm against him. He wanted to shout down the length of the shadowy road. The fire was out, the scrub would not burn to the river's edge, there had been no agents of the law on an inch of his land. There was no more danger, from fire or from folk, and Ardis sat next to him on the wagon-seat. He began to sing loudly in his high nasal minor. He sang "Comin' Round the Mountain" and Zeke hummed with him. Ardis laughed.

She said, "I like that. I forget it's dark when you're singing."

Where the road branched two ways, one towards Eureka, the other towards the Lantry clearing, he stopped the mule.

"Miss Ardis," he said, "hit's a two-hour job to git you home tonight. This way, or from my place acrost the river. If your daddy figgers you're with a passel o' gals, won't he figger you're stayin' the night with 'em?"

"I guess he will."

"You been promisin' to go fishin' with me one time. How 'bout you spendin' the night with Ma and me and we'll go fishin' in the mornin' and I'll git you home 'fore your daddy finds out which side o' the river you're visitin'."

Piety urged her. "You come spend the night now, Ardis. Lant's been wantin' you to visit the worst way."

She said after a moment, "All right."

At the house Lant walked aimlessly about, following Ardis from the front room to the kitchen and back again. The strangeness of her presence there was overwhelming.

Piety said, "Don't you try to he'p me. I'll fix us a bite o' supper. You jest set by the fire."

She sat in Piety's rocker and held the yellow cat. Lant brought out his box of alligator teeth. He showed her how they replenished themselves, new ones forming constantly, the new teeth nested inside the old.

"Alligators has lots o' use for teeth," he told her earnestly, "and the Lord takes keer o' the sons o' bitches."

He brought out hides and rattlesnake skins. She touched them gingerly. It delighted him to see her finger dart at them and away again. He left her and went to the kitchen for a bottle of wine. He leaned over Piety at the cook-stove.

He whispered in her ear, "Ma, ain't my girl sweet?"

She said loyally, "She's jest mighty sweet." She looked at him. "She won't think you're sweet, and the smut not even washed off you."

He said, "Great God!" and made for the wash basin.

It was after ten o'clock when they finished supper and Piety made up the small bed in the front room. She put a new sheet on the bottom and a clean quilt for cover. She brought out a clean flannel nightgown of her own and held it up.

"You one o' the few runty enough to git into this," she said.

Lant went into his room so that the women could undress by the fire. After his mother's door had closed and the creaking of the bed in the front room stopped, he opened his door a crack.

He whispered, "Good-night, Ardis."

Her voice came small and delicious from her bed.

"Good-night, Lant."

Then it was morning. Ardis and Piety were up ahead of him, and the smell of coffee and bacon drifted across the breezeway. Piety was at the side of the bed, bringing him clean clothes.

XXV

LANT POLED the rowboat by a short-cut to the river. Even in the bright November morning the way was gloomy, overhung with writhing black rattan. The ash and palms and cypress reared directly from the swamp water, their bases knotted in a torment of escape. Where a bar of sun-light came through the dense foliage, Lant pointed out to Ardis a water moccasin on a log. It was in the act of swallowing a frog. The frog was croaking lustily. The girl watched big-eyed, shrinking a little to the far side of the boat.

Piety said, laughing, "Listen to him squall and beller!"

"The frog's too big for the moccasin," Lant said. "He cain't git him swallered nor he cain't turn him loose."

He tried to pry out the frog with the end of an oar, but the pair slid under the water. The sunlight was blinding on the river as they swung into the current from the creek. Swamp laurel and holly leaves glistened in the sun.

Piety said, "I love the river, but I don't pertickler love the swamp. Hit's like travellin' thu Hell to git to Heaven."

Lant paddled down-stream with one oar, sitting in the stern seat of the rowboat. The muscles of his long arms were tough and stringy. Up or down the swift current, it made no difference to him. His mother sat contentedly hunched over in the bow. Ardis sat between.

"You figger you'll go to Hell, Ardis?" he asked.

She laughed. "I never thought about it."

"Since all the laws come in," he said, "I reckon we'll all go. And won't the ol' devil have a picnic when all us folks gits there! He'll have a pure fish-fry."

Piety chuckled from the bow, her chin in her hands.

The best bream holes were in back-waters of the river, around sunken logs and fallen tree-tops; or where the creeks flowed out between lily pads to join the current. They fished with tiny hooks and bonnet worms and long bamboo poles, for the smaller the bream, the better to the taste of the big bass. They caught a baker's dozen of red-breasts, from two to five inches long, put them in a bucket of fresh water to keep them alive, and turned back into the broadest of the creeks for Lant to set his lines.

He turned the boat over to Piety to paddle and directed her to places along the bank where ash saplings grew thickly. He drew up here and there and cut half a dozen, fifteen feet long and an inch or two in thickness. These he interspersed along the creek edge on the shady side, driving each sapling firmly into the muck so that it leaned over a dark pool. He measured heavy twine to reach from the top of the sapling to the surface of the creek water. On the end of the twine he noosed two heavy hooks, one hook put through the back of a live bream. The bream swam in a semi-circle, his backbone a fan reaching just out of the water. He made a tempting bass bait.

Ardis said, "This is lots of fun."

They paddled up and down the creek visiting the lines in turn. Sometimes they had no more than turned their backs on a freshly baited line when they heard a bass strike. He made a wild commotion. Sometimes he broke loose and got away, hooks, bream and all. When he was hooked, he thrashed on the line so that the ash sapling bent and swayed. Lant did not return to his first line when he heard a strike behind him. Piety said, "You better go back," but he was intent on the line ahead. When he made his round again, he found a ten-pound bass dead on the line. Its sides were slashed as though a jagged knife had hacked at them. A small alligator had sampled the meat.

Lant said, "He better git back in his winter quarters. I'll come up with him one o' these nights."

Several small bass were ambitious and hooked themselves. These Lant removed carefully, so as not to tear their mouths or gill them, and dropped them in the creek to swim away. He talked to them as he worked at the hook.

"You git you some size 'fore you come messin' up with me." He took over the paddling again.

He shot the boat up and down the creek with strong strokes. His lank body doubled up over the paddle. Sometimes he sent the boat under a tangle of briers, and Piety in the bow protested his roughness.

"I got to git there," he said. "What kin I do?"

"You kin pull up a leetle shorter," she complained.

When the boat passed near Sunday Bluff she turned excitedly. "I smell male hog!" she cried out.

"Oh, your ol' male hog. You won't never see him agin."

Ardis looked from one to the other. The older woman's vehemence puzzled her.

She asked, "What's the matter?"

Piety lamented her lost hogs at a moment's notice. "Why, half-breed Tine has been hog-stealin' around here the past two yare. Between him and the 'gators, you cain't raise you no hogs for market. We're doin' good to git down our own meat."

Lant said, "I'm about to catch up with the Half-breed. If I comes up on him tomorrer mornin', I'll cut his throat from ear to ear before night-fall."

Piety said, "You better not go on that-a-way. You'll find yourself in trouble. The law's gittin' mighty troublesome."

Lant said, "The law cain't do nothin' to you for lookin' out for your prop'ty. The law looks out for folkses' prop'ty."

Piety said, "Don't you go countin' on the law. Hit ain't on the side o' the pore man."

They had been a little late in getting out the set lines. Lant had tried to reach the creek at south moon over, but the moon was an hour past the meridian when they began to work the lines. The catch was only four fish. They were the true big-mouthed bass, and they weighed from four to ten pounds apiece. Lant took down his lines but left the saplings for another time. He paddled down the creek to his landing while Piety untied the hooks and put them carefully away.

Lant tied the rowboat to a small cypress. Ardis put her hand on the tree to steady herself.

He called anxiously, "Look out for that red cypress gum. It'll purely blister your skin."

Piety said, "Hit's a hide-raiser, all right, but they says it'll cure the cancer."

At the foot of the hammock Lant stopped.

He said, "Ma, you go on. I'll go up the trail a ways and cut us a swamp cabbage for dinner."

She took the string of fish from him.

"You want Ardis should go with you?" she asked.

"I thought I'd show her them two big hickories."

"They're somethin' to see, all right," she agreed.

She started up the ledge, her thin shoulders stooped, her stick-like legs pushing against the slope. She turned.

"Don't cut the cabbage too close to the swamp, for it'll be bitter."

Lant and Ardis went along the trail together. He carried his light axe over one shoulder. His gait, disjointed and awkward in a square-dance, fitted itself to the rough path like a stream flowing over stones. He was dark and vital, like the hammock and the swamp. Something stirred across the girl, as though a strong breeze blew suddenly across a shallow pond. When she stumbled in her thin shoes, she caught at him and then left her arm in his.

She asked, "Lant, how do you make your living?"

He thought, "I'll take her to the outfit."

He imagined her sitting on the platform under the sweet-gums, her hair as bright as the copper of the pot, while he explained the workings of the still.

She added, "Father and Cousin Bill were asking me."

He stiffened. He checked himself from blurting out, "It's none of their damn business." He thought, "I been at it a year and a half, and Bill Mersey ain't on to what I'm doing yet? And him snooping around asking questions all the time."

He said casually, "Oh, winter-times I trap, and summer-times I 'gator. I farm and I hunt and I raft and do all sich as that. I made a right smart piece o' money oncet, sendin' black haw roots to a drug comp'ny. They paid twenty cents a pound."

She said, "You must have sold almost every different kind of thing there is in the scrub to sell."

"I've done sold live rattlesnakes," he admitted.

He forgot his anger at Bill Mersey and warmed to the subject of rattlesnakes.

"The last I caught," he told her, "Cleve and me come up on a pair in the south-east fence corner. I stayed with 'em whilst Cleve goed to the house and fetched back a barrel and sack and fish-poles with loops on 'em. We stepped plenty lively gittin' 'em looped and the barrel over 'em and them in it. But we got four dollars apiece for them."

"Is that a good price?"

"Mighty good. You cain't git that money now. The snake-man to Eureka ain't payin' but fifty cents a foot. I'll not hunt 'em for that."

He held a wild grape vine aside for her.

"The risk's worth somethin'," he told her, "the same as the snake."

He was astonished that she knew none of the trees of the hammock except the magnolia and the holly. He pointed them out and described their peculiarities, so that she would surely know them again. Red bay and sweet bay, sweet gum and iron-wood— She followed his finger with her grave eyes. He stopped in his tracks and looked at her.

"What's wild mulberry good for?" he asked her sternly.

"Why—I suppose the birds eat the fruit."

"They ain't no finer wood in the world for oar-lock blocks," he informed her solemnly.

Every tree fitted into his life. Its beauty and its purpose were joined together, so that the most beautiful trees to him were those with the greatest use. For the slim white ash trees he felt a tenderness, gauging their probable length in terms of strands for firing in the furnace of his still. Near the Twin Sinks he led her up the ledge to the two giant hickories. He walked around and around them, warming to their straightness and good grain.

"They's hundreds o' feet o' timber in each o' them hickories," he said proudly. "I don't aim to cut 'em lest I got it to do. Trees like that is scarce."

She tipped her head back and stared submissively at the tops, where the leaves hung golden against the blue translucent sky.

Below the hickories again, where the hammock merged with swamp, he cut a low-growing palmetto. He trimmed down the ivory cylinder that was the heart of the palm and cut a shaving from the lower end, where the fan-like sections fitted intricately together. They tasted it. It was crisp and sweet, like chestnuts.

"That's a swamp cabbage that's fitten," he decided.

He dropped it on a clean palmetto frond and laid the axe beside it. He began to scratch himself thoughtfully.

"The red-bugs and ticks is gittin' into me," he said. "You set and rest whilst I dig the boogers out."

He rolled up his sleeves to the shoulder and investigated the length of each arm. He came to her where she sat with her back against a magnolia and showed her the microscopic mites and ticks. She could not make them out on his brown arm until he traced their movement with the tip of his pocket-knife.

"Them things gives me the devil," he said. "They don't bother Ma nary a mite."

He sat beside her and pulled up his trousers and bent to the same business about his ankles, bare of socks above his shoe-tops.

"I reckon I got 'em all 'fore they got too deep buried. If I ain't, I'll know it tonight."

He turned to her.

"They gittin' into you?"

"I don't feel anything. I got red bugs at a picnic at Orange Springs once, but I don't feel anything now."

"Lemme see."

He turned her arm, bare under short sleeves, to the sunlight sifting through the magnolia.

"God A'mighty, you 'bout covered. That's one thing I got agin hammock."

He bent earnestly and picked at her arm with his knife-point. He drew his hand against the skin and examined it closely again.

"Reckon I got 'em routed on that un. Gimme 'tother arm."

He leaned across her and picked with a complete absorption in his work, turning her arm this way and that. Suddenly he was weak and a little sick. The white flesh had changed under his touch. It was electric. It was soft, so soft it frightened him. A hot wave passed through him, and then he was cold. It was like malaria, but more terrifying. He wanted to look at her but he was afraid to lift his head. He dropped his pocket-knife and turned his head and rested his face against her throat. Her pulse beat rapidly, like a bird's. He held his breath. Slowly, as though a magnolia petal drifted down to him, she laid her check on his and he felt her eyelids flutter there like moth-wings.

There was no more hammock, no more swamp. Nothing existed

that had ever been before. There was only a soft pulsing under his lips and a magnolia petal against his cheek. It came to him like a revelation that he would kiss her. Her lips were cool and remote, as though he pressed a guava against his mouth. Then he was flooded with warmth. Her lips were warm, and all the torment that sometimes possessed him pushed against her mouth, like a man beating against a closed door.

He said, "Ardis honey, you so sweet."

She put the back of her hand across her lips.

She said, "I'm afraid."

The torment left him, and he was half-sick because he had frightened her. Her hands were cold and he rubbed them until the tips of the fingers were pink again. The sun stood at its zenith, but a chill November wind crossed the swamp and moved up the hammock ledge, rattling the thick leaves of the magnolia.

She said, "Let's go back."

He lifted her to her feet and picked up his axe and the white shaft of palm-heart. He wanted to take her hand, or put his free arm around her, but he walked stiffly beside her, looking ahead. After a while she put her arm through his and rubbed her face against his sleeve.

He said, "Honey, I jest ain't goin' to put my arm around you 'til you say so."

She said, "I say so."

They laughed and walked close together along the trail and through the hammock and across the clearing. Piety looked at them curiously.

She said, "Hit's too late to cook the cabbage for dinner, if you're takin' Ardis home soon like you said. Dinner's on the table."

In the early afternoon Lant rowed Ardis down the river to Iola Landing. He let the boat drift and she sat on the floor between his knees and leaned against him. The sun was warm and the river was brown velvet flecked with gold. When he drew her body closer and brushed his face across her hair and felt her throat with his fingers, a sharp sadness struck him. In the spring he had seen a red-bird singing from a wild plum tree white with bloom. The bird had almost instantly flown away, because the moment was too beautiful to endure.

XXVI

Lᴀɴᴛ was in Eureka the day before Thanksgiving.

The storekeeper said, "Your Uncle Abner left word for you to come out to his place and see him, the next time you were here."

He said, "I figgered on gittin' right home with my sugar. Did he say what-all he wanted?"

"He didn't say, but I imagine it's something about the cattle trouble."

"The Streeters raisin' Hell agin?"

"They penned half a dozen of Eph Wilson's yearlings last week. The way Abner spoke, I believe they got a bunch of his cattle this time."

Lant said, "Them damn Yankees better look out. Uncle Ab don't allow nobody to mess up with his prop'ty."

The storekeeper laughed.

"Lant, I'm a Yankee because I came from Massachusetts. The Streeters don't like the name. They claim men from Arkansas are Westerners."

"Hell," he grinned amiably, "you all the same. You all ol' furriners."

He had better see Abner, he decided. His rowboat was tied at Eureka bridge. He carried his sugar on his back and loaded it in and rowed down-stream and stopped on the piney-woods side and tied up. He walked through the woods to Abner's house. He had wondered how long the trouble could go on before the Streeters were jerked up with a short rope. They were comparative newcomers, farming in a cattle section, and from the first they had failed to mind their own business as was seemly for strangers to do.

The section had been always "open range." Miles of unfarmed, often ownerless land, valueless for crops, grew a lush growth of a coarse grass that fattened the free-ranging scrub-cattle without further feeding. As far back as Lant could remember—within his mother's memory, too—the poorest Crackers in the section had had their small herds ranging free. The more prosperous families were all cattle people. Abner had a thousand head in the woods. Each fall the herd, fat from the summer grazing, was driven in, the spring calves branded and the desirable beef animals sold for butchering.

Until the past year, Lant realized, there had been no question of fencing in the cattle. If a man had a field of corn or sugar-cane, a patch of peanuts or sweet potatoes, he threw a fence around it as a matter of course, to keep out stock; his own and that of his neighbours. But hard roads had replaced three of the old dirt wagon roads in the section, and auto traffic was coming through at a fast clip as far east as Eureka. It encountered herds of cattle, feeding along the shoulders of the roads, crossing from one side to the other, and slumbering placidly in the middle. Echoes of an urban outcry against the situation had reached the river. Lant had seen a newspaper from a town some thirty miles away, complaining of the savagery of cattle loose on the highways. Then, a few months ago, a distant legislature had closed the range. A man who owned cattle must keep them under fence, or be liable to damages if his stock strayed. A man finding stock on his land was legally privileged to impound them and to collect a generous fee for his trouble.

Lant remembered that Abner had said at first that the new law would make very little difference. Like the game and whiskey laws, he hoped that things would run by tacit consent much as they had run before. Almost every man in the section had stock that brought him in his chief cash income. Almost no one could afford to fence miles of pasture. There was no one to protest the free passage of cattle. True, the owner of stock was now liable for damages if a car struck one of his cows on a highway, but Abner believed the county itself would soon build fences along the county roads. Now the Streeters were intruding violently on the community agreement. They were impounding cattle with a reckless abandon.

Lant found Abner at his cane-mill, oiling the gears after the season's grinding. Old man Lonny Sours was with him. Abner swung his big stomach around, the oil can in his hand.

He said, "Hey, son."

"Hey, Uncle Ab. Hey, Lonny."

Abner said, "Looks like I'm 'bout to git you into another job like that one six-seven years ago with that Alabamy feller."

"That's about the way I figgered," Lant said.

They sat down on the cold brick furnace around the syrup kettle.

Abner asked, "Them damn Streeters been over on your side the river?"

"Now, Uncle Ab, I cain't rightly say. Monday, I believe 'twas, I was runnin' a charge and I thought I heered men hollerin' and a sound like cattle bein' drove into the river. I wa'n't in no shape to go messin' up with nobody. I jest laid low."

Abner said, "That was them, all right. Four of them pieded cows from the scrub herd was in with the bunch of mine them buzzards had penned yestiddy." He spat. "Claimin' the cattle come acrost their land—huh."

Old man Sours said, "Eph Wilson was comin' down the back-road Sat'day last, jest about dusk-dark, and he seed the Streeters drivin' four-five cows and calves, a good mile 'fore you git to their line. Eph said they jumped in the bushes and let the cattle go on and he never could find the men."

"Eph Wilson—huh! He never looked too long. Huh."

Lant asked, "What the Streeters gittin' out of it, besides the pure devilment?"

"Hell, they gittin' their fees for impoundin', pay for keepin' the creeters. And they tryin' to farm in a cattle country, and they figger they got the new law to he'p 'em."

Old Sours said, "But Ab, they got no right to interfere with folkses' livin'."

Abner said judiciously, "I ain't sayin' they got the right to do what they're doin'. The law's the law, and the law's always changin', but they's things beyond the law is right and wrong, accordin' to how many folks they he'ps or harms. I'm jest answerin' Lant's question, What is the Streeters gittin' out o' this?"

Sours said, " 'Twouldn't be so bad if they didn't leave the cattle go hongry and thirsty in the pen the way they done my milch-cow. Nor if they wa'n't drivin' in cattle from nowheres near their land. Nor if they hadn't acted so biggety, 'stead o' comin' to ever'body and askin' would we he'p 'em fence."

"What you tryin' to git at, Lonny," Abner said, "is, 'twouldn't be so bad if the Streeters wa'n't jest low-down, ornery Arkansas bastards."

Lant said, "I got to git goin', Uncle Ab. You wastin' my time, if you got me here jest to say you kin count on me. You knowed that."

Abner said, "I don't never like to take nothin' for granted. I'm givin' them Arkansas fellers one more chancet to go at this thing like white men. I'm payin' Cleve to ride range on my cattle, and I told John Streeter yestiddy to git me word ary day my stock was on his land and I'd have 'em drove off. We'll jest see. You done a good job for me when you was a knob-jointed, long-coupled young scaper, and I don't want you to miss no fun now you're a growed man. I'll git you and Zeke the word if the need come."

Lant went to the house to pass the time of day with Abner's wife, and then rowed home with his sugar.

A week later Cleve came to him in late afternoon at his still in the swamp.

Cleve said, "Come ahead, Mister."

"Streeters been at it agin, eh?"

"I mean. Penned a hull heap o' Uncle Ab's stock the day after Thanksgiving. Kep' 'em penned and never got Ab word and dogged if the sheriff didn't come today and hold a sale. Cost Uncle Ab 'bout two hundred dollars to bid 'em in and pay costs."

"You been to git Zeke?"

"He's waitin' at Otter Landin'."

The three men crossed the river by rowboat. At Abner Lantry's place they found gathered some twenty men from the vicinity.

They were waiting for dark, for there was no need to be recognized. There was a little discussion as to whether a preliminary warning to the Streeters was necessary. They agreed it was not.

Abner said, "I warned 'em ten days ago. Them scoundrels knowed the fust time they done it, hit were wrong, messin' up in other folkses' business. No use to do nary thing now but jest cold-out show 'em we'll not have it."

Under his silver-grey hair he was red-faced and sweating.

"Men," he said, "I jest as soon make this my business, if you say so. Man to man, me and the Streeters."

They thought the proposition over in silence.

Ase Wilson said at last, "Seems to me they've done harmed us all. They'll make trouble for the hull passel of us right on. Hit'll have more weight, like, more circumstance, do right smart of us whop it to 'em."

Old Jacklin spat the width of the Lantry porch and said, "Hit'll skeer 'em into mindin' their manners more to have twenty men put the strop to 'em easy, than for one man to fram the chitlin's plumb outen 'em."

When dark came the group set off down the lonely road towards the Streeter place in three old Ford cars. The piney-woods roads all looked the same in the night, their shallow ruts overgrown with grass, swerving erratically to avoid ancient stumps. The men drove with dimmed lights, but no one passed to see them. They stopped a hundred yards from the Streeter house and crept close in a semi-circle. The two Streeter men sat on the porch. The glow from their pipes showed their position. A kerosene light flickered from the kitchen, where their wives moved in a light clatter of supper dishes.

Abner said in a low voice, "A'right," and they moved to the porch. There was no hurry and they made no noise. The Streeters fought desperately, but a power as slow and deep as the river current laid itself on them, and they were no longer men, but trussed and frightened bundles. The cattle men dumped them in the two lead cars. The women came running to the porch. One held the kerosene lamp high over her head, her face drawn and puzzled in its glare. They screamed and ran after the cars. One of them looked Lant square in the face as she came up. The three cars ground off into the darkness.

Abner led the way to the swamp. The car lights were switched off and the Streeters were stripped in the dark to their waists. They were laid together across a fallen log and held at heads and feet. Each man in the gathering took his turn at the whipping. A piece of leather harness strap was used. The Streeters cried out and big hands covered their mouths in the darkness to muffle the sound. The whipping was dispassionate and thorough. It had been agreed to keep silence, but when Ase Wilson's turn came, he was excited. He brought down the strap in a burst of anger.

"Pen stock, will you!" he cried.

For terror, the Streeters did not move when the group had finished. When the sound of the cars died away, they broke free from their loose trussing and found their way home.

Abner and the Wilsons and the rest agreed that it was a good job done.

"Them low-down sorry varmints'll mebbe set down now and behave theirselves," they said.

Two days later the high sheriff and a swarm of deputies drove through the piney-woods serving warrants. One of the Streeter women had seen Lant's face distinctly. She did not know him by name, since he had never been a frequent visitor across the river. She looked in vain for him among the youths of her neighbourhood. The Streeter men had heard one voice, Ase Wilson's, in the darkness, but could not place it. They were all eyes and ears to locate the one face and the one voice. Meanwhile, they swore wholesale to warrants, naming Abner Lantry, Cleve Jacklin, the Wilson tribe and half the population of the piney-woods as the whippers.

The river-folk were aghast. Insult had been added to injury. They had given the law no trouble in their history. They had settled their own disputes among themselves, decently and quietly. When a man was found to be abusing his woman or his children, they had not bothered the sheriff nor called for a court. They had waited on the offending citizen and induced him, in one manner or another, to see the error of his ways.

When Jake Tanner felt sorry for the widow Lane and her six fatherless children and offered them all the shelter of his home, the community had waited a year for him to marry her. When he did not do so, they called in a body, a preacher in their midst, and informed him that for the sake of the common decency, the marriage must take place. Jake reported later that the wedding had put him in the widow's bed, where he had not been before and had no intention of going, but the proprieties were served.

On the rare occasions when a man was caught stealing, or lying to another's harm, he was dealt with as the Streeters had been, and the offender and the community were the better and the more peaceful for the settling of the matter. They knew what they would tolerate and what they would not. The Streeters had offended in the most grievous manner possible. Strangers, they had interfered with the community's living. And now the law upheld them. The county was backing up the Streeters. The county and the Streeters intended to send Abner and the Wilsons and other respectable citizens to Raiford prison, or even to Atlanta penitentiary.

Old man Lonny Sours said, "I never figgered I'd live to see the day. But you don't never know the luck of a lousy calf."

Lant went with Abner to the county seat one Saturday. Abner was talking with his lawyer and Lant walked idly about the town square. He met two men from a neighbouring county who sometimes hunted in the scrub and bought whiskey of him. He glanced up from his conversation. John Streeter's wife was staring at his red forelock, hanging from under his black slouch hat. By the time he had placed the woman in his memory, she had darted into the court-house and was approaching the group with an officer. Lant turned to run but the sight of the crowded town street stopped him. The group of three was placed under arrest as part of the flogging gang. The Streeter woman swore to a positive identification.

Abner went bond for Lant, as he had done for every one except the Wilsons, who were able to write their own. After conference with Lant's astonished acquaintances, and with his lawyer, Abner left the two in jail for a few days, for a purpose that at once occurred to him. He had drawn out money from his postal savings account and had counted the gold and silver buried under his rear stoop. Now he named to his attorney the amount he was willing to spend.

"If the Streeters wants law," he said, "by God, we'll give 'em law. Take the case to Tallahassee," he ordered, his big face florid and intent. "Take hit to Washin'ton to the pres-eye-dent. Take hit so fur them sons o' bitches'll be pantin' for water and their tick-bit tails torn and hangin'."

"Hit's a question," he added, "who's got the cash-money to hang on the longest, them or me. The longest pole reaches the persimmon."

XXVII

THE TRIAL of the cattle men was set for the first spring term of court. It seemed to Lant the winter would never be done with. He was restless. At his distilling he jumped like a cat at every sound. Zeke visited him occasionally in the swamp, unable to conceal his delight at being out of the trouble. When Zeke had gone again, Lant thought so fiercely about the Streeter business that he forgot Ardis.

Sometimes when he went to see her, the delicious closeness was gone and he came away in despair. He kept away from her as long as he could. Then the thought of her blended with his old torment. There was no more peace until he had rowed across the river to sit beside her at the Mersey hearth and perhaps, if she was in the mood, walk with her down the road and hold her desperately close, kissing her eyes and mouth and throat. The actual touch of her, cool and always faintly withdrawn, relieved his feverishness, as a little water quenches the worst of thirst. When he was away from her, the yellow hair seemed brighter, the unsmiling eyes warmer, the thin mouth and body inviting, even yielding.

Piety asked him, "You think Ardis'll have you?"

He said, "I think she'll have me. I aim to git it settled, time this cattle mess is over." He added, "If I gits out with a whole hide." He laughed shortly. "Here I been worryin' 'bout the moonshine business and then gits into deep water 'bout other folkses' cattle."

She said, "You had to he'p Abner."

"Oh, I ain't begrudgin' bein' in on it. Hit jest make me think the only thing do go right for me, is the whiskey."

"I cain't he'p lettin' it worry me right on."

"Bless Katy, Ma, you got you a decent livin' the first time since I been makin' one. The Prohis ain't goin' to come up with me 'less it's pure acceedent, and now you complainin'."

"I ain't complainin'."

She studied him, as she had once studied Lantry. Her stream of life had joined her son's, she thought, and was indistinguishable from it. She could conceive of no trouble that was not his trouble; no grief that was not his grief. Because his dark face was drawn, and the red-brown eyes a little sunken over the square cheekbones, she hoped the girl Ardis would come to him when he was ready for her. Abner had assured Piety that her son had nothing to fear from the trial, and she believed him. If worst came to worst, he told her, he would take the whole thing on himself.

Lant had money ahead at Christmas. He asked Kezzy's advice about a present for Ardis. Sears Roebuck had a fine pair of ladies' hunting boots that appealed to him. Kezzy sighed.

"Lant, if 'twas me, tromping thu the bogs and all over the way I do, it'd be different. You git that girl a double compact."

He was inclined to take offense at the suggestion.

She said tactfully, "You want her to know you think she's pretty, don't you? Nothin' don't please a young girl more than somethin' to use to make her pretty. Somethin' to put on her face or hair, or perfume to smell sweet on her." She blinked her eyes quickly. She said, choking a little, "I kin remember yit how tickled I were when Cleve come from the dime-store one day with a ol' shiny pin to stick in my hair."

He said, "Kezzy, look at me. Is Cleve workin'?"

She shook her head.

"Uncle Ab quit ridin' range on his herd mighty nigh a month ago," he commented. "Ain't Cleve done nothin' since then?"

"No."

"How you makin' out?"

"We makin' out all right. I butchered six hogs and I got my garden and my chickens and my own meal and 'taters."

"You fixin' to have another young un, ain't you?"

"Lant, I swear you the nosiest somebody."

"Somebody got to keep track of you. Cleve ain't doin' it."

She was silent.

He was buying parts to make a small radio for his mother for Christmas, he told her.

She said, "That ain't as bad as the huntin' boots for Ardis. Your mother's eyes is got to be so bad, I reckon it'll pleasure her to set and listen to a radio."

"What you want for Christmas, Kezzy?"

"I want a gallon o' your best 'shine, dogged if I don't. Time you drink some good 'shine, you don't notice if you've got nothin' else."

Abner and his wife had invited Cleve and Kezzy for Christmas dinner. Zeke and his wife were coming to Piety for the day.

Lant suggested, "How 'bout the day after Christmas, you and Cleve bring Ardis over in the evenin' and set and listen to the radio? I kin take Ardis home agin."

She laughed. "Got that part all figgered out, ain't you? Why yes, that'd be mighty nice."

He went away and she waved after him, smiling.

On Christmas morning Piety said dubiously of the radio, "I reckon I'll git used to it." The raucousness of the human voices distressed her and she did not like the music as well as Lant's banjo. She would rather have had curtains for the windows, she thought. She had never had any, and the shades Willy Jacklin had bought her twenty years before hung over the small panes in ribbons. Yet the old shingled roof leaked so badly that there would be no use in putting up curtains even if Lant would buy them. When it rained, she tugged the piles of heavy quilts from one room to another, and back again. When the rain was heavy enough the high peaked roof was no better than a sieve and the quilts got wet in spite of her. Perhaps another year Lant would re-shingle the roof and then she could have curtains.

She spent the morning after Christmas cleaning the house because Ardis was coming. She scrubbed the old pine floors until they were the colour of Jersey cream. She put fresh crimped paper over the mantel. She cut a picture from a magazine Lant had brought home from one of the hunting camps and pinned it on the board wall between a 'gator hide and his rifle. The fur company's calendar hung on the kitchen door. The cover this year was handsome. Lant still kept a few traps going through the winter season. She looked about. The Merseys had always had plenty to do with.

She said, "I wisht I had me a good house with somethin' in it, and then keep it nice."

Lant said absently, "This un's good enough."

She looked at him critically. He was ready to go to the still. His blue chambray shirt was ragged and he wore a cloth cap that was no more than a visor. His red-brown hair hung in back from under the naked band and stuck in straight spikes through the remnants of the front. He was most contented, she thought, when his elbows stuck out of his sleeves and his ribs showed white through long cool gashes in his shirt.

She said, "I jest as good to hold my breath, for you don't keer what you wear. You'll go to the outfit in a new shirt or new breeches and come back plumb ragged and better satisfied."

"I'll put on a white shirt this evenin'," he said.

"If 'twa'n't for Ardis, you'd go this-a-way all the time."

"I had me a white shirt 'fore I ever knowed her."

"Yes, and put it on mighty seldom."

She reached behind him and picked off the fragment of cap from his head and moved quickly to the hearth and threw it on the fire.

"I'll jest not look at that thing no longer."

He was forced to take from its hook the black felt that had been his Sunday best since he had been grown. Its wide brim annoyed him. He slapped it on the back of his head and went to his work.

He found one barrel of mash ready to run and decided not to risk waiting for the next barrel. He was out of ash and had to take time to cut fresh wood. It was after dark when he came to the house and Cleve and Kezzy and Ardis were ahead of him. He came in whistling. On his big head was perched the crown of the black felt hat.

Piety asked, exasperated, "Now where's the brim?"

"I made me a lantern wick outen the brim," he said complacently. "That-a-way I got me a extry benefit."

He washed and went to his room and put on clean clothes. Piety and Kezzy were talking in the bedroom where Kezzy had put the baby to sleep and Cleve was in the smoke-house getting a drink. Ardis stood alone in front of the hearth. He came from his room and stood beside her and watched her gravely. He said, "Le's go walk a piece" and took her arm and led her from the house and down the lane.

Piety said, "Kezzy, I'm like not to git a chancet with you alone agin. What you think of Lant's girl?"

"Well, I wouldn't say it to nobody but you—nor to you, if you hadn't asked me. Aunt Py-tee, she ain't got too much sense. She's pretty and soft-life. I reckon that's all a man wants."

The older woman said stoutly, "Well, 'tain't all a man needs. Pertickler a man fixed like Lant. She's too fine-haired. That's what she is."

"It's his business, Aunt Py-tee."

Cleve came in and in a short while Lant and Ardis were back again. Lant had little to say.

Piety said, "You've had no supper, Lant. Don't you want somethin'?"

He said, "I reckon."

They followed him to the kitchen and sat around the table while Piety gave him a cold supper.

She asked, "Cain't the rest of you eat?"

Cleve poked in the dish of meat.

"Any squirrel meat in here?"

Lant said, "I ain't shot none all week, Cleve. It's been blowin' too hard for 'em."

Ardis said brightly, "I suppose their tails are so big they can't balance when it blows."

Kezzy said, "I hope I ain't got to take to stayin' in on windy days."

Lant heard Ardis catch her breath. He looked at her. She stared wide-eyed at Kezzy, picking a chicken-wing, and flushed. She dropped her eyes and twisted her fingers in her lap.

Lant said sharply, "Kezzy, you quit talkin' so rough." He added, "Ardis ain't used to it."

"Ain't she? Mebbe you and I kin learn her somethin' she don't know."

Piety brushed some crumbs from the worn oilcloth cover on the table. Ardis watched her furtively.

Piety said, "I've got a white cloth."

"It's a good time to think of it," Lant said.

Kezzy's black eyes were on the girl.

She said hotly, "Oilcloth's good enough for anybody, I don't keer who 'tis."

Piety agreed, "I've always thought it was good enough."

Zeke Lantry called from the front door. They left the kitchen and went in by the hearth-fire. Zeke had slipped away from his wife to hear the radio. Lant sat by it and turned the dials. He stole a look now and then at Ardis, sitting stiffly between Kezzy and his mother. The girl's face was pale and clear beside the weather-beaten and serviceable hide that was his mother's skin. Ardis was no fairer than Kezzy. Or perhaps Kezzy's skin seemed so milk-white against the smooth blackness of her eyes and hair.

The radio was a disappointment. Its irritations outweighed its pleasures. The static was bad.

Lant said, "It sounds like a dirt-dauber in a tin can."

For a little time he had a jug band coming in. Many of the tunes were familiar. A stringed orchestra played sweetly and they listened with a deep pleasure. Suddenly a man's voice broke in harshly.

Piety shrilled indignantly, "Now that jessie had to put his bill in it!"

The stringed orchestra disappeared entirely and a "blues" singer began to wail. He lamented, "Why was I ever born?" They chuckled.

"He's in a bad fix," Kezzy said.

They were amused by the sorrowful songs that whimpered through the home-made loud speaker. After a time Zeke shuffled his feet and spat in the fireplace.

"Lant," he said, "turn that thing off and git out your banjo. Hit's a sight better'n that mess."

Piety said with enthusiasm, "That's what I say."

Lant clicked off the radio and brought his banjo from Piety's trunk. He sat by the fire and tuned it, his ear against the strings. Zeke looked hopeful, and Lant played his uncle's favourite piece, "Come all you Georgia boys." Zeke clapped his hands as Lant played and sang in his high nasal whine.

> *"Come all you Georgia boys and listen to my noise.*
> *Don't be deceived by the Deep Creek boys.*
> *For if you do, your portion it will be,*
> *Workin' in the cypress swamps is all you can see."*

There was a Deep Creek, north of the scrub, that flowed into the Ocklawaha. Zeke did not know whether that was the one named in the song, or not. A song was a song, and it made no difference where it came from.

> *"Go over to your neighbour's house, they'll set you out a chair.*
> *First thing you hear, 'Daddy killed a bear.'*
> *Draw up to the fire-place, pass the 'baccy 'roun'.*
> *'Mama, ain't your johnny-cake bakin' too brown?'*
>
> *"They'll go off to dress and put on their best—*
> *Daddy's ol' huntin' shirt—for that is their best.*
> *Ol' sock leg they wear the winter 'roun',*
> *Ol' palmetto hat, more rim than crown.*
>
> *"They go to the cow-pen and milk in a gourd,*
> *Set it in the jamb and kiver it with a board.*
> *That is the way they used for to do—*
> *For I was raised in the backwoods too!"*

Zeke listened to the words as intently as though he had never heard them before. He slapped his leg and shook his head and gave his sister a push.

"Ol' palmetto hat, more rim than crown, eh, Py-tee?"

She said, laughing, "Don't th'ow off on a palmetto hat to me. I got one on the nail right on."

There was no question about it. A banjo playing the old pieces had more satisfaction in it than all the radios in the county.

Zeke went home early for fear his wife would follow him.

Lant said bluntly, "I better git you home, Ardis. Let's go."

When he had gone with the girl, Piety said, "What you reckon ails him?"

Kezzy shook her head.

"I cain't quite figger. First I thought things jest wa'n't goin' right between the two of 'em, but I got a idee they's more to it than that."

Cleve stretched his legs to the fire. He said sleepily, "I been hearin' tell Tom and Bill Mersey is right thick with the Streeters."

Kezzy said, "I hated to say it."

Lant was home from the river in a short time. Cleve and Kezzy were ready to go. Kezzy was putting on her coat. Lant stormed at her.

"You wa'n't nice to my girl," he raged. He turned to include his mother. "Nor you neither. You was both throwin' off on her. I won't never take her around neither of you agin."

Piety put one hand half over her mouth and blinked her deep eyelids at him. He pushed past Kezzy to the front room. She followed him.

She said, "Lant—oh, Lant——"

He looked at her. Her head was thrown back and her eyes were closed. Her face was wax-white, like a palm-heart. Tears dropped slowly from under her long lashes. She lifted her arms from her sides and dropped them hopelessly.

She said, "I'd cut off my hands 'fore I'd mean to hurt you."

He remembered her hands the evening of the Big Burn when she had rowed across the river with word for Ardis from him. They had been blackened and raw. He took them and turned them over. They were square and strong. The palms were healed.

He said, "Kezzy, don't forgive me if it's too hard to do."

He tightened his hold and burst out, "I think I'm 'bout to go crazy. I don't know what-all's the matter."

She said, "I wisht I could he'p you."

XXVIII

THREE WEEKS before the trial, on the morning before the close of the legal deer season, Bill Mersey, the game warden, clicked the front gate of the Lantry clearing and walked up the fenced-in lane. Two red and brown hounds strained ahead of him on a leash. Piety saw him coming and hurried to Lant in the smoke-house.

"Bill Mersey's comin' to the house," she said.

"They ain't much here to bother him," he commented.

He looked up at the rafters where several year-old strips of jerked venison hung among the hams and bacons. He pulled them down and dropped them in a barrel in the corner and scattered a few ears of corn over the top. They walked into the yard together to meet Bill.

Lant said, "He's likely jest passin' by and bringin' some word from Ardis. He's a son of a bitch to be kin to her."

"Hey, Bill."

"Hey, Lant. Howdy, Mis' Jacklin."

Bill was cordial.

"What you think of my deerdogs, Lant?"

"They look all right. Kin they slow-trail?"

"I came to see if you didn't want to hunt deer with me this morning and find out."

Lant hesitated. He was not anxious to be seen in Bill's company. The game warden was always vaguely a pariah in the section. The man ahead of Bill had been corrupt. He had winked at fish-traps in the river bed; at wild turkeys in the oven in August; at fire-hunting by night; at the taking of doe-deer in season, or indeed of any deer at any time. The proper presents of liquor, the invoca-tion of a relative's influence, were all that was necessary to have him look the other way. Bill was reasonably honest. He took his job seriously. He was an object of profound mistrust.

Lant wondered what Bill wanted.

He said, "Bill, I ain't shot no doe-deer not scarcely no deer at all this winter, if you huntin' for somethin' more to git me to the court-house."

Bill laughed heartily.

"You don't think Ardis'd let me in the house if I was to make you any trouble, do you?"

Lant said, "I don't know who she'd let in. Times, I gits a idee she's 'bout not to let me in no more."

Bill said easily, "She's mighty sweet on you"; and after a moment, "How 'bout the huntin'?"

Lant said, "Why, yes. I'll go deer-huntin' with you."

He took down his rifle from the wall and slipped extra cartridges in his buckskin hunting vest. The two men walked down the lane together, the dogs snuffing at the path.

Bill asked, "Any special deer-run you know of, or good stand?"

Lant said, "You been in the scrub this winter more'n me, Bill. You'd orter know. I tell you what I think. Leave the dogs slow-trail north thu the upper hammock, see kin they jump a deer beddin' there. I've seed plenty of sign. Then if we don't jump one, work on up along the road. The woods is so full o' hunters now, and dogs, we stand jest as good a chancet havin' 'em drive a deer right to us."

Bill released the hounds and they loped forward.

Bill said, "It wasn't you, then, hung a fresh doe-skin on my gate last week?"

"You don't reckon I'd own to it, if 'twas, do you?" He added, "No, by God, nor tell you who done it if I knowed that."

Bill said comfortably, "It was likely some shirt-tail boy, thought it was funny."

Lant guffawed.

"It ain't nothin' I'm fixin' to cry about, right now," he said.

The warden flushed.

The deer season had been shortened this year, and the hunting camps in the scrub had doubled in number. There was a desperate attempt to take the camp bag-limit. The night before, Piety, wakeful, had heard several cars grind by, the deep sand tearing at the labouring motors. She had said to Lant at breakfast, "The pore deer'll ketch it today." North of the clearing the two men began to hear the sounds of a chase. A pack of deer-hounds and beagles yelped and bayed, and a hunting horn blew long and mournfully.

Lant said, "Listen! The deer's makin' for the swamp." He began to run. "Leave your dogs go. We'll cut down and lay for the booger. They's a trail all the deer's been takin' here lately."

They ran through the hammock and down the ledge to the swamp. The dogs were coming closer. The baying was deep and rich. It rolled like the notes of an organ through the dark swamp. Lant put Bill on a stand behind a clump of ash saplings at the swamp edge. He pointed out the deer tracks in the black muck. "Thick as a hog-trail," he whispered. The swamp dissolved here in a shallow creek. Across the creek lay a narrow swampy island. Beyond the island was the river. If a deer made the swamp and the creek, it was usually safe. Occasionally a dog would swim the creek to the island, but from that point the hunted animal had no trouble in making the river, and no dog would brave its depth and current. Lant took a stand above Bill, where swamp and hammock joined. The dogs were yelping with sharp excited cries. There was a dull thumping ahead, and two tawny bodies came slipping through the swamp with incredibly liquid motion. Lant lifted his rifle and eased it down again. The deer were an old doe and a maiden doe.

If he had been alone, or with Zeke or Cleve, he would have shot the old doe and left the maiden to breed in the spring. There were many old does, he knew, for whom there were no mates. Bill Mersey called up to him. "Too bad." They watched the pair take the creek, so that only the smooth heads and great brown eyes were visible, scramble to their sharp feet and bound away across the island. The dogs milled in a shrieking tumult at the creek edge and began to back-track. Three hunters came up.

Bill said, "A pair of does."

One of the men said, "We've been on their trail since daylight.

Picked it up about five miles into the scrub. We never even saw them. I'm having such rotten luck I'd have had a shot, doe or no doe."

One of his companions recognized Mersey and ground his elbow in the speaker's ribs.

Bill said, "Better luck next time."

The hunters blew in their dogs and cut wearily up the hammock. Lant lifted his nose and sniffed at a taint on the air.

He said, "They's a dead deer on the island agin."

Bill said, "Let's go see."

Above the deer-trail a log lay across the deep part of the creek. They walked across it. In the centre of the island lay the decaying carcass of a large buck. Lant cut away the antlers and handed them to Mersey.

Bill said, "I'll take 'em to Ardis for you."

Scarcely a day passed during deer-season, Lant knew, that a wounded animal did not slip through the swamp, spattering the palmettos with its blood, swim the narrow creek and take harbour on the island. If it recovered, it swam the river to the piney-woods after night-fall, or returned again into the scrub.

He said, "Dog take it, I got no use for buckshot. Half the time the deer jest gits tore up and dies tedious, or don't even die. I killed me a big ol' buck one year, had a game leg. You could see where the buckshot had messed it up. God know how long the creeter had laid up, and that thing a-healin'."

"A rifle's more sporting, all right."

"With a rifle, you got a quick kill or a clean miss." He went on, "If them scapers comes in here knowed how to track, they'd have no need to let the deer go off, like this un, and die this-a-way. They could foller and come up with it and git the good o' the hide and the meat."

But the hunters were not always good trackers, and the smell of carrion lay on the air and vultures wheeled above the swamp.

"Understand me, Bill, I ain't begrudgin' 'em their game nor their pleasure."

He thought, indeed, they were welcome to a share in the scrub. Except for the wanton wounding of deer, he minded only the noise they made. It fell offensively on ears accustomed to the soft sounds of birds and animals and river current. He was conscious always of a musical rustling in the scrub, where pine needles brushed on pine boughs like small bows on infinitesimal fiddles. On the stillest days, the tops of the trees stirred gently. The voices of men drowned out the sound, as the cries of hawks obscured the thrush-notes.

The two men followed the swamp to the north.

Bill said casually, "Your still anywheres around here?"

Lant's pulse jumped.

He thought, "I figured that was too fishy, you not knowing what I was doing."

He said, "No."

Bill let the subject drop. They cut up through the hammock. Across the road the dogs picked up a fresh trail leading into the scrub. The warden followed with a detachment peculiar, Lant thought, to a man on a deer-hunt. They walked side by side.

Bill said, "It's too bad the Streeters got all you fellows into trouble."

Lant said, "I reckon they figger they was pretty smart."

"I hope you get out of it all right. It's got Ardis worried. I don't think a jury'll convict you." He broke a twig of sweet myrtle and put it between his teeth. "You goin' to plead guilty?"

"Damn it, Bill, what you tryin' to find out? Snoopin' and pryin', and 'Ardis' this and 'Ardis' that."

"I'm not trying to find out a thing."

"Well, I tell what I got to tell, free—or I don't tell it. You go on with your huntin'. I'm goin' back."

He turned and walked angrily back to the road. Near the clearing he came across a lost dog. He whistled to it and it followed him. At the house he tied it, and fed and watered it.

"I'll find out where you come from, ol' feller," he said, "and git you home all right."

Dogs seemed to become bewildered in the scrub, he thought, by the same directionless confusion of pines that lost men. Each season he found several after the hunters had departed, gaunt with

starvation and thirst and half-wild with a dog's despair. Piety came
to the yard to look at the dog.

She said, "Where's Bill?"

"I let him go on. Damned if he wa'n't tryin' to git somethin' on
me. Wanted I should come right out and say I was in on the
whippin'."

"Lant, I'm goin' to tell you what Cleve said the night after
Christmas. He said he'd heerd tell the Merseys was in with the
Streeters."

"I shouldn't wonder," he said. He spat. He said bitterly, "Ma,
I ain't too sure where Ardis stand."

She hesitated. She said, "Kezzy wouldn't want I should tell you
this, but I'm goin' to. Kezzy said Ardis thought a heap of you, all
right, but she's timid. She's holdin' off, like, waitin' to see how
the trial come out."

"That do me a heap o' good now, don't it?"

The court-house was packed for the trial. Sympathy was sharply
divided. Piety and Zeke and Kezzy sat together. The early in-
dictments had been pared down to eight in number: Abner
Lantry, Cleve and Lant Jacklin, three of the Wilsons, and the
two men pointed out with Lant on the town square by Mrs. John
Streeter. The woman had clung hysterically to her identifications.

Abner breathed heavily but showed no distress. Cleve licked his
lips and turned his round pasty face furtively to look about the
court-room. The Wilsons stirred nervously on their hard chairs.
Lant's two acquaintances lifted their eyebrows at each other.
Abner Lantry was paying them well for their passivity. Lant
stared ahead of him, his arms folded, his forelock low over his eyes.

Ramrod Simpson drifted into the court-room, twisting a battered
hat. His pale eyes fell on Lant and the marshal had to dissuade
him forcibly from sitting with the defendants. The old man had
a hazy conception of the business and was tremendously excited.
Kezzy motioned him to a seat beside her.

The trial moved with startling speed. Abner's lawyer had arranged that the first to be tried should be the pair Mrs. John

Streeter had found with Lant on the town square. Even the other defendants were not prepared for the strategy. Mrs. Streeter identified them; swore tremblingly that they were of the group that had borne off her husband.

On cross-examination she insisted fervently that she was sure of her men.

"They were with the young man with the dark red hair in his eyes——"

"Never mind the young man with dark red hair. You could not be mistaken as to these two men? Not possibly mistaken?"

She said firmly, "I could not possibly be mistaken."

The attorney had kept the pair meekly in the background for a reason that became evident at once. He had no difficulty in proving that the two men in question lived in another county, forty miles from the scene of the whipping, were not acquainted with any of the defendants except Lantry Jacklin, with whom they had twice hunted, had been in their own homes on the entire day and night of the whipping, and knew nothing of the affair until they read of it in a newspaper a week later. When the Streeters identified the six other defendants with equal fervour, their oaths fell on the ears of a deaf jury.

The Streeters' venom made an unfavourable impression. On the morning of the fourth day of the trial, the jury retired to render its decision. In the light of the completely mistaken identifications of the two men from another county, it admitted something more than a reasonable doubt in favour of the river men. Somebody had assuredly administered to the Arkansas settlers a very thorough strapping, deserved or undeserved. For fear of doing injustice to an innocent man, the jury refused to read guilt in the enigmatic faces. The verdict was the same for all eight defendants, "Not guilty."

Kezzy gripped Piety's hand.

The older woman said, "Abner tol' me we had nothin' to fear."

Cleve came down the aisle grinning broadly. Abner's red face sweat and glowed. He shook hands right and left with his friends. The Wilsons shuffled their feet and were anxious to be gone.

Lant's face was set in hard lines. Piety, watching him, thought she had never seen him look so blackly. The Streeters were talking angrily. Mrs. John Streeter pointed a shaking finger at Lant and screamed across the intervening benches and tables.

"That man was in the bunch, as Jesus Christ is my witness."

The words released an old, well-oiled spring in Ramrod Simpson. He jumped up and down, his white hair fluttering, and out-shrieked the Streeters.

"I knowed it!" he shouted. "I knowed ol' Desus Chwist he'ped pen them cattle!"

Lant slipped through the crowd. He could see Kezzy craning her head for him, and his mother's turtle-lidded eyes blinking. He hurried away and out of the court-house. He picked up a ride in the first car he recognised as headed for the river. When he reached Eureka he walked through the piney-woods in the direction of Tom Mersey's place. Before he reached it, he turned off and paced the river trail for more than an hour; back and forth, his chin on his chest. At high noon he made directly for the Mersey house. Several cars stood in the yard under the live-oaks. The front door was open and he walked in. He heard Ardis' thin laugh in the dining room and made for it blindly. In the doorway he stopped short. The room was full of people. A Negress was putting dinner on the table.

He saw Bill Mersey standing with his arm across John Streeter's shoulders. The other Streeters were gesticulating in a corner. He recognised the high sheriff deep in talk with Ardis' father. Three or four deputies were in the group. He drew back his foot as though the men in the room were moccasins in a swamp. Ardis stared at him. Bill Mersey caught sight of him.

He called, "Come in, Lant. No need to look so scared of the sheriff even if you were raised on swamp cabbage and 'coon's milk."

The room shook with laughter. Ardis moved towards him. A cold horror flowed over him. Officers of the law—spies—aliens. He swung his body in the doorway and bolted through the house. He heard Ardis' light steps following. He moved quickly past the live-oaks in the yard and struck through the piney-woods towards the river. He did not want her. She was something he had bolted whole in his hunger and had spewed up.

XXIX

IN THE FALL Lant bought Abner's second-hand Ford car. Piety had begged for a new roof instead.

He said, "I kin make twicet as much money if I got a way to deliver to them city scapers. Then you kin have your roof."

Cleve brought him the car from Abner on a bright November morning. Lant ran to the gate to take possession. He called over his shoulder, "Come on, Ma, git you a ride," and she followed him, untying her gingham apron. The car was dingy and disreputable, but the motor was still good. Lant sat in the driver's seat with pride in the regular explosions. Piety climbed stiffly in the back and examined the worn upholstery with interest. Lant had driven occasionally for Abner and the mechanism was familiar. Cleve grinned at his excitement and slouched down beside him.

"We'll go see Uncle Zeke," Lant said. He added, "A pity Uncle Thad's dead, we could go see him, too."

Piety called loudly from the rear, "Kin go see the ol' place, anyways."

The small leaves of scrub oak and of sparkleberry glinted in the strong sunlight. The car passed Martha's old clearing, where she lay buried with Lantry and Thad and the Jacklin and Lantry infants. The blackjacks there were stained orange and red and cedar-brown by the first frosts. The sky bent down to them as indigo-blue as the quilt-backs Piety and Kezzy had made together. Piety thought a quilt would be pretty in the blackjack colourings, with the oak leaf itself for pattern. But it was lonely, piecing and quilting by herself. They stopped to wave to Zeke, then drove as far as Thad's old clearing and turned around. The cabin was in ruins, and only smilax and trumpet vines held the sides together. The roof slanted over them. More of her kin lay dead in the scrub than moved there alive. Piety was sorry she had come.

She thought, "Seem like makin' a show in front o' the dead."

Lant drove home in a high ecstasy, but she held tight to the frayed seat, her slight figure bouncing on every curve, remembering Thaddeus and Willy and Martha and her father.

Cleve said, "Kezzy said you should carry me home and stay to dinner. She says she cain't wait to see ol' Lant settin' up behind the wheel." He laughed derisively.

Lant said, "I kin be off today. How 'bout it, Ma?"

"Yes," she said decisively, "I want to go. I want to see Kezzy and the baby. He's six months old and I ain't seed him yit. You wait now, I want to take her somethin'."

She started up the fenced-in lane to the house.

"You ain't fitten to go through Eureka," she called to Lant.

He grumbled but gave in. Cleve walked about the yard as they changed their clothes. Piety washed hurriedly in the hand basin and took water to her bedroom to bathe her feet. She put on a grey and white print dress. Her face, thin and seamed, shone like clean polished horn. She put on a high brown straw hat with faded cloth roses on it. She moved quickly and had ready her bundles for Kezzy by the time Lant appeared in a clean blue shirt and grey cotton trousers. His red hair was brushed smooth.

"Now you look fitten," she said.

"Ne' mind the way I look. What-all you takin' to Kezzy?"

He pried into the paper sacks of sweet potatoes, turnip greens and a pan of cold fried squirrel.

"That's a sorry mess."

"Hit's all I got."

He groped through the kitchen safe and passed out a paper-covered glass of grape jelly, a Mason jar of peaches and another of wild honey.

"Them young uns o' hers don't git no sweetenin'," he said.

"Kezzy gives 'em sweetenin'," she said indignantly.

"When Cleve gits it there to give 'em."

Cleve was sulky when they joined him. He had been looking over Lant's belongings, handling the new focussing flashlight and the blow-torch.

"I wisht I could have me sich as this," he said.

Lant said, "All you got to do is work for 'em."

"They ain't no work."

"I'll give you work. Right now. You kin cut ash wood for me ary day you see fit."

Cleve did not answer.

"What you been usin' the blow-torch for?" he asked.

They walked to the car.

"He's been usin' it lately to try and burn the house down," Piety said. "That's jest what he's been a-doin' with it."

"How come?"

"Why, it's the antses," Lant said impatiently. "Them sons o' bitches has got a perfeck trail to the kitchen table. I found out where they was nestin' under the house and I put the blow-torch to 'em, is all."

"And set fire to the under-pinnin's," Piety declared. "Then it was to run with buckets o' water and th'ow sand. And him chasin' the antses with the blow-torch right on. When he take a notion that-a-way, a thing's as good as done time he think of it."

He grinned.

"You ain't woke up since to find them scoundrels kiverin' up the cold biscuits, have you? Well, then. Dogged if it ain't fight to git food, and then fight to keep it."

They drove the dim scrub road, turned to cross the bridge over the river, through Eureka and out the piney-woods road to Kezzy's small rented farm. She put down the new baby and came to meet them. The women embraced in silence. The men walked back of the house to look at the well Kezzy was having dug.

Piety said, "Hit's mighty good to be neighbourin' with you agin, Kezzy. How yuh?"

Kezzy laughed. "Well, we ain't starved to death yit."

"How you come out with your hogs?"

"Aunt Py-tee, they ain't bringin' but four cents a pound. We got a leetle corn left, and I declare hit's better to fatten 'em and kill 'em for lard and not have to buy no compound."

"You mighty right. You got to have grease. A man kin make out without meat but he shore cain't without grease."

"I declare, Aunt Py-tee, times is hard for folks around here. They's talk o' more trouble 'bout the cattle, and them as kep' stock will likely have to sell 'em, and them bringin' not much more'n the hogs. The pore people'll starve when you take the stock away from 'em. They cain't hardly make out as 'tis."

They sat on the rickety porch and Piety held the baby. The two-year boy played around their chairs. Kezzy leaned over and looked closely at the older woman.

"How you feelin', Aunt Py-tee? Your eyes looks bad agin."

"They is. I ain't got but a piece o' sight."

"You'd orter git you some glasses."

"I been to town with Lant one time. I been to the dime store and all over and I couldn't find none to fit."

"Hit's them cataracks, like."

"Must be. I've got to where I'm moon-eyed, Kezzy. I cain't hardly see, day-times, but when the moon's bright I kin see mighty plain."

"Aunt Py-tee, you know I kin hear you, times, acrost the river, callin' your hogs?"

"Kin?"

"I heerd you 'tother evenin' at dusk-dark, standin' at my water-shelf. I said, 'Wisht I could speak to her, pore ol' soul.'"

They rocked back and forth. Wasps buzzed in the clay-daubed rafters overhead. Kezzy rose from her chair and slapped at them.

"Them hateful dirt-daubers!" She dug at one with a stick. "I'll kill him if I kin rout him." She knocked the wasp to the floor, where the child crushed it. He said, "You'll quit totin' mud now!"

Piety said, "I carried you some sweetenin' and some squirrel meat."

"We been eatin' quail," Kezzy smiled. "I don't know what I'd of done for meat thouten my leetle ol' trap. We've got a bait of 'em—we're ready for squirrel." She frowned. "Aunt Py-tee, I'm mighty sorry you're porely."

"I ain't too young, Kezzy."

"You ain't old. You got no white hair to speak of. I'm like to turn white ahead of you."

"Your hair's so dark. Dark-haired people tarnish quicker."

Cleve and Lant came to the porch, talking of the well. Old man Lonny Sours was a well-finder. He had found the spot for digging. He had walked back and forth with a green forked persimmon switch, holding it ahead of him. It had turned down over the hidden water. The bark had twisted in his hands. He had approached the place from all angles to get the exact spot. He had said, "Dig here—here's your water." They expected to bring in the well in another day or two.

"Cain't ever' man find water," Kezzy said. "Ol man Sours has got the gift. He'll tell you to the foot how deep to go. He'll tie a string 'round a two-shillin' piece and lower it easy in a glass o' water and he'll tell you how many feet down your well-water'll lay."

"Where you been gittin' water?"

"Down to Ab's. Been a-totin' it. I catches rain water under the eaves, but the magnolia leaves colours it so's it's hardly fitten."

"How fur's it to Ab's from here?"

"They calls it a mile, but I figgers they measured the road with a 'coonskin, th'owed in the tail ever' lap."

Kezzy was expecting them for dinner and the food was plentiful. If rations would be scanty the rest of the week, she made no sign. She urged on them helpings of rice and home-cured bacon and cow-peas, white bread from the store, and her own cake.

"I do make good lard cake," she admitted.

Lant said, "I wisht you'd made hot bread 'stid o' this wasp's-nest light-bread. Put me some more grease on them swamp-seeds."

"Lant, you're a sight."

"He's a sight," Piety agreed with enthusiasm. "He's a pure sight. Look at him with them peas—he's eatin' nothin' but the soup on 'em."

"He knows what he likes," Kezzy said easily. "Leave him be."

"I wisht I had you cookin' for me, Kezzy," he said. "Hit's a pain to git what I want cooked."

"Now at my house," Cleve drawled, "the trouble is to git it there to cook."

They laughed comfortably.

Cleve said, "Anyways, I sold me a 'gator hide last week. Shot hit on the bank."

After dinner Lant took Kezzy aside.

"You jest ain't makin' out, Kezzy. What-all's Cleve been a-doin'?"

She was evasive.

"Oh—chippin' boxes now and agin."

"That's nigger work," he said. "Turpentinin' don't make a white man no livin'."

"He had a offer to go guardin' to the convict camp."

"Why'n't he take it?"

"Jest someway didn't suit him. Now, Lant, don't you pay us no mind. We'll make out."

"Zeke sent you five dollars, didn't he?"

"Pore ol' Zeke—I'll swear I hated takin' it the worst way."

"If 'twa'n't for Zeke," he said angrily, "somebody'd smell a patch in the fire."

"You ol' snoopy thing, you," she laughed. "You knows too much."

"I ain't meanin' to interfere," he said in alarm. "I offered Cleve work, cuttin' ash wood to burn at the outfit. I jest want to know, do he r'ally want it. I got to have me a piece o' he'p and the work's his if he'll take it."

"He'll take it," she said quietly. "He'll be there Monday-week."

Piety called from the porch.

"We better git goin'."

He started towards the door.

Kezzy laid a hand on his arm.

"Lant, did Cleve tell you about Ardis?"

He stopped.

"Cleve ain't said nothin' about her."

"She got married. A feller from the town they lived in."

A hot wave swept across him, picturing the small body in a stranger's arms. The wave receded.

He said, "Leave her git married."

Ardis was a stranger, too. Kezzy watched him closely. He drew a deep breath. He wanted a rattlesnake against him no more than he wanted the yellow-headed girl. He burst out laughing.

"By God," he said, "I hope she's got her a Prohi."

XXX

DEAD LIMBS were falling in the swamp. It was a certain sign of rain. They fell from the trees before and after, as though some dropped in terror of the moist burden, and others resisted a little longer. Limpkins were crying, and it would not be long before the grey curtain over the scrub and river dissolved into a sweep of rain. A drop spattered now and then like lead on a palmetto leaf. Lant and Cleve poled the rowboat noiselessly up the creek.

Lant said, "We kin git us them ash saplin's right yonder."

Cleve did not answer and he headed the boat between cypress knees. Cleve in the bow hauled it over a twisting mass of black rattan and looped the chain around a sweet gum. They clambered over fallen palmettos through the black muck of the cypress swamp. In wet weather the swamp was a bog, but the winter had been dry. Occasionally a spot was deceptive and they sank over their shoetops in mire.

Lant had used the same canopy over his still during the years he had been 'shining, changing the palmetto fronds each season. The sapling supports had buried themselves in the creek muck until the canopy came now too low for comfort. It would be easier to cut and sink new poles than to root out the old ones, only, perhaps, to find them rotting.

Cleve lagged behind while Lant picked ash saplings of the proper length. He felled each of the four with half a dozen axe-strokes. Cleve helped to trim them down. They walked lightly back through the swamp with the long poles over their shoulders. Cleve trailed them in the water against the boat-side while Lant paddled down-stream towards his whiskey outfit. He took the creek curves neatly, so that the poles should not become entangled in the overwhelming foliage. He made a comment now and then on the impending rain. Cleve made no answer.

Mash was working in the barrels on the platform. It was not yet ready to run, and they stirred it with heavy paddles. Lant scooped up a handful of the fermenting liquid from each barrel in turn and tasted it critically.

" 'Tain't fur from ready," he said.

He covered the barrels again and climbed an overhanging sweet gum to drive the sharpened point of the first sapling deep into the mud. He sat in a fork of the tree and wrapped his long legs around the trunk and drove the sapling with the axe-head. The entire outfit stood exposed, barrels, coils, cooker and drums, to any one who should come up the creek. But no one came except Cleve and Zeke and Abner. The Poseys, whose outfit was a mile and a half to the south, knew only the approximate location. There was only one entrance into the creek. It was masked and seemingly impenetrable.

As they worked, driving in the fourth sapling, they heard a distant whistle like a bird-call. It was almost certainly a hunter indicating his position to a companion on a deer-stand, but they took no chances. They dropped their axes and small equipment hurriedly in the boat, jumped in and were away in silence in an instant.

"Mought be the wrong cat-bird whistlin'," Lant said.

They poled out to the river and cut in again at Otter Landing. Lant hid the paddles and an empty demi-john in the myrtle bushes. They went a hundred yards farther south and into Lant's car to drive to his house.

The rain had begun when they reached the clearing. Large drops were falling like hail.

Lant said, "You comin' in, ain't you?"

Cleve spoke for the first time.

"I'm goin' to Zeke's."

"You best take the car then. You'll git plumb drownded time you git there."

"I don't want your damn car. I'd rather walk."

"Suit yourself. Hit's your business if you want to cut the fool."

Cleve slammed the car door and stalked down the road in the rain. His round pasty face was sullen. Lant left the car at the gate and hurried up the lane to the house. Piety shaded her half-blind eyes to see him.

She said, "I thought shore I heerd you speakin' to somebody."

"You done so," he agreed in exasperation. "Hit were Cleve. I be dogged if I know what ails him. He won't work and he won't work. He's been sulling from a ways back, and now he's actin' jest purely ugly. Ary other man, I'd crawl his frame."

"Wa'n't your wood up today neither?"

"Hit weren't up, and the last strand he cut were so sorry hit didn't outlast my second firin'. I had to git out and scratch for wood in the middle o' the run."

He sat down by the hearth and took off his wet shoes and stretched his feet to the fire.

"I b'lieve he's fixin' jest to walk out on me and go work for Poseys. I don't no more look for him to come back tomorrer than I look for the moon to drap in the river."

"If he'd only tell you," she said, rocking close to him, "you'd know how to figger."

"That's it. If he'd jest say. If he'll keep the work, I'll put up with it, and him so sorry. He talked all mornin' 'bout Poseys havin' a nigger to cut the wood. Then all evenin' he had nary word to say."

"Leave him go to Poseys," she said. "You don't keer, long as Kezzy and them young uns has somethin' on the table. Cleve's jealous, he's jest perfeckly jealous."

"Since I painted the car," he agreed.

"Since you painted the car and put a top on it. He cain't stand to see you goin' decent."

"I've done offered him a half interest in the outfit, if he'd divide the time. I need he'p bad. I could sell twicet as much agin, with a bigger outfit and good he'p."

"He won't do it," she said vehemently. "He jest won't do the work. You be glad if he do go to Poseys."

In the morning Lant went early to his outfit. His mash was ready to run. He had a small supply of ash wood. Cleve did not appear. Lant started a fire in his furnace and when his buck made its turn-over in the cooker, he capped it, slowed down his fire and went looking for Zeke. Zeke was not at home. Lant went home and called his mother from her work in the garden.

"Ma, you jest got to come watch my fire and my pot whilst I cut me some wood."

"I got a leetle stove wood here you kin have, and welcome," she told him.

They took the stove wood in their arms and she followed him back of the house to the swamp. She sat on her thin old haunches and tended the fire under the still. She heard him chopping in the lower hammock. He returned with armfuls of ash. Towards noon Zeke joined them.

"My old woman said you was lookin' for me," he said hopefully.

Lant said, "I don't miss it. Zeke, how good you these days, swingin' a axe?"

"Them ash saplin's, I kin cut them all day."

"Well, you got you a job right now, then."

"Cleve quit you?"

"Hit look that-a-way." He added, "Now I tell you, Zeke, if Cleve was to come back, I'd figger the work was his, right on."

Zeke agreed. "I wouldn't take the work from him, noways. But I jest as leave tell you, I'm glad to git a chancet at it. We ain't been eatin' too reg'lar to my house lately."

Zeke's strength was adequate for the wood-cutting. He turned out a comfortable strand a day. For three weeks there was no word from Cleve. Then Lant passed him on the river. He was with the Poseys. Lant saw their boat turn up the creek that led, he knew, to the Posey still.

The hunters left the scrub and the swamp. The red-bud bloomed above the river, the limpkins cried, the eagles nested and and it was spring. Cleve worked at the Poseys' still until May. Then Jim Posey fired him. Lant saw Kezzy at the store at Eureka.

"I hear Jim fired Cleve," he said to her.

She nodded.

"He got work agin?"

She looked at him.

She said quietly, "He ain't tried. I ain't hurryin' him this time, Lant. I got cow-peas and collards and meal, and a leetle bacon in the smoke-house. You know how Cleve is. Leave him loaf as long as I kin make out, is the way I figger it. Then when things gits bad agin, time enough for me to romp on him to git to work. God knows I cain't keep him at it all the time."

Drought set in early in June instead of the usual summer rains. Lant looked at his mother's parched garden.

He said, "If Kezzy's cow-peas and greens looks like ours——"

Lant went to his outfit on the first of July. He started, seeing a slouched figure on the platform. Cleve was waiting for him.

Cleve said sulkily, "I jest as good to cut your wood agin."

Lant said, "I've give that job to Zeke. You know that." He asked quickly, "Did Kezzy send you?"

Cleve said, "Yes."

"You lyin'. Kezzy said you should go anywhere but me. Didn't she?"

Cleve narrowed his pale eyes and did not answer.

"Kezzy told you not to interfere with Zeke," Lant said. "I ain't goin' to interfere with him. He's got to eat, same as you. He's been faithful. I ain't goin' to turn the ol' feller off and then you work a week maybe and go off the way you done before."

Cleve said, "Zeke don't need work. He's got money hid out."

"He do not. No use for you to talk, Cleve, I've give Zeke the work and you cain't ask me out of it."

Cleve said hotly, "All right. You be biggety now. You jest go right on bein' biggety."

He plunged angrily through the swamp to his boat.

At dinner Lant said to Piety, "Cleve come askin' for the wood-cuttin' back agin."

"You give it to him?"

"I ain't turnin' Zeke off for nobody."

"You got Kezzy to think of."

"I'm thinkin' o' Kezzy. She do better with Zeke workin' than Cleve. Zeke sends her money when things gits thick for her."

"You're makin' a leetle more'n we need. Seems to me you could save the quarrellin' and look out for Kezzy yourself."

He frowned.

"I cain't git her to take nothin'. I don't understand Kezzy noways. Now and agin she'll take it from Zeke, but I be dogged if she'll take it from me."

In mid-July Jim Posey stopped Lant as their rowboats, loaded with meal and sugar, passed on the river.

Jim asked, "Lant, you been missin' ary thing from your—place o' business?"

"Nary thing."

Jim flushed.

"I reckon they's no use you and me actin' too private. I jest as leave tell you, they's been ten gallons stole from back o' my outfit." He spat in the river. "Dog take it, I got no use for a thief. I make my money honest."

Lant said, "You got ary idee who 'tis?"

"I kin come all around namin' you the man."

Jim released his hold on Lant's rowboat and they began to drift apart.

Jim said, "If it's who I figger 'tis, I reckon you're not like to be bothered. The sorriest kind of a feller don't gin'rally steal from his own kin."

When his day's work was done, Lant sat in the cool of the July twilight, picking abstractedly at his banjo. Piety, watching his face, questioned him.

"Cleve's fixin' to git hisself into trouble," he admitted, and refused to tell her more.

Dog days came in and lay like hot lead on scrub and river. The August sun blazed on the pine trees and scorched the corn in the field. Chickens went with wings lifted to cool themselves and hounds panted in the shadows underneath the houses. Folk went to bed exhausted and awakened at daybreak smothered in an invisible blanket. The mocking-birds stopped singing and the snakes began to shed. Every one stepped warily, for the rattlesnakes had become blind and vicious. Sand gnats swarmed in clouds and passed the sore-eyes from one baby to another. Women who had saved May-water from the rains in May doled it out to cure the affliction. Children whimpered and fretted in the heat. The old folks grew irritable. Even soft-cooked grits did not feel smooth and good against the palate. Chills and fever went the rounds. Tempers were short.

On a white blinding day Jim and Martin Posey met Cleve on the Eureka bridge. They were riding in their car and Cleve was on foot. They stopped him.

Jim said, "I been wantin' to ask you about some whiskey o' mine showed up at Lynne."

Cleve said, "I don't know nothin' about your whiskey."

Jim said, "You say that oncet agin."

Cleve jumped on the running-board and leaned into the car. His right arm hung behind him, as though he held a gun. Jim picked up a hunting knife on the floor of the car and sliced at Cleve across the cheek and ear. Cleve dropped back with his hand against the bleeding streak. The Poseys drove on quickly.

XXXI

CANE-GRINDING at Abner Lantry's place began in the afternoon of the last day of October. Abner was the first to grind along the river, and every one would be there for the fresh cane juice and the fun. Cars and wagons began to pass Kezzy's house after dinner. Youngsters went by on foot, bare-legged and jostling. Kezzy watched the road for Lant's car. He swerved into the yard at three o'clock. Piety bounced beside him on the front seat.

Lant said, "You ready to go git your belly full o' cane juice?"

She picked up the small boy and the baby and dropped them into the back of the open car.

"I cain't hardly wait to git my nose in the bucket," she said.

Lant shut off the motor.

"Ain't Cleve goin'?" he asked.

"He ain't even here."

"Ain't he quit sullin' yit about Jim cuttin' him?"

She shook her head.

"Now, Lant," she said, "Cleve went off soon this mornin' and said he was gittin' a ride to Jacksonville. I don't know, did he mean it."

Piety asked, "Is his cuts healed good?"

"You cain't hardly see the scar. Hit didn't amount to nothin'." She threw back her smooth dark head and laughed.

"This is one evenin' I ain't goin' to set home and worry," she said lightly. "First day o' cane-grindin' don't come but oncet a year."

She loaded herself in with the children.

She said to them delightedly, "Ain't we the biggety things now, ridin' to cane-grindin' in a automobile."

She hailed the gathering with zest as they turned under the live-oaks into Abner's yard. She held the baby loosely in one arm like a bundle and waved her free hand to her friends.

"I swear, Ab," she called to the host, "you ain't growed enough sugar-cane to make all the juice I aim to drink."

"You go chase a hog!" he cried.

"I've done enough o' that!"

She handed Piety the baby. She ran to the mill, where boys pushed long stalks of sugar-cane into the gears as a slow horse walked around and around. Kezzy pushed the boys away and fed in a handful of stalks.

"The bucket o' juice I'm fixin' to drink," she told them, "I ain't got the heart to let nobody else do the mill-feedin'."

Abner followed her. "I hope you satisfied, Miss Kezzy. You been rarin' to feed the mill the first day o' grindin'." He looked at her closely. "Your old man Cleve got better comp'ny than ours this evenin'?"

She picked up a fresh handful of stalks and watched them attentively.

"Now, Ab," she said, "they's jest no sich thing as better comp'ny than yours."

He laughed and went across the yard to Lant and Piety and the children.

The juice gushed from the spout into a wooden bucket. It was green and clouded. Children dipped tin cups into its thin sweetness and ran away into corners to drink. The juice was chilled by the November air, and it seemed as if no one could get enough. Kezzy called Lant to take her place, and tipped back her black head to drink until she gasped for air.

Abner would not begin to boil syrup until the next day. Every one was thirsty for cane juice, and all the evening the horse would walk around the mill, with a child or two on his back. Some would take turns at feeding in the stalks while others satisfied a year-old longing. A mule and wagon were bringing in load after load of new-cut stalks. In the morning the great fire would be built under the syrup kettle and the juice would be boiled down in forty-gallon lots. The grinding and boiling would go on for two or three weeks. Today and tonight folk drank and laughed and children ran and romped.

Eph Wilson's wife had died and they talked of her and of Eph. He was mean and stingy and they said of him, "He'd favour a nigger a heap quicker'n one of his own young uns." Eph's wife had needed her teeth pulled and the man had refused her, saying he could not afford the work. They said, "She had beef cattle enough when she died, to fix her teeth. He sold her cattle right along with his." For the most part, the talk had no malice. There was much joking and pranking. When a commotion arose among the children, a mother of ten settled it by a general slapping of small ears.

"You have to frail all the young uns to git the right un," she explained. "Start with a big un and end with the least un."

Piety and Lant and Kezzy ate cold supper with Abner and his wife. As the autumn dusk sifted crisp and blue through the piney-woods, newcomers came for the night's cane-grinding and the night's frolic. Abner had a small talking machine with a horn, and the younger men kept one record going for an hour, "The Fox Chase." One called to another, "Come listen to this here ol' nigger playin' and singin' the Fox Chase!" They imitated the record. "Listen to them ol' dogs a-bayin'—*yip-yip-woo-o!*"

Lant said, "I'd like to have me a talkin' machine, jest to set and listen to the Fox Chase."

Martin Posey said, "The nigger do it all hisself, too."

Lant said, "He don't do it all. Them's rale dogs."

Martin insisted, "No they ain't. It's him."

Lant said, "Well, if he kin sound that clost to a dog, the Lord had orter give him a tail and call him 'Spot' and let him run rabbits and drink branch water."

Old man Lonny Sours began to play the fiddle in the desultory fashion of a dog scratching himself. He scraped the strings casually, then struck off tuneless phrases, looking around the room with a solemn detachment. The music took form in a tune. He played "The Rosewood Casket" and two children crossed hands and danced the schottische down the length of the bare pine floor. Abner's wife waddled in from the kitchen with an extra kerosene light to place on the mantel near the fiddler. Abner came into the room with Eph Wilson, holding out a white china pitcher of cane juice. He put his arm around his wife's thick waist as she passed.

"When you git you another wife, Eph," he said, "you want you a big woman like this un. Then you won't have to buy you no cover for winter."

She said behind her hand, "Now I jest wonder what my Uncle Ben would say if I was to go on home with you, Eph?"

"I might have somethin' I didn't know what to do with," Eph said. "I might have to call somebody to git me out from under Abner."

The fiddler played "Hog, Hominy and Grits," and Martin Posey eased into a chair beside him and joined in on a harmonica.

Lant said to Kezzy, "I'd a heap rather he'd play the jumbo jew's-harp. I don't like the way he chokes his mouth-organ."

A girl called from the doorway to the crowd around the cane-mill. A bonfire burned between the mill and the house for light and warmth. Boys foraged about the yard and down the road and threw on dry palmetto fronds and dog-fennel to make it blaze. Half a dozen couples detached themselves from the light, like shadows shifting, and ran into the house to join the set that was forming for the square-dance. Two or three older pairs entered the circle and stood with linked hands to wait for the calling. A boy, scurrying about for a partner, coaxed Ab's wife into the circle. She was an old hand and knew the figures, and moved her feet under her bulk as lightly as chipmunks. Martin Posey took his mouth from the harmonica.

"One more couple, and le's go. Lant Jacklin, you take out Kezzy."

The circle began to shuffle. The boys hailed Lant.

"Here, Blue-john! Here's your home!"

His head bobbed on his long neck. He grumbled good-humouredly.

"Dogged if I wouldn't rather be home in the scrub than messin' up in sich a ruckus with you sorry jessies."

They laughed. One said, "Lant, you a hell of a streaklin'."

Kezzy said affectionately, "Honey, you do favour a Blue-john somethin' turrible. You cain't quarrel with 'em about it no-ways."

He said, "You catch you another Blue-john for the next, then. One set and I'm done with you."

He had not danced since early spring. He unlimbered his long legs and swung Kezzy with gusto. Her white skin was flushed and her soft black eyes were shining.

"I was about to figger I was gittin' old," she panted when they were dancing close.

In the doorway he caught a sudden glimpse of a familiar round face. It was looking directly at him. It was white with hate. It could not be Cleve, he thought, staring at him so. When the change of partners in a figure brought him opposite the doorway again, the face was gone. He thought, "I'm gittin' bad as a damn nigger to see things." When the set was ended he left Kezzy abruptly and ran into the yard. There was no one there. Beyond, men and women and boys and girls ran and shouted about the cane-mill. The bonfire blazed between house and mill. Lant walked in and out among the groups. Cleve was not in sight. He thought, "That booger gittin' awful light-footed." He walked back across the yard and studied the footprints about the doorway in the light that came from the room. Kezzy stood by the hearth-fire. He walked across the room to her.

"Kezzy, was Cleve wearin' them big ol' boots he had half-soled in the spring?"

"I believe he did have 'em on this mornin', Lant." She looked at him curiously. "Why?"

"I jest wondered."

He stood beside her, warming himself at the fire. No one was dancing.

The fiddler and young Posey played "Double Eagle" and "Ninety-seven" and "Waiting for a Train." The music whined and squeaked unheeded. Even the young bloods preferred to be outside tonight, drinking cane juice and racing around the bonfire. The older folks had become chilled in the cool air, and most of them were gathered in the room for gossip near the fat-wood fire.

Here were lights and music and talk and gayety. A cane-grinding was the best of life, and a frolic warmed the blood like wine. Tonight there was a common safety; a common closeness and a common delight. The room grew warm and the old fiddler and young Posey were red and wet of face. Kezzy went to them and fanned them with a palm leaf while they played. She stood placid and maternal, smiling a little to herself.

The young baby slept in the adjoining bedroom with others of his age. Piety held the older boy on her thin lap, where he dozed uncomfortably, burrowing his head against her flat chest. It was good to be sitting with old women who knew the things she knew. Age marked these women early. The young girls were inclined to be plump and buxom, with heavy legs and large buttocks. They were dressed with much flimsy style. Their bland faces were painted. They were ripe and enticing. Life pared them down in a hurry. Here and there a middle-aged woman, prosperous as the section went, was fat and hearty. Almost without exception the older women were stripped gaunt and meagre, as though they had walked on foot a long sandy way.

But if the road had been hard, it was also pleasant. If a living was uncertain, and the sustaining of breath precarious, why, existence took on an added value and a greater sweetness. The tissues of life were food and danger. These were the warp and woof, and all else was an incidental pattern, picked out with varicoloured wools. Love and lust, hate and friendship, grief and frolicking, even birthing and dying, were thin grey and scarlet threads across the sun-browned, thick and sturdy stuff that was life itself. The old women sat together with bare, translucent faces, knowing that the pulse of blood through the veins was a rich, choice thing, and the drawing of a breath was good.

As the evening wore on, men joined them by the hearth, and then the young folks, surfeited and sleepy. They talked of hogs and cattle; of crops and the weather and the law. They spoke of a family of Yankee newcomers to the piney-woods, who had not come to the cane-grinding.

Kezzy said, "Them pore leetle ol' Yankees don't know what to make of us Crackers. I tell 'em I'm a fool and cain't he'p it and no use to hide it."

Old man Lonny Sours offered, "I hears tell they're Catholics."

"That's what they say."

Abner tilted back in a cow-hide chair and said, "Hit don't make no difference what a man perfesses. I been in a heap o' churches. There's the Nazarene Church and the Pentecost and the Holy Rollers and the Baptists and I don't know what-all. I cain't see much difference to nary one of 'em. There's a good to all of 'em and there's a bad."

Lonny Sours persisted, "All I got agin the Catholics now, is they got no freedom. Ary one seed them nuns with them bonnets, like, over their heads and faces? They has to wear them things all the time."

He added, nodding his head, "Even to bed."

Abner said, "Well, I never watched one of 'em go to bed."

His wife remarked, "Sho, ever'body goes in a Catholic church has to have his head kivered."

Lonny pondered. "Don't you reckon," he asked, "hit's an opinion they hold?"

Abner said, clearing his throat, "We been gittin' a magazine. Hit tells about a heap o' quare idees. Hit tells about the Muslems."

"I've heerd tell o' them, seems to me," Lonny said, "but I cain't rightly place 'em. Who was them Muslems? A form o' Catholics?"

"I cain't say as to that. But they pays right smart attention to the sun and figgers ever'thing comes fum the East, like. They think it's fitten and proper a man should keep hisself a hull mess o' wives."

"Seems to me that's all right," Martin Posey ventured mildly. The girls giggled.

They talked a while of all strange things and far-off people. The women gathered up the sleeping children and said, "Goodnight, all. Some kind of enjoyed the cane juice." The boys ran from the house and into the road in a last gust of energy.

Abner Lantry called, "Kezzy, you keep away from them Muslems."

She laughed.

" 'Tain't right to laugh," she said, sobering. "I declare, it makes me faint-hearted to think there's sich people with sich ways."

She carried the baby, sleeping, high on one shoulder. Piety led the small boy. They climbed into Lant's car. Lant's mouth was dry and he left them and cut across the yard towards the cane-mill to drink from the bucket of juice. His tread was light in the sand. He saw two men in the darkness under a shed roof. He recognised Jim Posey. Then he heard the voice of the storekeeper and postmaster.

He heard him say to Jim, "I'm not supposed to mention what goes through the mails. But you men have been good customers so long I feel obliged to warn you. A letter went to the Prohibition agents at Jacksonville yesterday. I'm pretty sure it was in Cleve Jacklin's writing."

Lant went to his car and drove Kezzy home through the spiced darkness of the piney-woods. A light was burning in her house when he stopped at the gate. He said "Good-night" and with Piety drove quickly away.

A week later he stood in the sandy yard under the live-oak oiling a steel trap. He heard the gate click at the rear of the garden and looked up. Kezzy was coming through the garden. She had not hailed jovially from a distance, as was her custom.

She walked to him without speaking. Her face was white and her eyes were red and swollen. Her mouth trembled. She spoke in a low voice.

"I don't know if I'm doin' right or not. I cried all night, studyin'. Hit ain't natural for a woman to go agin her husband, whatever he do. But 'tain't natural for Cleve to do what he's a-doin'."

"Come in the house and set down, Kezzy."

Piety joined them at the breezeway, holding to the wall as she walked.

"Who's there?"

"It's me, Aunt Py-tee. I jest now rowed acrost the river."

The younger woman laid her cheek a moment against the other's.

"I'm carryin' bad news, Aunt Py-tee. Hit concern you as much as Lant."

"Well, set down, anyway."

"Lant, Cleve's turned you up to the Prohis."

Piety said sharply, "He ain't done no sich thing."

"I know what I'm sayin'. Ain't I tried to ask him out of it, until it was me keep still or him to knock me down for it? He's turned you up, Lant, right along with Poseys and Luke Saunders. You ain't heerd about the letter he wrote to Jacksonville? I didn't know nothin' about that, but a letter come back to him. I went to the box for the mail and I seed where 'twere from, and it marked gov'mint business, or somethin' like that. He's been jest a-boilin' since Jim cut him, and right off I figgered what 'twas. Bless God, I no more thought you was in it—but I opened it, and that was it. The Prohis had done got a letter from him, sayin' they was three stills he could tell 'em about along the river. They was sendin' a man and wanted he should name a place and time to meet him. I jest nachelly tore the letter up. I reckon he kep' askin' at the post-office hadn't no letter come for him, and he found out. When he come at me about it, I faced him down about the hull mess. He said, Yes, he was turnin' you all up. I says, You got some complaint against Jim. He were hasty cuttin' you. You got nothin' agin Luke Saunders. God know you got nothin' agin Lant."

"What did he say then?"

"He think he do. He said you wouldn't give him work when he asked for it."

" 'Tain't so, not that-a-way. He quit me in the winter. Jest walked off to Poseys and said nothin'. I give Zeke the work and I couldn't see my way to take it from him agin, and Cleve mebbe do me the same way he done before. I'd done offered Cleve shares in the outfit and he wouldn't do the work."

"Don't tell me. Nobody on earth cain't git him to work. He won't work and he don't want the other fellow to git no beneeft from workin'. Time you painted your ol' car, and put a kiver to it, he acted like he had the itch ever' time he'd see you in it."

Piety said, "He wouldn't turn Lant up for sich as that?"

"Aunt Py-tee, there's twenty-five dollars in it. Ary still a man turns up, he's heerd tell the Prohis pays that much. He says if there's twenty-five dollars in it, he'll turn up all he kin find. I says to him, You cain't take a man's livin' away from him that-a-way, not even Jim. Hit's their livin', you got no right to tech it. Think of Lant and Aunt Py-tee, I says. What would Aunt Py-tee do if Lant was to have his livin' takened away? Cleve, I says, you cain't do it. Them's your kin-folks."

"What did he say?"

She drew a hand across her red, tired eyes.

"He said, 'Damn the kin-folks.' "

She rose to go.

"Like I say, mebbe I'm doin' wrong, but hit's my best opinion to tell you. I've done tole Luke and tole him to tell Poseys. A man's got nary right to interfere with another man's livin', I don't keer what he's done."

She leaned down to stroke Piety's cat, then hurried through the garden and across the clearing. The staunch figure disappeared in the hammock at the top of the ledge. Lant and Piety had not stirred from their places in the breezeway.

Piety asked, "You goin' to move the outfit, eh?"

"I dunno."

He began to walk up and down with his hands behind him and his chin sunk on his chest. Piety could make out his features dimly. A memory, as blurred as her sight, came to her of Lantry, her father, pacing in the same tense fashion. At last he stopped.

"I ain't a-goin' to move it. Hit's a heap o' work, and mebbe them scoundrels ketch me in the middle of it. Mebbe I'd git it moved, and them come up on the new place. Ain't no better place on the river no-ways, excusin' the Dread. I couldn't git the stuff down the river to the Dread now, and them not see me."

"Well, I'd move it," she said. "Cleve knows right where it's at."

"He cain't describe it so's no stranger in the world could find it."

"He mought show 'em the way hisself."

He snorted.

"That sorry bastard won't show his tracks nowheres along this river."

"Now you call him most ary name you're o' mind to," she said, "but Marthy were his mother and she were my sister, and she were a good woman. Don't you go callin' Cleve no bastard. Nor no son of a bitch, neither. You're awfu' free with your names."

"The pimp, then."

"That's better," she agreed cordially. "A whole heap better. The pimp."

XXXII

To the south a column of grey smoke ascended. It was not far off; no farther than a mile or two.

Lant said to Piety, "I know good and well Poseys ain't firin' that heavy, knowin' the Prohis'll be nosin' around."

The smoke darkened and grew thicker. A black cloud billowed towards the sky. The wind was from the west. It took the smoke in its sweep and spread it thinly over the scrub.

"I got to go see," Lant said.

"You look out, now. You'll run into them fellers, if that's what 'tis."

"I ain't goin' to run into no Prohis. I'm goin' up the river. They kin pass me much as they're o' mind to. I mought know them but how kin they know me?"

"Well, you be keerful, anyways."

Since her sight had failed her, the woman's hearing had become acute. She heard a dry branch crack on the hammock ledge as he passed through it; then the rattle of the chain as he loosened the rowboat in the creek below.

He had been gone from the house fifteen or twenty minutes when she heard a car grinding through the ball-bearing sand at the turn of the scrub road below the lane. She craned her neck and shaded her eyes, to see. She could make out nothing more than a dark streak, rounding the bend between scrub and hammock and moving to the north. Half an hour later she heard the sound of axes on wood and metal. The noise diminished and the west wind brought to her nose the smell of things burning that had not burned before. She knew the odours of burning pine, sweet and aromatic; of hammock, green and premature; of broom sage, that burned like paper. There was in the air an acridity that was unfamiliar. Then even her dim sight discerned the smoke, a broad column that reared from below the hammock ledge. It was rank and dark, as though the swamp itself were burning. The Prohis were at Lant's still.

She did not dare wait longer. She was afraid the house would be next invaded. Lant had twelve gallons unsold from his last run. There were two five-gallon oak kegs and two gallon glass jugs. The kegs were almost more than she could lift, but she made two trips with them to the hammock, stumbling blindly across the intervening clearing. She concealed them under palmetto clumps. She ran back and forth through the house with a gallon jug in either hand, then hid them, one deep in her flour-barrel, the other under the pillows of her bed.

She felt along the wall for her white sunbonnet, for it would be visible farther than her palmetto hat. She knew that Lant would return by river. It would be possible for the river-bends and the height of the ledge to conceal the smoke in the swamp until it was too late. She could see him rowing home unsuspecting, and the agents falling on him as he turned into the creek from the river. She could head him off if she could reach Otter Landing to the south before he passed it. The ledge dropped there to open river water and was visible for some yards. She could not be sure of seeing his boat, and as she reached the opening in the ledge above the landing, she began to wave her sunbonnet. She stood for some time, waving it back and forth, trying to distinguish one moving shadow from another. She heard the boat before she saw it. Lant's voice came close at hand.

"What's the matter, Ma? Did the Prohis tear up mine, too?"

"Hit's plumb tore up and a-burnin'. I could hear 'em maulin' on the barrels. They like to set the hull hammock afire."

He grounded his boat. The sides scraped against cypress knees.

"It's Cleve's work," he said.

" 'Tain't nobody else but Cleve," she agreed. "You jest mighty lucky I got here 'fore you goed on in to the creek and got ketched yourself."

"Cleve were right with 'em," he said quietly. "I been to Poseys' outfit. Wa'n't none of 'em there, but they ain't nothin' left but hoops and bricks. Couldn't nobody but Cleve of showed 'em the way in to Poseys and to mine too."

"I heerd a car go by 'bout two hour back."

"That was them, a'right. And Cleve with 'em."

Now that it had happened, he understood that he had always known that it would happen. But it was strange, after all these years of caution, that the danger should have been, not from strangers, but from Cleve. It was like Lantry's own dog, scavenging in his grave.

"I tole you to move the outfit," Piety said. She followed close behind him to keep herself on the path.

"I never figgered he'd r'aly do it. Go right with 'em and show 'em. I knowed he were sorry, but not that sorry. I never figgered he'd have the chitlin's when the time come."

They approached the house cautiously. It had not been entered. They stayed in quietly until the next afternoon. There had been no further sound. They went together to the swamp and looked at the ruins. The platform over the creek had made a fine bonfire for the barrels and the cooker. Nothing was left but twisted metal and blackened bricks. The trees in the swamp had burned for forty feet around, and the flames had licked far up into the hammock. Sweet gum and magnolia and hickory and palm stood sick and charred.

The woman watched him anxiously. He was trembling like a rabbit.

"Hit'll be a year 'fore the hammock's green agin," he said.

XXXIII

Abner Lantry and the Poseys and Luke Saunders came together across Lant's clearing at sunrise. Fog veiled the scrub, as though a grey misted sea washed through the stockade of the pines. The sun filtered through as they approached the cabin, so that bars of sunlight alternated with the shadowy bars that were the tree trunks.

Abner said, "I mind me comin' here to live when I were a young un. The scrub front o' the place were low and rollin', jest thick scrubby bush and palmettos. Hit's growed now to a perfeck wall."

"Like all the rest o' the scrub," Luke said.

"Like all excusin' the Big Burn. Give the rough five yare more thouten no farr, the hull scrub'll be thick-growed like that there."

"Hit's a mighty good place to be," Jim Posey said. "Pertickler right now, with sons o' bitches thick as they be, our side the river."

"A man that knowed the scrub," Abner said irrelevantly, "and somebody takened out arter him, he could jest cool out acrost it and nobody never ketch up with him."

They fell silent. Each man gnawed on the thought buried in him, as on a bone. Abner rapped on the floor of the breezeway and called "Hi!" There was no answer.

"You reckon they ain't up yit?"

"They up long 'fore crack o' day."

Piety's voice came weakly from the bedroom.

"Come in, unless it's strangers."

They stepped on the breezeway and sat down. Abner went into the room.

"You sick in the bed, Sis?"

"I'm right smart porely," she agreed. "I got the fever and I cain't eat. Ary mouthful gorges me. My spells is comin' frequent. I were dead most all yistiddy evenin'."

"I'm mighty sorry. Where-all's Lant?"

"He left for Jacksonville 'bout four o'clock this mornin'."

"I knowed he were goin'. I didn't know what for."

"Come clost and I'll tell you."

"Hit's jest the Poseys and Luke with me."

"You cain't tell who-all's fitten to hear things," she whispered hoarsely, "since Cleve done what he done."

He lifted the edge of the mosquito bar that enveloped the bed and sat beside her. She was grey-white and wasted. Her thin hair spread about her small face on the pillow, as though a child lay ill and prematurely old.

"Hit's been two weeks," she told him, "since Cleve takened the Prohis to the outfit, and Lant's jest now got his last whiskey sold. He figgered he'd best git him a new outfit goin' whilst he had the money to pay for it. He kin git the copper sheetin' to Jacksonville for half the price. Him and Zeke goed together. They're fixin' to come back thu St. Augustine and stop to the rep-tyle farm and see kin they mebbe sell some 'gator hides and snake skins."

"He ain't afeered the outfit'll git tore up agin?"

"Hit'll be tore up if the pimp finds it," she prophesied earnestly.

"What time he studyin' on gittin' back?"

"He said to cook noon dinner, if I kin git outen the bed."

"We'll set here and wait on 'em. You go back to sleep."

"I cain't sleep for the fleas," she complained, "and them a-runnin' and a-hoppin'."

"That ol' cat o' yourn sleepin' by the bed here on the deerskin, is what brings 'em in."

"That's what Lant say, but when he's gone, the cat's my only comp'ny. I figger hit's squirrel fleas. We been eatin' squirrel and Lant's keerless with the hides. I been dustin' insect powder 'round my shoulders."

"Insect powder won't kill 'em. Take a flea, all you kin do is git with him."

"Mebbe hit won't kill 'em, but it'll addle 'em to where they won't run nor hop."

The four men sat immobile in the breezeway. Towards noon Piety left the bed and dressed tremblingly. She started a fire in the kitchen-range, put sweet potatoes in the oven and filled the kettle. She felt in the flour-barrel for a quart bottle of raw white whiskey and poured herself three or four tablespoonfuls, which she drank with sugar and water. The bottle had raised letters that read, "Casper's Whiskey, Made By Honest North Carolina People." It had belonged to Lantry. She took it to the breezeway.

"If Lant was here, he'd say offer you the bottle," she said.

Abner and the Poseys drank from the tilted mouth.

Luke Saunders said, "I wouldn't keer for it." He added in apology, "Jest a leetle seem to make me drunk. I don't hold with gittin' drunk."

Abner said, "Nor me. When a man gits drunk, I don't want nothin' to do with him. But it's his business," he added.

Jim said, "I'm proud you got no objections, for many's the time I couldn't tell night from day. And some kind of enjoyed it."

Piety sat down with them.

"The on'y time I wants it, is when I first gits on my feet. Hit steadies me, like."

The talk turned to the one matter they mulled over in their minds. The old woman was the first to speak.

"Well," she asked querulously, "is Cleve still sayin' he weren't the one done it?"

"He's jest now quit lyin' about it," Abner said. "I faced him down yistiddy. He heerd Lant and Zeke was goin' to Jacksonville. You know what he figgered? He figgered Lant were goin' to the Prohis' office and git to look at their books, and see were Cleve's name there. I seed Cleve to the store yistiddy. I usually take up some time with him, but lately I ain't been speakin' to him, like ever'body else. I took the notion, jest to see what he'd say. Howdy, Cleve, I says, I hear tell Lant's fixin' to go to Jacksonville." He spat across the breezeway.

"What'd he say?" Piety leaned towards him.

"He said nary word. He jest turned as white as a log o' cotton."

"Well, I do know."

"Hit give me the idee. Cleve, I says, you're found out. No use lyin' no longer. Kezzy told it on you and you tried to make out like she were crazy. You was low-down enough to do it and you wa'n't man enough to own up to it. Now you're found out."

"What'd he say?"

"He said, 'What I done was lawful, and what the boys was doin' was on-lawful.' And Py-tee, when he said it, he were tremblin' like a bonnet-patch where the bream is feedin'."

"I do know. Do ary one know if he got the money from the Prohis?"

"Don't nobody know. They jest lately changed the rule, is what folks say, and the gov'mint ain't payin' for no more spies. Did Cleve git the money 'fore they changed the rule, I cain't say. He owes most that much to the store. He charged his rations as long as he was daresome to do so. He wouldn't dast show no money at the store, no-ways."

They sat in silence.

Luke Saunders said, "Sometimes Cleve look so piteeful. Then you think of what he done and you forgit to pity him."

Jim Posey asked, "Mis' Jacklin, what make Cleve like that?"

"I cain't figger. His ma were all right and Sylvester were all right. They wa'n't nothin' quare to neither of 'em."

"Well," he said profoundly, "hit's an awfu' way to be."

"Kezzy and the young uns is what worries me," she said.

"That were a pain," Jim said. "The way she were tryin' to make out. She were diggin' sweet pertaters to eat, and sellin' a few, to git somethin' to eat with 'em."

"I feels bad about cuttin' Cleve," Jim said. "I figgered shore he had a gun. I feels bad about firin' him, as things has come out. But hit weren't r'aly cold-out firin'. I jest said to him, Cleve, you ain't doin' the work I'm payin' you to do. Now you git, but ary day you take a notion to do a piece o' rale work, that day you come back. He never come. He jest goed to stealin' my whiskey and sellin' it at Lynne."

"If he'd told they was on starvation," Luke said, "ary one would of holped him."

"Starvation don't excuse him," Abner said. "His belly never pinched him. He ate hot dinner to my house nigh ever' day. Kezzy and them young uns was the ones went hongry. And Kezzy were the one jest wouldn't have it, when he goed to turn you fellers up."

Jim said, "Kezzy tells, the mornin' Cleve took the Prohis on the river, a rattlesnake struck at her three times thu the fence. She knowed right then what were happenin'."

"Who's a-feedin' Kezzy now?" Piety asked.

"Ever' one. Her and the young uns gits asked out twicet a day. We all sees to that. Nary man's fool enough to buy stuff for Cleve to tote off, but Kezzy and the young uns is welcome to what they kin carry away in their own bellies."

Piety put grits on the stove to cook and scalded white bacon to fry. She mixed biscuits and shaped them ready to bake. Lant and Zeke came a little after noon, carrying a sheet of copper between them. Abner pretended that he could not make out Lant's companion.

"Who that with you, Lant? Hit's Cleve, ain't it? Why, no, hit's ol' Zeke. I figgered shore you'd have your buddy Cleve along."

They slapped their thighs and laughed to hear Lant curse.

Jim Posey said, "Time you sees that pimp along with me, hit'll be his dead body."

Piety called shrilly from the kitchen door.

"Now you men quit a-talkin' that-a-way. Cleve'll be punished. Nobody don't need to go a-killin' of him. God will reward him for what he done."

Jim Posey said, "A man cain't starve to death waitin' for God to take a hand."

Abner said gravely, "That's what it comes down to. Long as Cleve's about, won't nobody have no peace nor make a livin' peaceable. He's done been talkin' 'bout goin' in with the Streeters to make trouble agin about the cattle. Tell what he know about the whippin', and sich as that. He says he'll turn up stills fast as he kin find 'em, and ary man shootin' deer and turkey out of season, he'll turn him up too."

"How long he been talkin' wild that-a-way?" Lant asked.

"Since yistiddy, when I got him to say he were the one done what were done. He broke out and said all them things."

Luke said, "If I was high sheriff, I'd have me a cellar dug under the court-house for jest sich fellers. I wouldn't see fit to put 'em in with men had done ordinary wrong."

Zeke offered mildly, "Lant and me jest come from a place'd 'bout suit him. We goed thu the ol' fort at St. Augustine. I mean, they got a dungeon there is some kind of a good place for Cleve. If you could git him in there now and roll a stone agin the door and leave him set there and think over what he done."

"He'd die," Lant said.

Jim said, "Well—" and they laughed.

Lant said, "That dungeon's a hell of a place. I felt faintified, thinkin' of all them people had died there. If I was to be shut up in there, I'd dig 'til I died."

"You'd die," Zeke assured him, "never fear it."

"Well, I'd have the satisfaction o' diggin'."

"You know," Zeke went on, "people must of purely dreaded that place in them days. You'd of thought they'd of kept out of devilment."

"Some of 'em hadn't done nothin'," Lant reminded him. "Like the Injun Osceola, where they showed he tried to git out and couldn't make it."

Zeke nodded. "He grieved hisself to death."

Lant said, "He jest couldn't make out without his freedom."

Piety called the men to dinner. They washed at the basin in the kitchen window and sat down in a comfortable hunger. They talked about the Indians and their dug-out canoes. They had all seen the canoe raised from the St. John's river.

Luke said, "I'll bet a bunch o' them fellers layin' on their oars could send them things along."

They agreed that white men had treated the Indians shabbily.

"Of course," Abner said judicially, "they was savage-like in a way o' speakin'."

They ate heartily and returned to the breezeway while Piety

washed the dishes. They had not yet said the thing they came to say. At last Abner shuffled his feet.

"What I want to know is, who's goin' to put Cleve where he won't interfere with nobody?"

Piety shrilled from the kitchen.

"You men quit a-talkin' 'bout killin'. If it was me, now, I'd jest have his credit stopped at the store. You'd bring him to time mighty quick. I'd jest say at the store, 'Hit's his trade or ours.' "

"Nobody ain't talkin' 'bout killin', Py-tee," Abner called. "But you think up a better idee than stoppin' credit, for that's been stopped a good whiles."

"We could write him a letter," Martin Posey suggested, "and git somebody to mail it off a ways."

"What'd the letter say?"

"Oh, tellin' him to be gone by Friday-week—" he waved his hand vaguely.

"And git the gov'mint nosin' around agin," Jim grunted. "The least I got to do with ary letter, the better it suit me."

"That's your house and land where they been livin', ain't it, Ab? Tell you, we'll give you two dollars for the house—jest so we kin say it's bought legal—and move the house right from offen him."

"He'd on'y set farr to hit."

"I'd like to burn his winter wood-pile," Lant said, "jest to see how he like havin' things tore up and burnt."

"Tell you, Lant," Martin offered, "le's four-five of us line up along the river-bank and hide in the bushes and all shoot buckshot under his boat. Jest riddle the boat, like, and if so it happened to sink, and him have to swim to the land, he might study 'fore he turned up the next feller."

"I wouldn't dast shoot at that rowboat," Abner said, "for I couldn't guarantee I wouldn't aim a leetle mite high."

They laughed lazily and stretched their legs.

"I reckon we're a sorry bunch," he said in the long easy silence. "In Clay County, Cleve'd never of got home."

Jim said apologetically, "We ain't never been bothered before, Ab. We ain't used to these here pimps."

Abner rose and hitched the straps of his overalls.

"We best to git goin'. Shore were a fine dinner, Py-tee. I hopes you feels some better."

She came to the breezeway to send them off.

"I hopes Cleve don't find your new outfit, Lant," Abner continued. "And I shore would venture to say, if he jest natchelly don't never come home agin, nobody won't never find hisself in no trouble about it. Ain't I right, Jim?"

"You mighty right."

They walked through the garden at the rear.

Piety said to Lant, "Them fellers is as good as tellin' you to kill Cleve and they'll be still about it. Ab had orter be ashamed."

Lant frowned.

"Ab don't want Cleve messin' up with the Streeters and startin' up the cattle trouble agin," he said. "I be dogged if I'll do it," he burst out. "I got no idee o' killin' Cleve. He better not mess up around me no more, but if he'll mind his business and leave me mind mine, I got nary call to harm him."

The garden gate clicked.

"Hey, Uncle Ab," he called loudly. "What you mean about Cleve not comin' home agin? Where-all's he at?"

Abner raised his voice, but it was bland.

"Don't nobody know, Lant. Must o' skeert him to hear 'bout you goin' to Jacksonville. His tracks stops 'tother side o' the river, 'bout opposite Zeke's place. Folks figgers he made for the scrub. Don't nobody know is he goin' for somebody—or from somebody. He's hid out."

XXXIV

LANT CUT across Thaddeus Lantry's deserted clearing. He had remembered an old rain barrel at one corner of the house, whose hoops could be salvaged and used for new barrels at the outfit he was piece by piece assembling. He stopped short at the over-grown stoop. Cleve's tracks were thick about it.

He thought, "This where you been layin' low all week, eh?"

He went cautiously into the dilapidated shack. No one was there, but a pile of fish-bones swarming with ants lay on the old clay hearth. A pallet of fresh Spanish moss was flattened out on the floor in a corner of the room. Cockroaches scrambled for shelter when he kicked it. He left the clearing without getting the hoops. He struck through the hammock, which thinned here to a bare fringe along the river. He hesitated. It might be wise to return over his own trail and then, walking backward, to efface it with a handful of brush.

He thought angrily, "Leave him know I've found him."

He wished now that he knew exactly what Jim and Abner had meant. He had ignored Kezzy's warning to move the still. He had been sure Cleve would not go through with the business. It occurred to him that perhaps Jim and Abner were warning him as Kezzy had done. They might know more than they had told him. Yet if they considered Cleve a graver menace, surely they would have said so. He was confused and anxious. At the edge of the swamp he saw a fresh chunk chipped from out a hickory.

He thought, "He's been lookin' for timber for a axe handle. I could of told him that hickory wouldn't split."

He followed the swamp to the site of the burned still. He had salvaged the bricks and stacked them neatly to be moved to Taylor's Dread. The barrel hoops were twisted but he had beaten some back into form. At the house, his copper pieces were already cut and shaped. He had new barrel staves piled under clumps of palmettos and he set to work to assemble these inside the hoops.

He noticed that the sun was setting earlier. Soon the winter would begin, with cool bright days and hearth-fires in the evenings. The burned swamp and hammock about him began to grow dark. Ahead of him shafts of sunlight shot among the sweet gums and magnolias. Squirrels moved quickly and in silence along the limbs, hurrying to their beds. A chill air wavered from the brown creek water as the last of the sunlight left it. It was too dark to work longer. He piled staves and hoops again under the palmettos, slung his rifle across his shoulder and started up the ledge.

Suddenly he knew that something was behind him. He had

heard no sound, but a movement, impalpable as a breath, had stirred between him and the swamp. He took a quick step forward and was conscious of a similar step behind. He was chilled, as though a gust of cold wind had moved across him. He had never before been followed. He had stalked deer and tracked wild cat and panther and bear. Nothing in his life had moved like this to the rear of him, stepping when he stepped, halting when he halted. He felt his lips dry and thicken. He turned sharply in the middle of his paces.

The white face that looked at him from behind a clump of sparkleberry belonged to Cleve—and it did not belong to Cleve. The light in the hammock was green and murky. It picked out the sick grin and exposed gums above the teeth that were Cleve's. The resemblance ended. A lifted gun-barrel glinted under the face. The face was round, like an obscene moon strayed from a strange and evil universe.

All his life, he knew now, he had been afraid of something. He had drunk a fear in his mother's milk and in the buck Zeke Lantry had given him in a hollow gourd. He had sucked it from the air old man Lantry had puffed out from his dying lungs. A fear pulsed in his veins like poison. And of what was he afraid? A soundless tracking at his back and a white pasty moon above the sparkleberries— He was blind with fear. Danger was a remembered danger, remembered in his bones and in his blood. He lifted the rifle and did not know he fired.

He had once shot a rattlesnake in such numb terror. He had put his foot across a log and had held it in mid-air while he blew the snake head from the body, flexed to strike.

He heard the echo of his shot die away through the hammock and across the scrub. His sight cleared. He moved woodenly to the clump of bushes, where a wisp of smoke still hovered. The evil moon was gone and the danger was gone. The twitching body was Cleve's and the face was Cleve's, with the eyelids fluttering and the mouth gaping and blood flowing smoothly over the chin. He leaned his rifle against a tree and sat down with his back pressed to the trunk. The last of the light faded. Nothing was left of Cleve but a prone shadow near him. Someone might come, but it did not matter. He was purged of fear. In its place was sickness. He buried his face in his hands.

He thought over and over, "I never studied on killin' him."

A flock of ducks flew down the river. Overhead he heard the measured sweep of their flight. Then for a long time there was silence. The hammock was black, yet when he took his hands from his eyes, he thought the white of Cleve's face was visible. The magnolia leaves rustled and he heard the beat of great wings. The hoot-owls began to cry. He lifted his head. South moon was under. On the other side of the earth the moon rode high, and it had power to move the owls and rabbits. He closed his eyes and listened in the darkness to the rhythmic call.

He wondered if it might be so with men. Perhaps all men were moved against their will. A man ordered his life, and then an obscurity of circumstance sent him down a road that was not of his own desire or choosing. Something beyond a man's immediate choice and will reached through the earth and stirred him. He did not see how any man might escape it.

Neither river nor swamp nor hammock nor impenetrable scrub could save a man from the ultimate interference. There was no safety. There was no retreat. Forces beyond his control, beyond his sight and hearing, took him in their vast senseless hands when they were ready. The whole earth must move as the sun and moon and an obscure law directed—even the earth, planet-ridden and tormented.

A rabbit startled him with its sneezing. He sat quickly alert. He could not leave Cleve's body to be found here. No one visited the island above the landing. It merged imperceptibly into creek and swamp. It was a succession of boggy pools from which cypresses and palms grew thickly. It was covered with hollow logs. He acted swiftly.

He dragged Cleve to the rowboat at the creek landing and poled up the shallow channel to the island. He felt his way among the trees and through the muck. He groped to the spot where a great cypress log had lain hollow for years. He lit a match. The openings were clogged with cobwebs and the fine powder of decay. He crawled in backwards and edged along on his belly.

Inch by inch he dragged Cleve after him. He backed out and wiped the sweat and dust from his face. He filled the openings with muck and humus. The ants would make a fine trail through it and clean the bones. He poled down the creek and walked up the ledge to the cabin.

Piety was in bed. She called to him.

"Where you been so long? I done had me a bad spell while you was gone."

He did not answer. She heard him take out the whiskey bottle from the flour-barrel. His chair scraped in front of the hearth and she could hear him blowing the embers and putting on fresh fat-wood. The light flickered over the rafters and lit her bed across the room-high partition. His shoes dropped on the pine floor. A match scratched and the sweet rankness of his corn-cob pipe drifted through the rooms. The chair scraped again. He was pacing up and down in his bare feet. Up and down, up and down, like a panther in a cage.

"Lant?"

He did not answer.

"Lant!"

A match scratched again. He was smoking a cigarette.

"You come here now! I want to see you."

He came to the side of the bed. She sat upright, leaning on one hand, and lifted the mosquito bar. The light from the hearth-fire was bright through the opened door. She shaded her eyes.

"I wisht I could see you," she said.

His face was a red-brown blur. She could not see the torment. But a panic and a distress came to her from him as tangibly as though she touched it.

"You tell me!" she wailed. "What is it? You tell me!"

"You lay down and be still," he said. "You won't git you no sleep, rarin' so."

He went out and closed the door behind him. He sat by the fire until midnight. The woman lay on her back until the pillow was damp with tears. She made no sound. She moved the pillow to one side to dry. The rest of the night she heard him tossing in his bed. Towards morning a rain fell. It was a rain heavy enough to wash out tracks.

XXXV

Piety fought for breath. She dug her old horny toes into the foot of her bed and struggled like a bass on a set-line. Lant had gone for Kezzy. He had not seen her since she clicked the garden gate behind her and walked away across the clearing with swollen eyes. He had avoided her. He crossed the river by boat and found her watering rutabagas in her garden.

He said, "Ma's 'bout done for," and she answered, "I'll come with you."

They returned together in silence. The two children chattered like birds. Kezzy shook her head when the older one asked her questions. She dropped them both in the Lantry yard to play and went into the house ahead of Lant. He noticed that she was thin and the black eyes seemed deep-sunken. She went to the bed.

"How yuh, Aunt Py-tee? It's Kezzy speakin'."

"I'm sick, Kezzy, and dyin'."

Kezzy drew a chair to the side of the bed and reached in to take the old knotted hands.

"Tell me 'bout it. Your spells comin' frequent?"

"Mighty frequent and mighty bad. The doctor were here 'fore Lant goed for you. I heered 'em talkin'. I cain't see, but I kin hear."

"What's it like when you're takened?"

"Things gits grey and distant, Kezzy. I go off into the twilight. Into some lonesome-lookin' place."

The winter afternoon darkened early.

Kezzy said, "I'll go to the kitchen and cook a leetle hot supper. Kin you eat a mite o' somethin' tasty?"

"I couldn't."

"You want your snuff?"

"Nary thing."

Kezzy cooked supper. She and Lant and the children ate hungrily. She put the children on the couch near the hearth-fire in the front room and covered them with a quilt. Lant followed her into Piety's bedroom. The old woman was losing consciousness. She roused as they came in.

"That you, Kezzy? Kezzy! Where's Cleve?"

The woman caught her breath.

"He's gone, Aunt Py-tee."

"He been gone long?"

"Since 'way before last new moon."

"Kezzy?"

"Here I be."

"Folks think ary thing?"

"Folks thinks nary thing, Aunt Py-tee," she said quietly. "Nobody jest don't look for him back."

Piety sighed.

"Lant," she complained, "outen that light."

"They ain't no light lit."

" 'Tis, too. Hit scalds my eye-balls."

She relaxed and breathed steadily through the night. Lant and Kezzy sat unmoving on stiff chairs. A screech owl quavered and Kezzy found an old hat and turned it inside out.

"To stop that quiverin' fuss," she said.

At daylight the cat stirred from his nest on the foot of the bed. He walked across it and sniffed at the lean face with its closed eyes. He bristled and jumped from the bed and scrambled out of the room.

Kezzy said, "Oh, my God."

She covered Piety's face with the counterpane. Lant moved his chair to the window at the far side of the bed and sat with his back to the room, looking out into the scrub. A streak of saffron spread across the east. Kezzy walked around the bed and stood beside him. She put one hand on his forehead and began smoothing back his shaggy forelock. The window framed the grey slat fence, with coral honeysuckle blooming across it. The sun swung up above the scrub and the dew glistened across the red-top.

Kezzy said, "You never been lonesome, young feller. Scaperin' around in the scrub, a-huntin' and a-trappin'. You like to be mighty lonesome now."

He did not answer.

"Don't you reckon you better leave me and the young uns take up with you?"

She drew his head to her.

"You and me git married, and me to he'p you at the outfit?"

He turned and buried his face against her breast.

"I've always thought a heap o' you, Lant."

His voice was muffled.

"My God, Kezzy, how kin I?"

"What you mean?"

"I shot Cleve."

The gentle stroking was suspended a moment and then continued.

"You think I didn't know?"

The steady heart-pulse under his ear did not change its beat.

"I been grievin' for all two of you—you and Cleve. But most pertickler for you. I reckon you had it to do."

"I don't know. I cain't be shore, did he mean me harm."

"Well, it's done."

She left him and pressed her face against the cool moist window.

"Man, the scrub's a fine place to be," she said. "If things ever gits too thick, you and me jest grab us each a young un and a handful o' shells and the guns and light out acrost it. I'd dare ary man to mess up with me, yonder in the scrub."

The growing sunlight wakened the children on the couch. The man and woman went into the front room and closed the bedroom door after them.

Kezzy said, "Your Aunt Py-tee's dead. You young uns be nice and quiet."

She cooked breakfast and they left for the river.

Lant said, "I don't reckon it's right to leave the house, but I belong to go down the river to the Dread and look at my mash."

"I'll hurry," Kezzy said. "I'll git somebody to come lay her out and I'll see the preacher for the buryin' and be back by noon."

At the edge of the creek she stopped short.

"Lant," she burst out, "where-all's he at?"

The hair rose on his neck. Kezzy would go where he went. She had hunted the swamp islands with him. She would visit them again. Long storms might rot the hollow log where Cleve lay. 'Possums were scavengers. They might drag out the bones, one by one. He could not have Kezzy stumble up on anything that had been Cleve. He decided at once to come at night and drag the log with its contents to the river.

He said, "Kezzy, don't ask me sich as that. I'll give my promise you won't never see him."

She nodded, white of face.

"That's good enough."

Sweat stood out around his eyes. The log might not sink before it was seen. It might lodge up against a lower bank and fall to pieces and Cleve's bones lie suddenly white under over-hanging elder. He wondered if the rifle bullet through the chest had left its record on a bone. He would have to risk it.

He thought desperately, "The law's like to come up with me yet."

Kezzy held the children in front of her in the rowboat. He poled through the creek to the river. The woman pointed out a motionless grey form on a limb above them. She tilted the children's heads to show it.

"Lookit the ol' mammy cat-squirrel settin' so still. She's likely got leetle ol' squirrel young uns a-waitin' in the nest."

from
CROSS CREEK

Hyacinth
Drift

O NCE I LOST touch with the Creek. I had had hardships that
seemed to me more than one could bear alone. I loved the
Creek, I loved the grove, I loved the shabby farmhouse. Suddenly
they were nothing. The difficulties were greater than the com-
pensations. I talked morosely with my friend Dessie. I do not
think she understood my torment, for she is simple and direct
and completely adjusted to all living. She knew only that a friend
was in trouble.

She said, "We'll take one of those river trips we've talked about.
We'll take that eighteen-foot boat of yours with a couple of outboard motors and put in at the head of the St. John's River. We'll
go down the river for several hundred miles."

I agreed, for the Creek was torture.

Men protested.

"Two women alone? The river runs through some of the wildest
country in Florida. You'll be lost in the false channels. No one
ever goes as far as the head of the river." Then, passionately,
betraying themselves, "It will be splendid. What if you do get
lost? Don't let any one talk you out of it."

The river was a blue smear through the marsh. The marsh was
tawny. It sprawled to the four points of the compass; flat; interminable; meaningless.

I thought, "This is fantastic. I am about to deliver myself over
to a nightmare."

But life was a nightmare. The river was at least of my own
choosing.

The St. John's River flows from south to north and empties into the Atlantic near the Florida-Georgia line. Its great mouth is salt and tidal, and ocean-going vessels steam into it as far as Jacksonville. It rises in a chain of small lakes near the Florida east coast, south of Melbourne. The lakes are linked together by stretches of marsh through which, in times of high water, the indecisive course of the young river is discernible. Two years of drought had shrunken the stream and dried the marshes. The southernmost sources were overgrown with marsh grass. Water hyacinths had filled the channels. The navigable head of the St. John's proved to be near Fort Christmas, where the highway crosses miles of wet prairie and cypress swamp between Orlando and Indian River City.

There is a long high fill across the marsh, with a bridge over the slight blue twisting that is the river. We drove car and trailer down an embankment and unloaded the small boat in the backwaters. The bank was of black muck, smelling of decay. It sucked at our feet as we loaded our supplies. We took our places in the boat and drifted slowly into mid-channel.

Water hyacinths began to pass us, moving with a faint anxiety in their lifted leaves. The river was no more than a path through high grass. We swung under the bridge and the boy at the wheel of our car lifted his hand in parting and shot away. Something alive and potent gripped the flat bottom of the boat. The hyacinths moved more rapidly. The river widened to a few yards and rounded a bend, suddenly decisive. Dess started the outboard motor. I hunched myself together amidships and spread the U. S. Coast and Geodetic Survey river chart on my knees and clicked open my compass. I noticed disconsolately, "Lights, Beacons, Buoys and Dangers Corrected for Information Received to Date of Issue." There would be neither lights, beacons nor buoys for at least a hundred miles. Bridge and highway disappeared, and there was no longer any world but this incredible marsh, this unbelievable amount of sky.

Half a mile beyond the bridge a fisherman's shack leaned over the river. For sociability, we turned in by the low dock. The fisherman and his wife squatted on their haunches and gave us vague directions. We pointed to Bear Island on our chart.

He said, "You won't never see Bear Island. Where they got a channel marked on your map it's plumb full o' hyacinths. Down the river a ways you'll see a big ol' sugar-berry tree stickin' up in the marsh. That's your mark. You keep to the left. The next mark you'll get is a good ways down the river. You go left by a pertickler tall piece o' grass."

The woman said, "You just got to keep tryin' for the main channel. You'll get so you can tell."

The man said, "I ain't never been as far as you-all aim to go. From what I hear, if you oncet get through Puzzle Lake, you got right clare river."

The woman said, "You'll some kind of enjoy yourselves. The river life's the finest kind of life. You couldn't get you no better life than the river."

We pushed away from the dock.

The man said, "I'd be mighty well obliged if you'd send me a postcard when you get where you're goin'. That-a-way I won't have to keep on worryin' about you."

Dess cranked the motor and they waved after us. Dess began to whistle, shrilly and tunelessly. She is an astonishing young woman. She was born and raised in rural Florida and guns and campfires and fishing-rods and creeks are corpuscular in her blood. She lives a sophisticate's life among worldly people. At the slightest excuse she steps out of civilization, naked and relieved, as I should step out of a soiled chemise. She is ten years my junior, but she calls me, with much tenderness, pitying my incapabilities, "Young un."

"Young un," she called, "it's mighty fine to be travelling."

I was prepared for marsh. It was startling to discover that there was in sight literally nothing else. Far to the west, almost out of sight to the east, in a dark line like cloud banks was the distant swamp that edged this fluid prairie. We may have taken the wrong channel for a mile or so, for we never saw the sugar-berry tree; nothing but river grass, brittle and gold, interspersed, where the ground was highest, with butter-yellow flowers like tansy. By standing up in the boat I could see the rest of the universe. And the universe was yellow marsh, with a pitiless blue infinity over it, and we were lost at the bottom.

At five o'clock in the afternoon the river dissolved without warning into a two-mile spread of flat confusion. A mile of open water lay ahead of us, neither lake nor river nor slough. We advanced into the center. When we looked over our shoulders, the marsh had closed in over the channel by which we had come. We were in a labyrinth. The stretch of open water was merely the fluid heart of a maze. Channels extended out of it in a hundred directions—some shallow, obviously no outlets; others as broad as the stream we had left behind us, and tempting. We tried four. Each widened in a deceptive sweep. A circling of the shore-line showed there was no channel. Each time we returned to the one spot we could again identify—a point of marsh thrust into the water like a swimming moccasin.

Dess said, "That map and compass don't amount to much."

That was my fault. I was totally unable to follow the chart. I found later, too late for comfort, that my stupidity was not entirely to blame, for, after the long drought, half the channels charted no longer existed. The sun had become a prodigious red disc dropping into a distant slough. Blue herons flew over us to their night's quarters. Somewhere the river must continue neatly out of this desolation. We came back once more to the point of land. It was a foot or two out of water and a few square yards of the black muck were comparatively dry. We beached the rowboat and made camp.

There was no dry wood. We carried a bag of fat pine splinters but it occurred to me desperately that I would save them. I laid out a cold supper while Dess set up our two camp cots side by side on the open ground. As the sun slid under the marsh to the west, the full moon surged out of it to the east. The marsh was silver and the water was steel, with ridges of rippled ebony where ducks swam in the twilight. Mosquitoes sifted against us like a drift of needles. We were exhausted. We propped our mosquito bar over the cots on crossed oars, for there was no bush, no tree, from which to hang it.

We did not undress, but climbed under the blankets. Three people had had a hand in loading our cots and the wooden endpieces were missing. The canvas lay limp instead of taut, and our feet hung over one end and our heads over the other, so that we were disposed like corpses on inadequate stretchers. The crossed oars slid slowly to the muck, the mosquito bar fluttered down and mosquitoes were about us in a swarm. Dess reached under her cot for her light rifle, propped it between us, and balanced the mosquito bar accurately on the end of its barrel.

"You can get more good out of a .22 rifle than any other kind of gun," she informed me earnestly.

I lay on my back in a torment of weariness, but there was no rest. I had never lain in so naked a place, bared so flatly to the sky. The moon swung high over us and there was no sleeping for the brightness. Toward morning dewdrops collected over the netting as though the moonlight had crystallized. I fell asleep under a diamond curtain and wakened with warm full sunlight on my face. Cranes and herons were wading the shore near me and Dess was in the rowboat a few hundred yards away, casting for bass.

Marsh and water glittered iridescent in the sun. The tropical March air was fresh and wind-washed. I was suddenly excited. I made campfire with fatwood splinters and cooked bacon and toast and coffee. Their fragrance eddied across the water and I saw Dess lift her nose and put down her rod and reel. She too was excited.

"Young un," she called, "where's the channel?"

I pointed to the northeast and she nodded vehemently. It had come to both of us like a revelation that the water hyacinths were drifting faintly faster in that direction. From that instant we were never very long lost. Forever after, where the river sprawled in confusion, we might shut off the motor and study the floating hyacinths until we caught, in one direction, a swifter pulsing, as though we put our hands closer and closer to the river's heart. It was very simple. Like all simple facts, it was necessary to discover it for oneself.

We had, in a moment, the feel of the river; a wisdom for its vagaries. When the current took us away that morning, we gave ourselves over to it. There was a tremendous exhilaration, an abandoning of fear. The new channel was the correct one, as we knew it should be. The river integrated itself again. The flat golden banks closed in on both sides of us, securing a snug safety. The strangeness of flowing water was gone, for it was all there was of living.

In midmorning, solid land made its way here and there toward us, and then in time withdrew. For a mile we had a low rolling hill for company, with traces of ancient habitation at its peak: a few yards of rotting fence, a crepe myrtle, an orange tree.

We passed a lone fisherman hauling his seine. His legs were planted cranelike in the water. His long arms looped up folds of the gray net with the rhythm of a man swinging a sickle. We told him our origin and our destination. Because we were now a part of the river he offered us a fish. His catch was meager and we refused it. We passed cattle, wild on the marsh. They loomed startlingly above us, their splotched black and brown and red and white luminous against the blue sky, like cattle in Bonheur pictures hung high above the eye-level.

The river dissolved into shallow pools and was interspersed with small islands, palm-crowded and lonely. It was good to see trees, lifting the eyes from so many miles of flatness. The pools gathered themselves together and there was under us again a river, confined between obvious banks. Sometimes the low-lying land was dry for a great distance, specked with soapberry bushes, and the wild cattle cropped a short grass that grew there.

We had Puzzle Lake and then Lake Harney, we knew, somewhere ahead of us. We came out from a canal-like stretch of river into a body of open water. Dess and I stiffened. She shut off the motor.

Far away across the marsh there was a long white rolling as though all the sheep in the world were being driven through prehistoric dust clouds. The mad thought came to me that we had embarked on the wrong river and had suddenly reached the ocean, that the vast billowing in the distance was surf. But something about the thing was familiar. That distant line was a fill, a forty-foot sand embankment across the marsh between the St. John's

River and the east coast town of Mimms, and I had driven its one-rut grade two weeks before. The marsh had been even more desolate from the height of that untravelled, unfinished roadway. The fill ended, I remembered, in a forty-foot drop to a decrepit ferry that crossed the river. The billowing we now saw was loose white sand moving along the embankment ahead of a high wind. I ran my finger along the chart. There was no ferry mapped for the far side of Puzzle Lake. A ferry was indicated, however, on the far side of Lake Harney.

I said, "Dess, we've come through Puzzle Lake and didn't know it. We've reached Lake Harney."

She did not question my surety. She spun the motor.

"All right, young un. Which way across?"

I compared chart and compass. I pointed. She headed the boat as I directed. I split nautical points to keep our position exactly. I took her across water so shoal we had to pole through it; under overhanging banks and through dense stiff sedge, when often a plainly better channel swung a few feet away in another direction. The extreme low water, I called, had evidently dried Lake Harney to this confused alternating of open lake and maze. Dess whistled dubiously but asked no questions. We struck deep water at last and were at the ferry I had indeed remembered. The old ferry-man peered from his hut and came down to meet us, shading his eyes. He seemed to find us very strange indeed. Where had we come from?

"We put in yesterday at Fort Christmas," I answered him, "and I'm glad to say we've just finished navigating Lake Harney."

He stared in earnest.

"Lady," he said, "you haven't even reached Lake Harney. You've just come through Puzzle Lake."

The ferry here simply was not charted, and the episode proves anything one may wish it to prove. I felt contentedly that it proved a harmony with the river so complete that not even the mistaking of whole lakes could lose us. Others of more childish faith were sure it proved the goodness of God in looking after imbeciles. I know only that we were congratulated by fishermen the entire length of the river on navigating Puzzle Lake successfully.

"I brought our boat through Puzzle Lake," I told them with simple dignity, "by the sternest use of chart and compass."

And it was only in Dess' more evil moments that she added, "—in the firm belief that she was crossing Lake Harney."

Lake Harney itself was four miles long, unmistakably broad and open. We crossed it in late afternoon with the westerly sun on our left cheeks and a pleasant March wind ruffling the blue water. Passing out of the lake we brought roe shad, fresh and glistening from the seine. The current quickened. The hyacinths plunged forward. The character of the river changed the instant the lake was left behind. It was deep and swift, the color of fine clear coffee that is poured with the sun against it. It was mature. All its young torture was forgotten, and its wanderings in the tawny marsh. The banks had changed. They were high. Tall palms crowded great live oaks and small trees grew humbly in their shadows. Toward sunset we swung under the western bank at one of those spots a traveller recognizes instinctively as, for the moment, home.

If I could have, to hold forever, one brief place and time of beauty, I think I might choose the night on that high lonely bank above the St. John's River. We found there a deserted cabin, gray and smooth as only cypress weathers. There was no door for its doorway, no panes or shutters for its windows, but the roof was whole, with lichens thick across the shingles. Dess built me a fire of red cedar. She sat on the sagging steps and whittled end-pieces for our cots, and I broiled shad and shad roe over fragrant coals, and French-fried potatoes, and found I had the ingredients for Tartar sauce.

Dess nailed a board between low rafters in the cabin from which to hang the mosquito bar over our cots, and said, "Young un, Christopher Columbus had nothing on us. He had a whole ocean to fool around in, and a what-do-you-call-it:—a continent, to come out on. Turn that boy loose in the St. John's marsh, and he'd have been lost as a hound puppy."

We had hot baths out of a bucket that night, and sat on the cabin steps in pajamas while the fire died down. Suddenly the soft night turned silver. The moon was rising. We lay on our cots a long time wakeful because of beauty. The moon shone through the doorway and windows and the light was patterned with the shadows of Spanish moss waving from the live oaks. There was a deserted grove somewhere behind the cabin, and the incredible sweetness of orange bloom drifted across us.

A mocking-bird sang from a palm tree at sunrise. We found by daylight that the cabin sat among guava trees higher than the roof. The yard was pink and white with periwinkles. Dess shot a wild duck on the wing with the .22 and I roasted it in the Dutch oven for breakfast. We lay all morning on the bank in the strong sunlight, watching the mullet jumping in the river. At noon we went reluctantly to the water's edge to load the boat and move on. The boat was half filled with water and was resting with an air of permanence on the river bottom.

My first thought was of pure delight that it was no longer necessary to leave this place. But Dess was already stepping out of her sailor trousers. I too removed superfluous clothing. We bailed the boat and found two streams of water gushing in steadily under bow and stern seats. We managed to drag the boat on shore and turn it upside down. We found that the caulking had worked loose out of two seams. Dess donated a shirt, and for two hours with pocket knives we stuffed strips of cloth into treacherous cracks. When we put the boat in the river again, the caulking held.

I begged to stay another night, but Dess was restless. We pushed on for the few hours left of daylight. The shore line narrowed to thin strips of sand with tall twisted palms along them. The clear brown river was glassy in the windless evening. The palms were mirrored along both banks, so that when white ibises flew over in a rosy sunset, the river might have been the Nile.

We camped that night in comparative comfort under an upturned tree root. The spot was not tempting from the water, but once we were snugged down, it proved cavelike and cozy. A moccasin slithered from under my feet at the edge of camp and went harmlessly about his business. Dess cut down a young palmetto and we had swamp cabbage for dinner. I cooked it with a piece of white bacon and baked corn sticks in the Dutch oven to go with it.

In the morning we watched the hyacinth drift closely to be sure of taking the cut to Prairie Landing instead of wandering into Lake Jessup. A highway crossed the river here and folk waved down to us. In the cut a woman was running a catfish line. She was gaunt and sun-tanned, ragged and dirty. She pulled in the line, hand over hand, with a quick, desperate accuracy. She lifted a shaggy head when we called "Howdy" and said "Hey," and bent again to her line with a terrifying absorption. Something about her shamed all soft, clean women.

We cut across the south end of Lake Monroe and found that it was Sunday in the city of Sanford. We had reached the outpost of large-vessel traffic on the St. John's, and we put-putted under the bow of an incoming freight steamer. We had meant to bathe and put on clean shirts and slacks that morning, but there had been no landing place among the marshes. Dess strapped around her waist the leather belt that held her bowie knife at one hip and her revolver at the other, and felt better prepared for Sanford than if we had been clean. She landed us neatly at the city dock, in the lee of an immaculate pleasure yacht from Long Island Sound. The owner, trim in double-breasted blue, came to the rail and looked down at us. We had also intended to do a better job of stowing. The bow end of our boat was piled untidily with our supplies, our folded cots, our extra outboard motor and our gasoline tins. Dess stood up in the stern and stretched and shifted her armored belt.

She called up to the yacht owner, "Safe to come into this town?"

"That depends on what you are coming for," he said, and smiled.

"Not a thing but gasoline. Where's the nearest place a fellow can fuel up?"

"All the filling stations near the docks are closed this morning. But I'm having my yacht refuelled, and a station is opening for me. How much do you need?"

Dess checked our tins with her eye.

"Five gallons is about right."

He smiled again.

"I'm sending my car to the station. If you will bring your tins up, I'll be very happy to have my man take you along and bring you back."

"Thanks, fellow," Dess said. "You're a white man."

There was a sound inside the yacht. There simmered up the companionway a woman, magnificent in pink spectator sports costume. The crew jumped almost to attention and escorted her down the yacht's gangplank.

The woman snapped over her shoulders, "I must have the car at once. I cannot be late to church for this nonsense."

Our white man turned rosy and made a comradely gesture to us.

He leaned over and whispered, "The car will be back in just a moment. If you don't mind waiting—. Please wait."

"O.K., fellow," Dess said.

The pink spectator sports swept into a limousine. In a few minutes the car had returned. We were driven in style to a filling station and our tins filled with gasoline. We bought the New York Sunday papers. The yacht crew brought the tins down to us and helped us re-stow our duffle. Dess outlined our trip briefly to the owner. She cranked up and we were off again.

"Good luck!" called the yacht owner. "The very best of good luck!"

He waved after us as far as we could see him, as though reluctant to break a mystic thread. His face was wistful.

"The poor b—," Dess said pityingly and indignantly. "I'll bet he'd give his silk shirt to go down the river with us instead of with Pink Petticoats."

We used the gasoline and forgot to read the papers.

Out of Lake Monroe we began to see fishermen pulling seines every few miles along the river. Here and there was a camp. Once a palmetto thatching made a tip-tilted shelter and a startlingly pretty girl in overalls looked out with a placid face. We passed an old fisherman and a little girl in a boat. The child was rowing. We encountered a tall lumber steamer in mid-stream. The book of

Pilot Rules on my lap provided that the boat in our position should swing to starboard, passing to port, and should give two short distinct blasts on the boat's whistle to signify its intention. Two lusty blasts on my dog whistle brought no answering blow from the steamer, but the cook, paring potatoes in the open stern, waved to us as we angled to cross their wake.

We had "right clare river" now, the river life was indeed the finest of lives, and there was no hurry left in the world. We put up a golden-brown deep creek and fished all afternoon. A white egret fished companionably with us a few yards away, and water turkeys flapped their wings lazily from high cypresses. A water moccasin arched his six feet of magnificent mottled hide between a spider lily and a swamp laurel. The laurel was in full bloom and the sunny creek was a wedge of fragrance. We found a white sand bar and had a swim in water clear as amber.

Camp that night was on a pine bluff, very high and dry and decent after the tree root and the moccasin. Storm threatened for the first time and we stretched a tarpaulin between slash pines to make a shelter. We were on the east bank. The moon and sun rose behind us. In the morning we found that small animals had dug holes all about us while we slept.

We pushed the motor that day. The river was deep and narrow. The banks were dense swamp, black with undergrowth. A landing would have been, for the most, impossible. We ate a cold lunch as we travelled. Beyond Deland Landing we called at a houseboat tethered to the bank. Its owner had been captain of the old Clyde River Line, and he received our request for advice on crossing Lake George with the old-school graciousness of large craft meeting small. He took my compass well forward of the houseboat, away from its metal stanchions, to chart our course across the fourteen-mile lake the more precisely. I made the mental note that perhaps I had better move the cast iron Dutch oven from under my seat. He gave us a set of distance cards and a choice of courses. The more sporting course was the main channel used by large steamers. In a boat as small as ours we should be out of sight of land for nearly an hour. The west channel never entirely lost the land, but if it came on to blow, we would do best by

taking neither, and hugging the west shore. He bowed us courteously on our way.

We planned to camp as close as possible that night to the
Volusia bar. We wanted to cross Lake George in the early morning before the wind rose. Beyond the village of Astor the scrub
reared high against the west. Cypress swamp bordered the river.
There was scarcely a patch of ground large enough to step out
on. We pushed on to a cluster of fishing huts at the junction
of lake and river. Hyacinths moved here in vast green flexible
sheets. The huts were on stakes over the river and were not
inviting.

Only one stood on enough ground to offer camping facilities.
We poled through the hyacinths and called from the rickety small
dock. A sullen-faced woman spoke curtly from the doorway. We
could see the interior of the shack. There were pallets on the
floor; a table; a chair or two. A dirty child peered from her skirts.
We were not wanted here, it was plain, but she was a squatter,
with no right to refuse us. Dess and I debated the matter in low
voices. The woman, the place, seemed to me preferable to the
dark swamp to which we must return. But the wind was freshen-
ing from the west. Even now, hyacinths were piling in behind us.

Dess said, "I'd rather sleep with a moccasin over each shoulder
than get caught in a hyacinth block."

We swung about to turn back up the river. As we pushed
away, the child dropped to the doorsill and began to pat his hands
together. He chanted with shrill delight, "They're going away!
They're going away!" I wondered what life had done to this
woman and this child, that, among a friendly fisher-folk, they
should know such fear and hate of strangers.

When the sun dropped behind the scrub, swamp and river
were in darkness. At twilight we had retraced several miles. When
we landed at the only promising opening, we found a comfortable
square of high ground. As we were making camp three fishermen
hailed us excitedly. Were we the women who had put in at Fort
Christmas nearly a week before? If so, they must know. Word
had been sent down the river from other fishermen to watch for
us and to report our safety. The three were camped across the river

from us. They had a trail cut into the swamp to a spot of sound dry earth. Their campfire flickered sociably all night.

The course for the main channel was, simply, north by east. But there was fog at daylight, and when the fog lifted a little the wind came freshly from its week-long westerly quarter. Boats twice our size had been in trouble on Lake George. Its squalls were notably dangerous. It seemed needlessly heroic to deny ourselves the comfort of the sight of land. We had no intention of hugging the safe shore, so we compromised on the west channel. We left the great channel markers behind and a gust of wind twisted our stern. There was a half hour when the haze threatened to obscure all visible shore lines. Then Drayton's Island lifted ahead.

Midway, the wind was blowing the whitecaps off the waves, but it was helpfully behind us. With both arms braced against the steering handle of the motor, Dess kept the boat headed when water that rolled like surf lifted our stern. The propeller churned high out of the water. When it dropped again the boat lunged and turned.

I called, "She's slueing badly!"

Dess shouted, "Young un, if you had this wind under your stern, you'd slue, too!"

The distant shore seemed stationary. We passed the north point of Drayton's Island, where the main channel joined the west, with the lake boiling after us. At the first sheltered dock we stopped to rest and an old Negro gave us fresh drinking water. We had been some two and a half hours in crossing the lake.

The river resumed its broad quiet way as though it had left no tumult behind it. It had the dignity of age, was not now in that dark hurry to reach the sea. At Welaka one afternoon we left the hyacinths swirling leisurely and turned up our home river, the Ocklawaha. I thought in a panic, I shall never be happy on land again. I was afraid once more of all the painful circumstances of living.

But when the dry ground was under us, the world no longer fluid, I found a forgotten loveliness in all the things that have nothing to do with men. Beauty is pervasive, and fills, like perfume, more than the object that contains it. Because I had known intimately a river, the earth pulsed under me. The Creek was home. Oleanders were sweet past bearing, and my own shabby fields, weed-tangled, were newly dear. I knew, for a moment, that the only nightmare is the masochistic human mind.

Antses
in Tim's Breakfast

I HAVE USED a factual background for most of my tales, and of actual people a blend of the true and the imagined. I myself cannot quite tell where the one ends and the other begins. But I do remember first a place and then a woman, that stabbed me to the core, so that I shall never get over the wound of them.

The place was near the village on the Creek road, and I thought when I saw it that it was a place where children had been playing. A space under a great spreading live oak had been lived in. The sand was trodden smooth and there were a decrepit iron stove and a clothes line, on which a bit of tattered cloth still hung. There were boxes and a rough table, as though little girls had been playing house. Only opened tin cans and a rusty pot, I think, made me inquire about it, for children were not likely to carry a game so far. I was told that a man and woman, very young, had lived there for a part of one summer, coming from none knew where, and going away again with sacks over their shoulders when the autumn frosts came in.

What manner of man and woman could this be, making a home under an oak tree like some pair of woods animals? Were they savage outlaws? People who might more profitably be in jail? I had no way of knowing. The Florida back country was new and beautiful but of the people I knew nothing. The wild home at the edge of the woods haunted me. I made pictures to myself of the man and woman, very young, who had come and gone. Somehow I knew that they would be not fierce, but gentle. I took up my own life at the Creek.

The answer to my wonderings was on my own grove and for a long time I did not know that it was there. A tenant house stood a few hundred yards from my farmhouse. It was placed beautifully under a vast magnolia tree and was all gray age and leaning walls. It was a tall two stories and had perhaps been the original home on the grove. It was windowless and seemed on the point of collapsing within itself. The occupants were Tim and his wife and their baby. I saw only Tim, red-haired and on the defensive and uninterested in his work. His job with the previous owner of the grove had been his first of the kind, he said. His weekly wage was low but I did not question it. He had come with the place. His passion was for trapping and the hides of raccoons and skunks and opossums and an occasional otter or wild-cat hung drying on the walls of his house. He trapped along the lake edge back of the grove, and I would see him coming in of an early morning with a dead creature or two in his hands. The well at the barn, in front of the tenant house, was sulphurous and fit only for the stock, and Tim came to my pump by my back door for water for his family use. I saw his wife only from a distance and made no inquiries about her.

Callousness, I think, is often ignorance, rather than cruelty, and it was so in my brief relation with Tim and his wife. My excuse is that at the time I myself had so much hard physical work to do and was so confused with the new way of living that I did not understand that life might be much more difficult for others. The woman came striding to my back door one day. She had her baby slung over one hip, like a bundle. She walked with the tread of an Indian, graceful and direct. She was lean and small. As she came close I saw that she had tawny skin and soft honey-colored hair, drawn back smoothly over her ears and knotted at her neck. She held a card in her hand and she thrust it at me.

"Please to read hit," she said.

I took the card, addressed to Tim, and turned it over. It was only an advertisement from a wholesale fur house, quoting current prices on such pelts as Tim trapped for. I must have seemed very stupid to her, for I did not know what she wanted. At last

I understood that she could not read, that the card had come in the morning's rural mail while Tim was at work at the far side of the grove. Mail, all reading matter, was cryptic and important and it was necessary to know whether she should call Tim from his work because of the card. I read it aloud and she listened gravely. She took it from me and turned to walk away.

"I thank you," she said.

Her voice was like the note of a thrush, very soft and sweet.

I called after her, seeing her suddenly as a woman, "Tell me, how are you getting on?"

She looked at me with direct gray eyes.

"Nothin' extry. They ain't no screens to the house and the skeeters like to eat us alive. And I cain't keep the antses outen Tim's breakfast."

Her statement was almost unintelligible. I myself was troubled by the mosquitoes, for they came up through holes in the kitchen floor and had my legs swollen to twice their size. But my bedrooms were tight and comfortable, and when sleep is possible, one can stand much in the daytime. I had actually not noticed that the tenant house was wide open to the intrusion not only of insects, but of wind and weather. The matter of ants in the breakfast was beyond me. It was only as I came to know the backwoods cooking customs that I knew that enough food was cooked once or at the most twice a day, to last for the three meals. The people were up long before daylight and the remnants of the previous evening's biscuits and greens and fat bacon were set aside for the early breakfast, eaten by lamplight. Where a house was rotting to the ground, ants and roaches inhabited the very wood of floors and walls and swarmed over the family's edibles. The situation of Tim's wife puzzled but still did not concern me. I did not yet understand that in this way of life one is obliged to share, back and forth, and that as long as I had money for screens and a new floor, I was morally obligated to put out a portion of it to give some comfort to those who worked for me. I took others' discomfort for granted and the only palliation of my social sin is that I took my own so, too.

I made another profound mistake in my short time with these

two. I asked Tim one day if his wife would do my washing for me. He looked at me, and looked away angrily and spat.

"A white woman don't ask another white woman to do her washin' for her, nor to carry her slops," he said. " 'Course, in time o' sickness or trouble or sich as that a woman does ary thing she can for another and they's no talk o' pay."

There was a fierce pride here, then, and above all, services that would be gladly given but could not be bought. I began to understand and then Tim announced they were leaving.

I asked, "Are you going to another job?"

"No'm. I ain't made for this kind o' work. I don't do it to suit and it don't suit me."

"Where will you go and what will you do?"

"Same as we done before. I only takened this on account o' the baby comin'. A woman's got to have a roof over her then. Us'll git along better thouten no house, pertickler jest a piece of a house like this un here. In the woods, you kin make a smudge to keep off the skeeters. Us'll make out."

They moved on, the proud angry man and the small tawny lovely woman and the baby. But they put a mark on me. The woman came to me in my dreams and tormented me. As I came to know her kind, in the scrub, the hammock and the piney-woods, I knew that it was a woman much like her who had made a home under the live oak. The only way I could shake free of her was to write of her, and she was Florry in *Jacob's Ladder*. She still clung to me and she was Allie in *Golden Apples*. Now I know that she will haunt me as long as I live, and all the writing in the world will not put away the memory of her face and the sound of her voice.

'Geechee

THE BLACK GIRL came on foot the four miles from the village. She was barefooted. She strode up the path to the back door, thick-legged, her big toes splayed in the sand. She stopped short and glared at me, as though she meant to strike me. She wore one garment, too short for her erect height. It was of muslin flour sacking, so tattered that the full length of one sweating thigh showed through its multiple rents. She was the dusty black of teakwood. Two short tufts of hair were braided over her temples. They were stiff, a trifle curved, like horns.

She said fiercely, "I hear tell you want a girl. You take me."

She seemed impossible. She looked capable of murder. It would be like having a black leopard loose in the house.

I said, "I wanted a young girl."

"I be's young."

"No. One young enough to teach my ways."

"If I don't do to suit you, you can cut my throat."

It occurred to me that displeasure might work two ways. It seemed necessary to placate her rather than, simply, to reject her.

I said, "A girl your age wouldn't be satisfied four miles from town."

She stepped closer as in menace.

"Town ain't nothin' to me. You don't know. I don't do no courtin'. I don't want no man around me. You jes' don't know."

I said helplessly, "I'm sure you wouldn't suit me."

"Time to say, time you've done tried me. All you got to do is try me."

Futility possessed me.

292

I said, "I can't pay very high wages."

"Any wages is better than nothin'. I got to get work. I got a use for my pay."

It was her eyes, I decided, that were frightening me. One was blind and white, fixing me with an opaque, unseeing purpose. I made a gesture of despair.

"Right now, this porch floor ain't scrubbed," she said. "You got to have things clean. I be here soon in the mornin'. I got to fotch my things."

She turned on her bare heels to go.

I called after her, "But I don't know anything about you. What's your name? Where do you come from?"

"Name be's Beatrice. I be's 'Geechee. Folks jes' calls me 'Geechee."

She was gone, striding down the path toward some black and Amazonian army that awaited her coming that the battle might begin. I felt dazed and foolish, as though I had been hypnotized by a grotesque idol. She was the ugliest Negress I had ever seen.

The Ogeechee River is tidal and its salt tongue licks far into Georgia. The Negroes of the region, cotton Negroes, sugar Negroes, rice or tobacco Negroes, the sons and daughters of slaves, are of a special African tribe and have kept their identity. They are very black; strong, with a long stride; their bodies straight as palm trunks; violent, often, and as violently loyal. Another black will say, "He's 'Geechee. I'se skeert of him," and a Georgia plantation owner will say, "There's no better Negro in the world if you get a good one."

'Geechee came the next day at daylight and had good strong coffee and crisp small biscuits ready when I awakened. Her "things" were a comb, not the straightening comb of sophistication, but the ordinary kind, toothless from struggles with her knotted wool—and a bundle of letters. That was literally all. I had never seen material possessions at a more irreducible minimum. Even the letters, I thought, were a fancy and could have been dispensed with. I did not know my 'Geechee. She had nothing to wear but the torn shift in which she had appeared, challenging me to accept her. I dressed her. She was bigger-boned than I, but leaner. In my clothes she looked like a battered black rag doll. As the weeks passed I bought her a cautious cheap uniform or two. Even in their white formality she seemed always about to burst into a belligerent dance, tearing her garments from her, prancing naked in a savage triumph. The effect came from her lioness stride, from her unkempt hair which shot in black electric spirals from her skull, and from the white eye with its hypnotic probing. She had been blind in it, she said, since the big fight.

"I dis-remember did I get the lick before they put me in the jailhouse or en-durin' the time they was puttin' me in the jailhouse."

I could have beaten her raw those first months and it would not have mattered. She cleaned my house. She began with the painted wooden ceilings, the hand-hewn rafters where generations of dirt-daubers had built their mud homes. She continued down the painted walls, where roaches had trailed and long-vanished children had drawn pictures. She included the furniture in her sweep, so that polished mahogany emerged pale and unshining. She washed rugs that would go in the washpot. Those that would not, she beat until they hung limp and dustless over the clothesline. She thrashed mattresses in the sunlight. Their tufting covered the yard like full-blown thistles. She ended with the floors. She used six cans of potash, and where there had been soot and grease and streaked varnish and the ochre-colored paint dear to all the South, there were now soft pine boards, luminous with age. There was a hole in the middle of the kitchen where she had followed a stain quite through the flooring.

I shall never have a greater devotion than I had from this woman. She was, as I had thought, not young. Within a week, all fear of her was gone and in its place came the warmth of being watched over and served and cared for. Then she began to drop unintelligible hints. There was something back of the service, something back of the fierce woman. I remembered my first sensing of a fixed purpose.

She said, "I'm doin' to suit you?" and I said, "Yes," and she said, "You trust me, enty?" and I said, "Yes."

One day when she had been with me for some months, making life a good smooth thing, she said, "I got a thing to tell you. I got to have help."

It seemed to me then that I had always known that we were building up to this; that it was not she who was serving me, but I who was destined to serve her.

I said, "What is it?"

She brought a mass of crumpled paper from her breast.

"These is from my man," she said. "Read them."

"My sweet Beatrice," they read, "you got to get me out. I can't stand it. You got to get me out."

One after another, they sang the same refrain. They were written from the state prison.

"You know people," she said. "You can git him out. I got to git him out. You can do it."

I felt like a pawn in the hands of dark forces. Her man was named Leroy. He was serving a twenty-year sentence for manslaughter.

"He didn't do a thing," she said. "This other nigger was layin' for him. He went at Leroy and he bopped him one and Leroy be's strong and he made a pass at him and it done killed this nigger. And you got to git him out."

The 'Geechee had become a part of me. I had little of comfort and that little stemmed from her.

I said, "I'll do what I can," and did not mean to. I needed her more than did Leroy.

I wrote a bland letter to the superintendent of the prison. It was answered as blandly, for I think he understood me. Time passed. Then one day I got the mail from the rural mail-box instead of sending 'Geechee for it, and in the mail was a letter addressed to her from a lawyer. I questioned her.

She said, "You ain't done nothin' for Leroy, when you could. A lawyer that visits at the prison done tol' him he could git him out for two hundred dollars. I wrote him I'd git it, did he give me time."

No shyster lawyer could liberate a killer. I could not endure to have her slave and save and throw away her money on one such. And surely, if this fierce good woman believed in Leroy, he must be entitled to consideration. I felt an unreasonable trust in her judgment and her loyalty.

I said, "Don't pay this lawyer another dollar. I'll see what we can do."

I drove to Raiford and interviewed the superintendent. Leroy had been a model prisoner. The superintendent was an idealist.

"If you can give Leroy a job," he said, "I see no reason why he shouldn't return to normal living. Lack of work when a man first gets out is the usual stumbling-block."

I had made good friends; a state senator, the president of a university. I asked them to wire the Pardon Board, asking for the black man's parole to me. I had a hearing at the state capitol and Leroy was paroled in my care. I drove back to the grove to gather up 'Geechee to go to the prison to collect the man for whom she had starved and toiled and gone ragged.

Leroy was not at the prison when we reached there. He had headed on his release, an hour before, not for the black woman who had done so much for him, but direct to Jacksonville for a round of carousing. He showed up at the grove four days later. He was a slim, sullen, light-brown man with shifty eyes. 'Geechee walked on air. I would pay him, I told him, the customary rural wages, his house and fuel free, and he might have the use of the farm truck once or twice a week. The grove work was not too hard and I would show him all that must be done. I had bought clothes for him, and I gave them a real wedding, with good food afterward.

For a week he languished comfortably under his wife's care. He made no effort to learn the grove work but I did not hurry him. Four years in jail would surely do something to a man's initiative. He could not plunge at once into living. There must be a period of adjustment, as for one who long blind should come with new sight into the sunlight. I made my excuses for him and 'Geechee lost her air of ecstasy. She worked harder than ever, for now she had Leroy's comfort to look after. My own work was never slighted.

At the end of the second week he came to the back door for

his Saturday wages. I hold no brief for Southern wages, yet many
Negroes supported in a rudimentary comfort large families on
Leroy's pay, and must pay rent and buy fuel to boot, without the
extra wages that 'Geechee brought in. Instead of standing at the
door to receive his money, the man pulled it open and brushed
past me and seated himself insolently on the bench. He crossed
his legs and threw back his head, narrowing his eyes at me. In a
loud voice he began to recite his grievances. He could not live
on his pay. He wanted better clothes than those I had bought
him. Nobody could be expected to live out here in the woods. It
was too far from town. A man had to have his own automobile.
He stopped shouting and began to mutter. There was more than
a hint of threat in the low growling voice. I who had freed him
was an object of hate. My friend Dessie was in the house. She
was so certain that the man was about to spring at me that she
slipped to her car for her revolver.

He said, "I jus' as soon be in jail as out here in the woods."

I saw 'Geechee slip into the kitchen with tears raining down
her black cheeks. I was sick at heart. I ordered him back to the
tenant house. I locked my house, which stands for weeks in my
absence without even the latching of a screen, and drove to town
to put in a long distance call to the prison superintendent. There
was a silence at the end of the wire.

At last, "The prison is crammed full. We have absolutely no
room for him. Send him away at once. You are running a great
personal risk. If he can keep out of serious trouble, we'll let him
go his way. If he gets into trouble, he'll automatically be picked
up again." He sighed. "If I live long enough, I'll learn to recognize the true criminal nature. This man has it."

It was dusk when I reached the grove. 'Geechee, I knew, with
her fierce loyalty, would go with him. I could not send her off in
the night. I slept uneasily that night, my revolver under my pillow.
In the morning she brought my coffee. Her face was drawn and
inscrutable.

I said, "Leroy must leave as soon as you've had breakfast. I
know you'll want to go with him. I shall be very sorry to be
without you. I've become attached to you, 'Geechee."

She said, "I ain't goin' with him. I don't mind him doin' me wrong. He ain't never done anything but wrong to me. But nobody ain't never done for him what you done. He ain't worth killin', the way he talked to you. I wanted to die, listenin' to him."

The world seemed suddenly a brighter place. Then I knew that no new treachery would alter her long loyalty to the man she had known always was worthless.

I said, "It will be better for you to go with him. Then if you still prefer to be with me, you can come back. I'll wait a week or two to get another girl."

She said, "You cain't get along without me. I'se seed. You needs me. I'll go with him. I'll make sure he goes off far enough. I be back Tuesday mornin' on the nine o'clock train."

Sunday and Monday were long. I could not concentrate on my work. I did the household chores absently. I milked the cow and fed the chickens. The grove seemed very silent with no human being about, no man to care for it, no kind black hands serving me in the house. I was so sure that 'Geechee's loyalty to her man would not waver that I very nearly did not go to the village on Tuesday. I made an excuse to myself to go to the village store at train time. The local puffed to a stop at the dingy station and 'Geechee was there. We lonely humans need very little of devotion for contentment. For the moment, this black one-eyed savage woman was all I needed. I touched her calloused dark hand.

She said, "Us'll make out all right. Us'll do better alone."

We drove home to the grove and Mandy the pointer dog leaped up to lick her face in welcome. She celebrated by putting on one of the uniforms in which she was patently uncomfortable and set about putting the house in proper order. The day was fine and sunny, and she drove the cow in at evening and we managed the milking together. After supper she went alone to the tenant house of which she had hoped to make a home. We got along very well on our own. She was sad and quiet. Leroy was living in Jacksonville with another woman and quarrelling with all around him. She had done her best and now a thing was ended and a book was closed. I urged her to let me drop her off in Citra where

the Negroes are gay and light-hearted of a Saturday night. I told
her to invite them out to her house.

"Surely you can get a new beau," I said.

She said gravely, "You'd ought to know, jus' anybody won't do."

She was as wild-looking as some fresh-caught African slave, but
she had given her big heart for life.

It made her happy for me to have parties. She seemed to think
that I needed the gayety I urged on her. When the house was full
for a buffet supper, she put on her best apron and tied a handkerchief over her tufted head and dashed in and out among the
guests, crying the flavor of our foods. When it was time to pass
the dessert, she raced through the house with a loaded tray, shouting at the top of her voice, "Sherbet comin' up! Sherbet comin'
up!" Her delight was infectious, and friends complain mournfully,
now she is gone, that they never had better times at the Creek
than when 'Geechee rushed among them, pressing them to drink
deep and eat hearty. Once my friend Norton slipped away to my
room to steal a nap and 'Geechee discovered him and routed him
out. He grumbled that he was sleepy and the room was quiet and
her mistress would not mind.

"I minds," she said severely. "You git right out o' here."

She carried her protective instinct to embarrassing lengths. One
Saturday night we had the house full after a football game. Half
a dozen decided to spend the night. In the morning there were
not enough eggs for making the unexpected breakfast and I sent
her down the road to Old Boss to see if he could spare a dozen.
She reported on their conversation, proud of the way she had
protected me.

"Well, 'Geechee," Old Boss said to her, "your Missus had quite
a party last night."

"I looked him right in the eye," she said, "and I says to him,
'No, sir, that wasn't no party. That was jus' a few of her kin-
folks dropped in to visit her, and she was so proud to see 'em.'"

My life was circumspect, but if I had lived in scarlet sin, 'Geechee would have covered my tracks. A man came from the citrus
packing house on business. I was ill in bed and she showed him in

to my bedroom without consulting me. I was a trifle embarrassed and when he came again the next day to report on the matter, I said to her, "When I'm in bed and a man comes to see me, I'd a little rather you stood near the doorway."

She showed him in and disappeared. After he had gone and I questioned her, I found that, loyal soul, all the while he was there she had stood sentinel at the front door—watching the highway.

It was after Leroy had gone that I began to realize the source of her occasional high spirits. There were times when she sang so infectiously from the kitchen or over the washtubs that I would stop my work and follow the old spiritual with her. That anomaly, "Prohibition," was still in force, and our liquor was good moonshine from the Florida scrub. We bought it almost openly, bringing it home in five-gallon glass demijohns and siphoning it off into charred oak kegs to ripen. The local sheriff was in cahoots with the moonshiners, arresting only those who did not pay his weekly tribute. A plutocrat was one who could buy 'shine enough ahead of his needs to have always a fully matured supply on hand. The riff-raff drank from hand to mouth of improperly aged liquor, and it was a mark of caste to serve one's "corn" not less than six or eight months old. I managed to put by two five-gallon kegs, for it was enough for friends to drive twenty-five miles to call on me, without offering them raw liquor.

When I breached the first keg, there were only three gallons in it. I was appalled at the rate of evaporation and decided that the modest original price did not prove out so cheaply after all. When I siphoned off the second keg, the contents were two gallons. On that day 'Geechee was unusually blithe. An unhappy suspicion came to me. I questioned her. One may usually spare one's breath in questioning a Negro about a theft, especially that of liquor. The slave status has made the lie a social necessity. 'Geechee freely admitted having helped herself. She had not even bothered to use the siphon. She had simply heaved the keg up on her shoulder when she wanted a drink and poured out a tumblerful.

"It's the onliest way I can make out," she said. "It's the onliest thing lifts my heart up, times I think I'm jus' obliged to die."

There could be no answer. We compromised by my parcelling out as much as I thought she needed, but it was never enough. Her grief, her burden, was too great. She found her way, like water seeping through a crack, to whatever stores I had locked or hidden. Once when I was away I left her a quart and locked a new keg in my own bedroom cupboard, taking with me the key. When I returned, the lock was undisturbed and the keg was half empty. She had taken the door off the hinges, she told me. Her despair was greater than I knew. I thought that we were getting on very well, when suddenly, just before Christmas, she got hold of a gallon of her own, got rousing drunk, and simply walked away. I woke up to a strangely silent house, with no good sounds from the kitchen of stove lids thumping, no sweet smell of coffee, no murmur of 'Geechee's morning humming.

A freeze came in the night before Christmas. On Christmas morning the pipes were frozen solid, there was no water for coffee, the woodpile was depleted and I had to chop enough for a fire in the living room. I sat huddled over it, longing for the black girl's feet shuffling toward me with comfort and help. There came instead a message from a passer-by that 'Geechee had told that she had not quit me nor been fired. She was only taking a vacation. Time proved what I suspected. She had taken her savings and gone to Jacksonville to make sure that Leroy was being properly cared for.

I waited a long time for her to come back to me. The weeks passed and there was no word. I believe that she was too ashamed of having abandoned me to return without word from me. If I had understood the Negro psychology as well then as now, I should have gone after her. Exasperated with too much cow and too little firewood, I hired a Negro couple, Kate and Raymond. We settled down into a semblance of comfort, and while Kate was pretty and flip and impudent, she was clever and willing, and Raymond's long arms swinging the axe at the woodpile looked to me like the flutter of angels' wings. But life was not the same. That small bright flame of loving devotion was put out, and sitting in front of Raymond's roaring log fires, I was still cold. More than a year went by. It was a good year, with a new gay friend to initiate me into duck-hunting. The hunt on the lake was good, and coming home at night, with supper of quail and red wine and biscuits, and good talk by the fire. But 'Geechee was gone.

In late spring I sailed comfortably from off an intractable horse and broke my neck and fractured my skull. I rode the horse back to the stables and dismissed the incident. No one has ever had an easier experience with a serious accident. I put in a week not too badly, ending with paddling a boat all day while my friend cast for bass. Then the pain became a nightmare and I was a little out of my mind. My good Tampa doctor friend came with Dessie, his wife, for the week end, and said, "You don't seem to know it, but you have a broken neck." X-rays confirmed his easy diagnosis. There were weeks nursed by them in Tampa and the doctor fitted me with a steel brace that I thought gave me the noble look of Joan of Arc in armor, chin lifted, listening to the Voices, but that seemed to strike others dumb with horror. I was ready to go home. I could drive a car, could go on with my work, but I could not bathe nor dress myself nor adjust the brace. Dessie had already given me too generous a share of her time. The doctor knew of a good practical white nurse who would go home with me. I did not want her. I was re-writing a book and I did not want to take time out from it to be polite to her. I wanted 'Geechee.

Dessie drove me to Hawthorne where 'Geechee's mother lived. The girl had been following the strawberry season as a picker. We followed two blind trails. The third took us south to the outskirts of Plant City. We inquired at a Negro soft-drink stand. She was not known by her name of Beatrice. I described her big-boned frame, her one blind white eye. The Negro chuckled.

"You mean 'Geechee. There's a gal us don't fool with. An' you won't find her around no soft-drink stand. 'Geechee got to have somethin' stronger'n that."

He knew where she was living and we drove into the yard. She came out to the car. At sight of me in my apparatus tears streamed down her face.

"Oh, my white lamb," she cried out, "what they been doin' to you?"

She knew why we had come before we told her. She gathered up her pitiful belongings—she was sending her money to Leroy. Dessie drove us home to the Creek. It was like being in the hands of a black Florence Nightingale. All of us, no matter how self-reliant, long, I think, for tenderness. Her big rough hands touched me as gently as though I were made of glass, instead of being almost as sturdy as she. In the bath, she washed and dried me with a feather touch. She lingered over it, giving great attention at last to the toes, and once she chuckled and whispered under her breath, "Such little white footses—." They were little and white only in comparison with her own.

For two weeks she did not touch a drop of liquor. Then the old need came over her, and her breath reeked, and she wavered in helping me from the tub. Sometimes when I called she did not hear me, and Kate came saucily to report that " 'Geechee asleep—leas', I reckon she's asleep," and laughed. My heart ached. One Sunday morning two months after she had come, I awoke to pandemonium. Stove lids were being dropped on the floor, or thrown there. Dishes crashed. I heard shrieks from the tenant house. After a long time, 'Geechee reeled into my room.

"Kate an' Raymond's fightin'," she announced. "But don't you worry."

She staggered out and the racket began again in the kitchen.

She came to my door and said, "The bacon done burnt itself up, but don't you fret."

After half an hour she appeared to say, "Kate is chasin' Raymond thu the grove with a butcher knife. But you jes' lay still and don't worry."

I did not see her again. I lay helpless and hopeful, but there was no further sound. It was all hopeless. My breaks were nearly healed, and in her many deliquencies I had found that I could adjust the brace myself. I got myself dressed after a fashion and went to the back door and called her. There was no answer. In late afternoon she appeared, half sober.

She said, "I know I got to go. I ain't no use to nobody. It

comes over me and I can't help it. No use foolin' with me, I won't never be no different."

Kate and Raymond appeared sheepishly.

"It was me got 'em drunk," 'Geechee said. "They didn't aim to do it. Kate an' Raymond's all right."

I paid her and told Raymond to drive her home in the truck to her mother.

"I hate to part this way," I said.

"Me, too," and she was gone.

No maid of perfection—and now I have one—can fill the strange emptiness she left in a remote corner of my heart. I think of her often, and I know she does of me, for she comes once a year to see me. I put my arms around her big bony shoulders and she pats my back comfortingly. She is always a little drunk. She goes from one job to another, losing it always for the same reason. The last time she came I was away.

Little Will reported, "The 'Geechee girl was her to see you. She sure was high. She said she tried to go without drinkin', times, but seemed like she'd lose her mind, didn't she have it. She said she knowed she'd still be here with you, could she change. She said tell you they ain't nothin' nobody can do about it."

Taking Up
the Slack

IT IS ALWAYS bewildering to change one's complete way of life.
I was fitted by temperament and by inheritance for farm and
country living, yet to take it up after some thirty years of urban
life was not too easy. I had known my maternal grandfather's
Michigan farm, but there I was both guest and child, and the
only duties were to gather the eggs from the sweet-smelling hay-
loft. I had known my father's Maryland farm, but that farm was
his love, his escape from Washington governmental routine, and
we lived there only in the too few summers. I had no duties there
at all. There was only delight; the flowering locust grove; the
gentle cows in pasture; Rock Creek, which ran, ten miles away
from its Washington park, at the foot of the hill of the locusts,
where my brother and I learned to swim and to fish for tiny and
almost untakable fishes; long walks with my father through the
woods where he hoped some day to build a home; jaunts with
him behind old Dan in the carriage, to the county seat of Rock-
ville, or to buy mules at Frederick. These things got in the blood
but were no preparation for running a farm oneself. When I
bought the Florida orange grove with my inheritance that repre-
sented my share of the Maryland farm, my father's sister Madeline
wrote me in lament.

"You have in you," she said, "that fatal drop of Pearce blood,
clamoring for change and adventure, and above all, for a farm.
I never knew a Pearce who didn't secretly long for a farm. Mother
had one, Uncle Pierman was ruined by one, there was your
father's tragic experience. I had one, once——."

I see no reason for denying so fundamental an urge, ruin or no. It is more important to live the life one wishes to live, and to go down with it if necessary, quite contentedly, than to live more profitably but less happily. Yet to achieve content under sometimes adverse circumstances, requires first an adjustment within oneself, and this I had already made, and after that, a recognition that one is not unique in being obliged to toil and struggle and suffer. This is the simplest of all facts and the most difficult for the individual ego to accept. As I look back on those first difficult times at the Creek, when it seemed as though the actual labor was more than I could bear, and the making of a living on the grove impossible, it was old black Martha who drew aside a curtain and led me in to the company of all those who had loved the Creek and been tormented by it.

Martha welcomed me with old-fashioned formality. She came walking toward me in the grove one bright sunny December day. I turned to watch her magnificent carriage. It was erect, with a long free graceful stride. It was impossible to tell her age. She walked like a very young woman and walks so to this day. She is getting on to seventy, yet glimpsing her down the road she might be a girl. She was dressed neatly in calico, with a handkerchief bound around her head, bandana fashion. She was a rich smooth brown. She came directly to me and inclined her head.

She said, "I come to pay my respecks. I be's Martha. Martha Mickens."

I said, "How do you do, Martha."

She said, "I wants to welcome you. Me and my man, Old Will, was the first hands on this place. Time the grove was planted, me and Will worked here. It's home to me."

"Where do you live now?"

"T' other side o' the Creek. We too old now to do steady work, but I just wants to tell you, any time you gets in a tight, us is here to do what we can."

"How long has it been since you worked here on the grove?"

"Sugar," she said, "I got no way o' tellin' the years. The years comes and the years goes. It's been a long time."

"Was it the Herberts you worked for?"

"Yessum. They was mighty fine folks. They's been fine folks here since and they's been trash. But Sugar, the grove ain't trash, and the Creek be's trashified here and there, but it's the Creek right on. I purely loves the Creek."

I said, "I love it, too."

"Does you? Then you'll make out. I reckon you know, you got to be satisfied with a place to make out. And is you satisfied, then it don't make too much difference does you make out or no."

We laughed together.

She said, "Heap o' folks has lived here. Ain't nobody has lived here since the Herberts but had to scratch and scramble. The ones loved it, stayed 'til death or sich takened 'em away. The ones ain't loved it, has moved on like the wind moves." I said, "The grove hasn't always made a living, then."

" 'Pends on what you calls a livin'. To get yo' grease an' grits in the place you enjoys gettin' 'em, ain't that makin' a livin'?"

"Yes."

"Then lemme tell you. Ain't nobody never gone cold-out hongry here. I'se seed the grove freeze to the ground. I'se seed it swivvel in a long drought. But Sugar, they was grove here before my folks crossed the big water. They was wild grove here as long back as tongue can tell. Durin' the war for freedom the white ladies used to drive out here in wagons and pick the wild oranges to squeeze out the juice and send it to the sojers. And they'll be grove here right on, after you and me is forgotten. They'll be good land to plow, and mast in the woods for hogs, and ain't no need to go hongry. All the folks ahead o' you has fit cold and wind and dry weather, but ain't nary one of 'em has goed hongry."

Hunger at the moment was not immediate, but when it menaced later, I remembered the things the old black woman said, and I was comforted, sensing that one had only to hold tight to the earth itself and its abundance. And if others could fight adversity, so might I.

"I won't keep you," she said. "I jes' wanted to tell you I was here."

She bobbed her head and went away.

She lived at the time four miles away, across the Creek, in an old gray house immaculately kept, with oleanders and dogwood in the clean bare yard. She had always "porch plants" about, grown from slips, of geranium and aspidistra; fuchsia, "the Georgia flower," sansevieria and elephant's-ear and impatient Sultana, all blooming lushly in containers of old tin. She walked the four miles back and forth to help in the bean field or the cucumber patch, to nurse the sick, to wash and clean for Old Boss or the Mackays or, as time went on, for me. About her, the nucleus, were her sons and daughters and their wives and husbands, who worked transiently for the rest of us. The best of her daughters, to my personal knowledge, is Estelle. There is a very elegant daughter who works for a wealthy family outside of Baltimore, and of her I know nothing, except that she sends her mother good clothes not too much worn. Estelle and her husband Sam worked many years for Old Boss. They lived at the edge of the road and were patient and faithful, except that Sam had an unwonted impudence "under the influence." A son-in-law of Old Boss was somehow unable to deal with Sam, and in a huff he took Estelle and moved off to Hawthorn. Estelle is gentle and soft-spoken like her mother.

For a long time I knew of Zamilla only that she was "the one what got shot." I pictured a leaf-brown hussy subject to brawling, whose wild life finally caught up with her. I was never more mistaken. When Sam and Estelle cleared out in righteous indignation, Old Boss notified Martha that it was up to her to replace her delinquent offspring. Henry and Sissie appeared on the scene and took over the small cabin. Sissie, too, was gentle, bearing Henry's abuse when he was drunk and, absurdly, jealous. One day I discovered that Sissie was the wounded Zamilla, shot innocently in a jook from which she was trying to extricate her husband. The shot was probably intended for Henry, and much as I like him, sober, I know of no darky who more deserves shooting when drunk.

Adrenna is a daughter whose life became so involved with mine that I have wondered where one ended and the other began. She was a lean angular creature whom at first I took to be a girl, but found to be of my own age. She was shingle-butted, but what there was of butt stuck out sharply. She was a *femme fatale,* and I have never been able to identify any possible appeal she might have for the colored men, unless it be that little square boxlike rear. She was careless in her dress and cleanliness, to Martha's distress, and mine, and usually wore her hair in Topsy pigtails that stuck out around her face like a halo. She could seduce any man she wanted, for the moment, but she could not hold them, or, if they were faithful, she grew tired of them. She did my work for several years and there was true love and exasperation between us. Our involvement came through her attempts to capture a husband. The husband must serve a dual purpose. He must provide her with whatever she wanted of a husband, and me with a good grove and yard man. Adrenna and I fell constantly between the upper and the nether millstone.

"Little Will" Mickens, her brother, is my grove man at this instant, and while all seems well, I can guarantee nothing by the time this chronicle goes to press. Other sons and daughters of Martha are scattered here and there through the state.

"I was a fast-breedin' woman," Martha says with dignity and without apology. Such things are elemental, a matter of fact. "I got sympathy for a woman is a fast-breeder."

When any of the daughters working at the Creek are ill or absent or brought to child-bed, or the sons or husbands are drunk and cannot do their work, Martha takes their places. Last winter a freeze menaced and Little Will was taken suddenly drunk. Martha came without notice to gather Spanish moss to cover the flower plants in my garden. I drove in from town and found her bending over the plants.

"I always like to take up the slack," she said.

There have been occasions when her slack-taking has been so zealous as better to have gone untaken. I left the Creek for a vacation at a beach cottage seventy miles away. Adrenna left behind by accident six napkins that I had picked up at the dime store for twenty cents. The morning after our arrival at the cottage, my farm truck clattered up to the door. Little Will presented me breathlessly with a neatly wrapped package.

"Mama sont me to carry you these. She say she jes' know you

wanted 'em. She say, tell you you don't never need worry when
Adrenna forget things. She see you gets 'em."

The parcel contained the twenty cents' worth of napkins. The
round trip for the truck stood me several dollars. Will had left
the grove fertilizing in the very middle, while the extra hands
must sit idle, waiting for the return of the truck to move the
fertilizer. I accepted the napkins and sent him on his way. Two
hours later he returned on foot. The truck had broken a spring
on a rough back road. I was editing a story to meet a magazine
deadline and was obliged to drop my work, arrange for a new
spring and a repairman from the nearest city. The job cost fifteen
dollars, the details filled my day, and it was night before Little
Will reached the grove again. I take a rueful satisfaction in using
the flimsy napkins, saying to friends, "Please be careful. These
napkins are worth about six dollars apiece." My only dividend on
the investment is their puzzled expression at my bad taste and
the obvious worthlessness of the napkins. I take no more chances
on Martha's slack-taking. Whenever I leave the Creek for the
beach, I say, "If we leave anything behind, do not send the truck
with it." I have probably deprived her of many triumphs in
despatching a pound of butter or a magazine by farm express.

We call Martha "old-timey." That means specifically that to
our white faces she presents a low-voiced deference, to our backs
an acute criticism, and to the colored world a tongue before which
it bows as before a flail. She has an inviolable sense of proportion.
It comes of the gift, and I think it is a gift, that many of her
alleged superiors do not possess, of seeing people as they are.
Wealth does not impress her, on the rare occasions when she
encounters it. "Fame" is a word without meaning. Those few of
the worldly great who have paused briefly at the Creek have
passed before her silent appraisal as they must pass that of St.
Peter. On the other hand, the poorest tramp receives a kind word
from her if she senses in him that integrity that even the most
unfortunate often possess. I fed one such one day, for at the Creek
the hungry have a great claim on us. The ragged creature blessed
me as he went away with his full stomach and small gifts.

"It will all come back to you," he said, "many times over."

It was of course the ancient response of the mendicant, through whom the charitable curry favor in the sight of the gods, but the man had something more.

Martha said, "That ain't no beggar. That's a person."

She has her own standards of payment for services rendered. She accepts nothing from those too poor to pay. When I came to my own lean period, and found that I could not carry all the manual labor alone, she washed and cleaned for me, at the current rate of ten cents an hour. She would not cheapen herself by loitering over her work, to draw a higher pay, and was always finished in a few hours. I paid her the small sums with guilt and necessity. She accepted with infinite politeness. Now, when accident has raised my fortunes, I pay her generously for the smallest labors, and she accepts the over-pay with equal understanding. Who knows better than she that one pays as one can, and that the Lord giveth and the Lord taketh away? Blessed be the name of the Lord.

None of her get is of the same stuff as her own. If she were white I should call her a natural aristocrat, and I see no reason to withhold the adjective because of color or race. She is illiterate, she can tell a judicious lie when necessary, she does not know sterling silver from aluminum, and scours old English Sheffield along with the cooking pots and pans. But she is well-bred. Breeding is after all a matter of manner, of social adjustment, of exquisite courtesy. Perhaps she is descended from old African kings and queens. At any rate, the hallmark is on her.

Old Will, her husband, some ten years older than she, is almost of her breed. He has the arrogance of the elite but not the graciousness. Many of the quarrels at the Creek have been of his instigating. Perhaps he too came of a regal line but a more belligerent one. He looks for all the world like Uncle Tom, with grizzled hair and whiskers, and walks with a cane. The cane is a badge of his independence, indicating that he is frail and cannot or will not stoop to labor. But he was a hard worker in his day and made money on cotton and at sharecropping of all sorts.

When I am his age, if I have no other subsistence, I think that I too shall walk with a cane and accept a livelihood as my right, after years of toiling.

Martha is a Primitive, or foot-washing, Baptist, militant and certain of her doctrines. She does not go often to church only because there is none nearby of her denomination. There was a Primitive Baptist church across the Creek when I first came, but the leader absconded with the hard-saved church funds, and his house, which was also the meeting-house, was quite properly struck by lightning and burned to the ground by the wrath of the Lord. Martha is an inexhaustible fount of old spirituals. When we get hungry for song, she gathers several of her family together, lines them up in a row and "leads off." Her voice is high and reedlike and utterly true. The other voices weave in and out of her melody, sometimes only humming, for some of the songs are so rare and old that only she is familiar with the words. Her favorite, and mine, is "Come, Mary, toll the bell." For this, she throws back her kerchiefed head, closes her eyes, pats her foot and accompanies herself with an intricate syncopation of hand clapping. Rhythm-minded friends attempt to follow her timing, charmed by its perfection, and can never duplicate the fine shading of beats. Her son-in-law Henry is her favorite to sing with her, for he too knows many of the old songs, and has a rich sweet bass that ripples like velvet under the silver of her voice. Unfortunately Henry is often in disfavor and we must sing without him. It is of no use ever for me to ask him to sing "St. Louis Blues" or "Coon-shine Baby."

"Mama don't let me sing them low-down songs where she can hear it," he says.

I wonder often what she thinks of the mysterious business that is my writing. Once in the midst of creative difficulties, I said facetiously, "Martha, I'm in trouble. I'll do the washing if you'll write this chapter for me."

"Sugar," she said gravely, "God knows I'd do it if I could."

I recall the time I rang late for my breakfast coffee. It seemed necessary to apologize for the hour, for at the Creek one is not quite decent who is not up with the red-birds.

I said, "I'm sorry to be so late. I worked very late last night at my writing."

She said compassionately, "Oh Sugar, I knows you're tired in the arms."

There is indeed much writing that sounds as though the only possible fatigue to the author were manual, but working as I do with great mental anguish, I could hope that a trace of cerebration might register, even for Martha. Pride pricked me, I think, or the need of self-justification that Martha is likely to impose on one, and that day I showed her my published books. She recognized my picture on a jacket and turned the unintelligible pages with a cautious black finger. She put her hands on her hips and threw back her head.

"Sugar," she said, "they ain't nobody at Cross Creek can do that."

from
THE YEARLING

Penny Is Bitten
by a Rattlesnake

THE QUAIL were nesting. The fluted covey call had been silent for some time. The coveys were dividing into pairs. The cocks were sounding the mating call, clear and sweet and insistent.

One day in mid-June Jody saw a cock and a hen run from the grape arbor with the scuttling hurry of paternity. He was wise enough not to follow them, but prowled about under the arbor until he found the nest. It held twenty cream-colored eggs. He was careful not to touch them, for fear the quail might desert them, as guineas did. A week later he went to the arbor to look at the progress of the Scuppernongs. They were like the smallest pellets of shot, but they were green and sturdy. He lifted a length of vine, imagining the dusty golden grapes in the late summer.

There was a stirring at his feet, as though the grass had exploded. The setting was hatched. The young quail, each no bigger than the end of his thumb, scattered like small wind-blown leaves. The mother quail cried out, and made alternate sorties after the brood, in defense, and at Jody, in attack. He stood quiet, as his father had taught him to do. The hen gathered her young together and took them away through the tall broom-sage grasses. Jody ran to find his father. Penny was working the field peas.

"Pa, the quail has hatched under the Scuppernong. And the grapes is makin'."

Penny rested on the plow handles. He was wet with sweat. He looked across the field. A hawk flew low, quartering.

He said, "If the hawks don't git the quail, and the 'coons don't

317

git the Scuppernongs, we'll have a mighty good meal, about first frost."

Jody said, "I hate the hawks eatin' the quail, but I don't someway mind the 'coons eatin' the grapes."

"That's because you love quail-meat more'n you love grapes."

"No, 'tain't. Hit's because I hate hawks and I love 'coons."

"Fodder-wing learned you that," Penny said, "with all them pet 'coons."

"I reckon so."

"The hogs come up yit, boy?"

"Not yit."

Penny frowned.

"I purely hate to think the Forresters has trapped 'em. But they ain't never stayed off so long. If 'twas bears, they wouldn't all be gone to oncet."

"I been as far as the old clearin', Pa, and the tracks goes on west from there."

"Time I git done workin' these peas, we're jest obliged to take Rip and Julia and go track 'em."

"What'll we do, do the Forresters have 'em trapped?"

"Whatever we got to do, when the time comes."

"Ain't you skeert to face the Forresters agin?"

"No, for I'm right."

"Would you be skeert if you was wrong?"

"If I was wrong, I wouldn't face 'em."

"What'll we do, do we git beat up agin?"

"Take it for our share and go on."

"I'd ruther let the Forresters keep the hogs."

"And go without meat? A black eye'll quiet down a heap quicker'n a empty belly. You want to beg off goin'?"

He hesitated.

"I reckon not."

Penny turned back to his cultivating.

"Then go tell your Ma please Ma'am to fix us early supper."

Jody went to the house. His mother was rocking and sewing on the shady porch. A small blue-bellied lizard scuttled from under her chair. Jody grinned, thinking how quickly she would heave her frame from the rocker if she had known.

"Please, Ma'am, Pa says to fix us supper right now. We got to go huntin' the hogs."

"About time."

She finished her seam leisurely. He dropped on the step below her.

"We likely got to face the Forresters, Ma, if they got 'em trapped."

"Well, face 'em. Black-hearted thieves."

He stared at her. She had been furious at both him and his father because they had fought the Forresters at Volusia.

He said, "We're like to git beat up and bloodied agin, Ma."

She folded her sewing impatiently.

"Well, pity on us, we got to have our meat. Who'll git it if you don't?"

She went into the house. He heard her thumping the lid on the Dutch oven. He was confused. His mother talked much of "duty." He had always hated the very word. Why was it his duty to let the Forresters maul him again, to recover the hogs, if it had not been his duty to let them maul him in order to help his friend Oliver? It seemed more honorable to him to bleed for a friend than for a side of bacon. He sat idly, listening to the fluttered whirring of mocking-birds in the chinaberry. The jays were chasing the red-birds out of the mulberry trees. There was a squabble for food even in the safety of the clearing. But it seemed to him there was always enough here for every one. There was food and shelter for father and mother and son; for old Cæsar; for Trixie and her spotted calf; for Rip and Julia; for the chickens, clucking and crowing and scratching; for the hogs, grunting in at evening for a cob of corn; for the song-birds in the trees, and the quail nesting under the arbor; for all of these, there was enough at the clearing.

Out in the scrub, the war waged ceaselessly. The bears and wolves and panthers and wild-cats all preyed on the deer. Bears even ate the cubs of other bears, all meat being to their maws the same. Squirrels and wood-rats, 'possums and 'coons, must all scurry for their lives. Birds and small furred creatures cowered in the shadow of hawk and owl. But the clearing was safe. Penny kept it so, with his good fences, with Rip and old Julia, with a wariness that seemed to Jody to be unsleeping. Sometimes he heard a rustling in the night, and the door opened and closed, and it was Penny, slipping back to his bed from a silent hunt for some marauder.

There was intrusion back and forth, as well. The Baxters went into the scrub for flesh of deer and hide of wild-cat. And the predatory animals and the hungry varmints came into the clearing when they could. The clearing was ringed around with hunger. It was a fortress in the scrub. Baxter's Island was an island of plenty in a hungry sea.

He heard the trace chains clanking. Penny was returning to the lot along the fence row. Jody ran ahead to open the lot gates for him. He helped with the unharnessing. He climbed the ladder into the loft and pitched down a forkful of cowpea hay into Cæsar's manger. There was no more corn and would not be until the summer's crop was made. He found a pile of hay with the dried peas still clinging to it and threw it down for Trixie. There would be more milk in the morning for both the Baxters and the spotted calf. The calf was inclined to leanness, for Penny was weaning it from the cow. The loft was heavy with heat, trapped under the thick hand-hewn slabs of the shingled roof. The hay crackled with a dry sweetness. It tickled his nostrils. He lay down in it a moment, abandoning himself to the resiliency. He was no more than comfortable when he heard his mother call. He scrambled down from the loft. Penny had finished milking. They went to the house together. Supper was on the table. There were only clabber and cornbread, but there was enough.

Ma Baxter said, "You fellers try to git a shot at some meat while you're off."

Penny prodded.

"I'm totin' my gun o' purpose."

They set off to the west. The sun was still above the tree-tops. There had been no rain for several days, but now cumulus clouds were piled low in the north and west. From the east and south, a steel grayness crept toward the glaring brilliance of the west.

Penny said, "A good rain today'd near about leave us lay by the corn."

There was no breeze. The air lay over the road like a thick down comforter. It seemed to Jody that it was something that could be pushed away, if he could struggle up through it. The sand burned his bare calloused soles. Rip and Julia walked listlessly, heads down, tails sagging, their tongues dripping from open jaws. It was not easy to follow the tracks of the hogs where the loose soil had been so long dry. Penny's eye was keener here than Julia's nose. The hogs had fed through the black-jack, crossed the abandoned clearing, and then headed for the prairie, where lily roots could be dug, and pools of cool water could be muddied and wallowed in. They did not range so far when food could be had close at home. Now was a barren and parlous season. There was no mast yet, of pine or oak or hickory, except what could be rooted deep under the leaves from last year's falling. Palmetto berries were still too green, even for the undiscerning taste of a hog. Three miles from Baxter's Island Penny crouched to examine the trail. He picked up a grain of corn and turned it over in his hand. He pointed to the hoof-marks of a horse.

"They baited them hogs," he said.

He straightened his back. His face was grave. Jody watched him anxiously.

"Well, son, we're obliged to follow."

"Clare to the Forresters?"

"Clare to wheresomever the hogs be. Mought be, we'll find 'em in a pen some'eres."

The trail zigzagged where the hogs had weaved back and forth for the scattered corn.

Penny said, "I kin understand the Forresters fightin' Oliver and I kin understand them rompin' on you and me. But I be dogged if I kin understand cold-out meanness."

A quarter of a mile beyond stood a rough hog-trap. It had been sprung but the pen was now empty. It was made of untrimmed saplings and a limber sapling had been baited to spring the gate behind the crowding hogs.

"Them rascals was nearby, waitin'," Penny said. "That pen wouldn't hold a hog no time."

A cart had turned around in the sand to the right of the pen. The wheel tracks led down a dim scrub road toward Forresters' Island.

Penny said, "All right, boy. Here's our way."

The sun was near the horizon. The cumulus clouds were white puff-balls, stained with the red and yellow wash of the sunset. The south was filled with darkness, like the smoke of gunpowder. A chill air moved across the scrub and was gone, as though a vast being had blown a cold breath and then passed by. Jody shivered and was grateful for the hot air that fell in behind it. A wild grape-vine trailed across the thin-rutted road. Penny leaned to pull it aside.

He said, "When there's trouble waitin' for you, you jest as good go to meet it."

The rattler struck him from under the grape-vine without warning. Jody saw the flash, blurred as a shadow, swifter than a martin, surer than the slashing claws of a bear. He saw his father stagger backward under the force of the blow. He heard him give a cry. He wanted to step back, too. He wanted to cry out with all his voice. He stood rooted to the sand and could not make a sound. It was lightning that had struck, and not a rattler. It was a branch that broke, it was a bird that flew, it was a rabbit running——

Penny shouted, "Git back! Hold the dogs!"

The voice released him. He dropped back and clutched the dogs by the scruff of their necks. He saw the mottled shadow lift its flat head, knee-high. The head swung from side to side, following his father's slow motions. He heard the rattles hum. The dogs heard. They winded. The fur stood stiff on their bodies. Old Julia whined and twisted out of his hand. She turned and slunk down the trail. Her long tail clung to her hindquarters. Rip reared on his hind feet, barking.

As slowly as a man in a dream, Penny backed away. The rattles sung. They were not rattles— Surely it was a locust humming. Surely it was a tree-frog singing— Penny lifted his gun to his shoulder and fired. Jody quivered. The rattler coiled and writhed in its spasms. The head was buried in the sand. The contortions moved down the length of the thick body, the rattles whirred feebly and were still. The coiling flattened into slow convolutions, like a low tide ebbing. Penny turned and stared at his son.

He said, "He got me."

He lifted his right arm and gaped at it. His lips lifted dry over his teeth. His throat worked. He looked dully at two punctures in the flesh. A drop of blood oozed from each.

He said, "He was a big un."

Jody let go his hold on Rip. The dog ran to the dead snake and barked fiercely. He made sorties and at last poked the coils with one paw. He quieted and snuffed about in the sand. Penny lifted his head from his staring. His face was like hickory ashes.

He said, "Ol' Death goin' to git me yit."

He licked his lips. He turned abruptly and began to push through the scrub in the direction of the clearing. The road would be shorter going, for it was open, but he headed blindly for home in a direct line. He plowed through the low scrub oaks, the gallberries, the scrub palmettos. Jody panted behind him. His heart pounded so hard that he could not see where he was going. He followed the sound of his father's crashing across the undergrowth. Suddenly the denseness ended. A patch of higher oaks made a shaded clearing. It was strange to walk in silence.

Penny stopped short. There was a stirring ahead. A doe-deer leaped to her feet. Penny drew a deep breath, as though breathing were for some reason easier. He lifted his shotgun and leveled it at the head. It flashed over Jody's mind that his father had gone mad. This was no moment to stop for game. Penny fired. The doe turned a somersault and dropped to the sand and kicked a little and lay still. Penny ran to the body and drew his knife from its scabbard. Now Jody knew his father was insane. Penny did not cut the throat, but slashed into the belly. He laid the carcass wide open. The pulse still throbbed in the heart. Penny slashed out the liver. Kneeling, he changed his knife to his left hand. He turned his right arm and stared again at the twin punctures. They were now closed. The forearm was thick-swollen and blackening. The sweat stood out on his forehead. He cut quickly across the wound. A dark blood gushed and he pressed the warm liver against the incision.

He said in a hushed voice, "I kin feel it draw——"

He pressed harder. He took the meat away and looked at it. It was a venomous green. He turned it and applied the fresh side.

He said, "Cut me out a piece o' the heart."

Jody jumped from his paralysis. He fumbled with the knife. He hacked away a portion.

Penny said, "Another."

He changed the application again and again.

He said, "Hand me the knife."

He cut a higher gash in his arm where the dark swelling rose the thickest. Jody cried out.

"Pa! You'll bleed to death!"

"I'd ruther bleed to death than swell. I seed a man die——"

The sweat poured down his cheeks.

"Do it hurt bad, Pa?"

"Like a hot knife was buried to the shoulder."

The meat no longer showed green when he withdrew it. The warm vitality of the doe's flesh was solidifying in death. He stood up.

He said quietly, "I cain't do it no more good. I'm goin' on home. You go to the Forresters and git 'em to ride to the Branch for Doc Wilson."

"Reckon they'll go?"

"We got to chance it. Call out to 'em quick, sayin', afore they chunk somethin' at you or mebbe shoot."

He turned back to pick up the beaten trail. Jody followed. Over his shoulder he heard a light rustling. He looked back. A spotted fawn stood peering from the edge of the clearing, wavering on uncertain legs. Its dark eyes were wide and wondering.

He called out, "Pa! The doe's got a fawn."

"Sorry, boy. I cain't he'p it. Come on."

An agony for the fawn came over him. He hesitated. It tossed its small head, bewildered. It wobbled to the carcass of the doe and leaned to smell it. It bleated.

Penny called, "Git a move on, young un."

Jody ran to catch up with him. Penny stopped an instant at the dim road.

"Tell somebody to take this road in to our place and pick me up in case I cain't make it in. Hurry."

The horror of his father's body, swollen in the road, washed over him. He began to run. His father was plodding with a slow desperation in the direction of Baxter's Island.

Jody ran down the wagon trail to the myrtle thicket where it branched off into the main road to Forresters' Island. The road, much used, had no growth of weeds or grass to make a footing. The dry shifting sand caught at the soles of his feet and seemed to wrap clinging tentacles around the muscles of his legs. He dropped into a short dog-trot that seemed to pull more steadily against the sand. His legs moved, but his mind and body seemed suspended above them, like an empty box on a pair of cart-wheels. The road under him was a treadmill. His legs pumped up and down, but he seemed to be passing the same trees and bushes again and again. His pace seemed so slow, so futile, that he came to a bend with a dull surprise. The curve was familiar. He was not far from the road that led directly into the Forrester clearing.

He came to the tall trees of the island. They startled him, because they meant that he was now so close. He came alive and he was afraid. He was afraid of the Forresters. And if they refused him help, and he got safely away again, where should he go? He halted a moment under the shadowy live oaks, planning. It was twilight. He was sure it was not time for darkness. The rain clouds were not clouds, but an infusion of the sky, and had now filled it entirely. The only light was a strand of green across the west, the color of the doe's flesh with the venom on it. It came to him that he would call to his friend Fodder-wing. His friend would hear him and come, and he might be allowed to approach close enough to tell his errand. It eased his heart to think of it, to think of his friend's eyes gentle with sorrow for him. He drew a long breath and ran wildly down the path under the oak trees.

He shouted, "Fodder-wing! Fodder-wing! Hit's Jody!"

In an instant now his friend would come to him from the house, crawling down the rickety steps on all fours, as he must do when in a hurry. Or he would appear from the bushes with his raccoon at his heels.

"Fodder-wing! Hit's me!"

There was no answer. He broke into the swept sandy yard.

"Fodder-wing!"

There was an early light lit in the house. A twist of smoke curled from the chimney. The doors and shutters were closed against the mosquitoes and against the night-time. The door swung open. In the light beyond, he saw the Forrester men rise to their feet, one after the other, as though the great trees in the forest lifted themselves by their roots and stirred toward him. He stopped short. Lem Forrester advanced to the stoop. He lowered his head and turned it a little sideways until he recognized the intruder.

"You leetle wild-cat. What you after here?"

Jody faltered, "Fodder-wing——"

"He's ailin'. You cain't see him no-ways."

It was too much. He burst out crying.

He sobbed, "Pa— He's snake-bit."

The Forresters came down the steps and surrounded him. He sobbed loudly, with pity for himself and for his father, and because he was here at last and something was finished that he had set out to do. There was a stirring among the men, as though the leavening quickened in a bowl of bread-dough.

"Where's he at? What kind o' snake?"

"A rattlesnake. A big un. He's makin' it for home but he don't know kin he make it."

"Is he swellin'? Where'd it git him?"

"In the arm. Hit's bad swelled a'ready. Please ride for Doc Wilson. Please ride for him quick, and I won't he'p Oliver agin you no more. Please."

Lem Forrester laughed.

"A skeeter promises he won't bite," he said.

Buck said, "Hit's like not to do no good. A man dies right now, bit in the arm. He'll likely be dead afore Doc kin git to him."

"He shot a doe-deer and used the liver to draw out the pizen. Please ride for Doc."

Mill-wheel said, "I'll ride for him."

Relief flooded him like the sun.

"I shore thank you."

"I'd he'p a dog, was snake-bit. Spare your thanks."

Buck said, "I'll ride on and pick up Penny. Walkin's bad for a man is snake-bit. Fellers, we ain't got a drop o' whiskey for him."

Gabby said, "Ol' Doc'll have some. If he's purty tol'able sober, he'll have some left. If he's drunk all he's got, he kin blow his breath, and that'll make a powerful potion."

Buck and Mill-wheel turned away with torturing deliberation to the lot to saddle their horses. Their leisureliness frightened Jody as speed would not have done. If there was hope for his father, they would be hurrying. They were as slow and unconcerned as though they were burying Penny, not riding for assistance. He stood, desolate. He would like to see Fodder-wing just a moment before he went away. The remaining Forresters turned back up the steps, ignoring him.

Lem called from the door, "Git goin', Skeeter."

Arch said, "Leave the young un be. Don't torment him and his daddy likely dyin'."

Lem said, "Die and good riddance. Biggety bantam."

They went into the house and closed the door. A panic came over Jody, that they did not mean, any of them, to help at all; that Buck and Mill-wheel had gone away to the corral for a joke, and were laughing at him there. He was forsaken, and his father was forsaken. Then the two men rode out and Buck lifted his hand to him, not unkindly.

"No use to fret, boy. We'll do what we kin. We don't hold nothin' agin folks in trouble."

They touched their heels to the horses' flanks and shot away. Lightness filled him where he had been heavy as lead. It was only Lem, then, who was an enemy. He settled his hate on him with satisfaction. He listened until the hoof-beats faded from his hearing, then set out down the road for home.

Now he was free to accept the facts. A rattlesnake had struck his father, who might die of it. But help was on the way, and he had done what he was supposed to do. His fear had a name, and was no longer quite so terrible. He decided not to try to run, but to walk steadily. He should have liked to ask the loan of a horse for himself, but dared not.

A pattering of rain passed over him. A hush followed. The storm might go around the scrub entirely, as often happened. There was a faint luminosity in the air around him. He had scarcely been conscious that he was carrying his father's gun. He swung it over one shoulder and walked rapidly where the road was firm. He wondered how long it would take Mill-wheel to reach the Branch. He wondered, not whether old Doc would be drunk, for that was known, but just how drunk he would be. If Doc could sit up in bed, he was considered fit to go.

He had been at Doc's place once when he was very young. He remembered still the sprawling house with wide verandas, decaying, as old Doc was decaying, in the heart of a dense vegetation. He remembered the cockroaches and the lizards, as much at home inside the house as in the thick vines outside it. He remembered old Doc, deep in his cups, lying under a mosquito canopy, staring at the ceiling. When he was called, he sprawled to his feet and went about his business on uncertain legs, but with gentle heart and hands. He was known far and wide as a good doctor, drunk or no. If he could be reached in time, Jody thought, his father's life was certain.

He turned from the Forresters' lane into the road that ran east to his father's clearing. He had four miles ahead of him. On hard ground, he could make it in little over an hour. The sand was soft, and the very darkness seemed to hold him back and make his steps uneven. He would do well to reach home in an hour and a half, and it might take two. He broke now and then into a trot. The brightness in the air dropped into the darkness of the scrub like a water turkey dropping into the river. The growth on either side of the road pressed closer, so that the way was narrow.

He heard thunder in the east, and a flash of lightning filled the sky. He thought he heard foot-steps in the scrub oaks, but it was drops of rain, striking like shot on the leaves. He had never minded night or darkness, but Penny had always been in front of him. Now he was alone. He wondered, sickened, whether his father lay now in the road ahead of him, swollen with poison, or perhaps across Buck's saddle, if Buck had reached and found him. The lightning flashed again. He had sat with his father through many storms, under the live oaks. The rain had then been friendly, shutting them in together.

A snarl sounded in the bushes. Something incredibly swift flashed across the road in front of him and was gone, soundlessly. A musky taint lay on the air. He was not afraid of lynx or wild-cat, but a panther had been known to attack a horse. His heart thumped. He fingered the stock of his father's gun. It was useless, for Penny had shot both barrels, one at the rattler, one at the doe. He had his father's knife in his belt, and wished he had brought the long knife Oliver had given him. He had no scabbard for it, and it was dangerously sharp, Penny had said, to carry. When he was safe at home, lying under the grape arbor, or at the bottom of the sink-hole, he had pictured himself thrusting it with one sure plunge into the heart of bear or wolf or panther. There was no flush of pride now in the picture. A panther's claws were quicker than he.

Whatever the animal, it had gone its way. He walked more rapidly, stumbling in his haste. He thought he heard a wolf howl, but it was so far away that it might only have been the wind. The wind was rising. He heard it far off in the distance. It was as though it were blowing in another world, across a dark abyss. Suddenly it swelled. He heard it coming closer, like a moving wall. The trees ahead thrashed their limbs. The bushes rattled and flattened to the ground. There was a great roaring and the storm hit him like a blow.

He lowered his head and fought against it. He was drenched

to the skin in an instant. The rain poured down the back of his neck and washed through his breeches. His clothes hung heavily and held him back. He stopped and turned his back to the wind and propped the gun at the side of the road. He took off his shirt and breeches and rolled them into a bundle. He took up the gun and went on naked through the storm. The rain on his bare skin made him feel clean and free. The lightning flashed and he was startled by his own whiteness. He felt suddenly defenceless. He was alone and naked in an unfriendly world; lost and forgotten in the storm and darkness. Something ran behind him and ahead of him. It stalked the scrub like a panther. It was vast and formless and it was his enemy. Ol' Death was loose in the scrub.

It came to him that his father was already dead, or dying. The burden of the thought was intolerable. He ran faster, to shake it off. Penny could not die. Dogs could die, and bears and deer and other people. That was acceptable, because it was remote. His father could not die. The earth might cave in under him in one vast sink-hole and he could accept it. But without Penny, there was no earth. Without him there was nothing. He was frightened as he had never been before. He began to sob. His tears ran salt into his mouth.

He begged of the night, as he had begged of the Forresters, "Please——"

His throat ached and his groins were shot with hot lead. The lightning showed an opening ahead of him. He had reached the abandoned clearing. He darted into it and crouched against the old rail fence for a moment's shelter. The wind washed over him more coldly than the rain. He shivered and rose and went on again. The stop had chilled him. He wanted to run, to warm himself, but he had strength only to plod slowly. The rain had packed the sand so that the walking was firm and easier. The wind lessened. The down-pour settled into a steady falling. He walked on in a dull misery. It seemed to him that he must walk forever, but suddenly he was passing the sink-hole and was at the clearing.

The Baxter cabin was bright with candles. Horses whinnied and pawed the sand. There were three tethered to the slat fence.

He passed through the gate and into the cabin. Whatever was, was done. There was no bustle to greet him. Buck and Mill-wheel sat by the empty hearth, tilted back in their chairs. They were talking casually. They glanced at him, said "Hey, boy," and went on with their talk.

"You wasn't here, Buck, when ol' man Twistle died o' snake-bite. Penny must o' been right about whiskey not doin' no good. Twistle were drunk as a coot when he stepped on the rattler."

"Well, do I ever git snake-bit, fill me full jest for luck. I'd ruther die drunk than sober, ary day."

Mill-wheel spat into the fireplace.

"Don't fret," he said. "You will."

Jody was faint. He dared not ask them the question. He walked past them and into his father's bedroom. His mother sat on one side of the bed and Doc Wilson sat on the other. Old Doc did not turn his head. His mother looked at him and rose without speaking. She went to a dresser and took out a fresh shirt and breeches and held them out to him. He dropped his wet bundle and stood the gun against the wall. He walked slowly to the bed.

He thought, "If he's not dead now, he'll not die."

In the bed, Penny stirred. Jody's heart leaped like a rabbit jumping. Penny groaned and retched. Doc leaned quickly and held a basin for him and propped his head. Penny's face was dark and swollen. He vomited with the agony of one who has nothing to emit, but must vomit still. He fell back panting. Doc reached inside the covers and drew out a brick wrapped in flannel. He handed it to Ma Baxter. She laid Jody's garments at the foot of the bed and went to the kitchen to heat the brick again.

Jody whispered, "Is he bad?"

"He's bad, a'right. Looks as if he'd make it. Then again, looks as if he won't."

Penny opened his puffed eyes. The pupils were dilated until his eyes seemed black. He moved his arm. It was swollen as thick as a bullock's thigh.

He murmured thickly, "You'll ketch cold."

Jody fumbled for his clothes and pulled them on. Doc nodded.

"That's a good sign, knowin' you. That's the first he's spoken."

A tenderness filled Jody that was half pain, half sweetness. In his agony, his father was concerned for him. Penny could not die. Not Penny.

He said, "He's obliged to make it, Doc, sir." He added, as he had heard his father say, "Us Baxters is all runty and tough."

Doc nodded.

He called to the kitchen, "Let's try some warm milk now."

With hope, Ma Baxter began to sniffle. Jody joined her at the hearth.

She whimpered, "I don't see as we'd deserve it, do it happen."

He said, "Hit'll not happen, Ma." But his marrow was cold again.

He went outside for wood to hurry the fire. The storm was moving on to the west. The clouds were rolling like battalions of marching Spaniards. In the east, bright spaces showed, filled with stars. The wind blew fresh and cool. He came in with an armful of fatwood.

He said, "Hit'll be a purty day tomorrow, Ma."

"Hit'll be a purty day iffen he's yit alive when day comes." She burst into tears. They dropped on the hearth and hissed. She lifted her apron and wiped her eyes. "You take the milk in," she said. "I'll make Doc and me a cup o' tea. I hadn't et nothin', waitin' for you-all, when Buck carried him in."

He remembered that he had eaten lightly. He could think of nothing that would taste good. The thought of food on his tongue was a dry thought, without nourishment or relish. He carried the cup of hot milk carefully, balancing it in his hands. Doc took it from him and sat close to Penny on the bed.

"Now, boy, you hold his head up while I spoon-feed him."

Penny's head was heavy on the pillow. Jody's arms ached with the strain of lifting it. His father's breathing was heavy, like the Forresters' when they were drunk. His face had changed color. It was green and pallid, like a frog's belly. At first his teeth resisted the intruding spoon.

Doc said, "Open your mouth before I call the Forresters to open it."

The swollen lips parted. Penny swallowed. A portion of the cupful went down. He turned his head away.

Doc said, "All right. But if you lose it, I'm comin' back with more."

Penny broke into a sweat.

Doc said, "That's fine. Sweatin's fine, for poison. King of the jay-birds, if we weren't all out of whiskey, I'd make you sweat."

Ma Baxter came to the bedroom with two plates with cups of tea and biscuits on them. Doc took his plate and balanced it on his knee. He drank with a mixture of gusto and distaste.

He said, "It's all right, but 'tain't whiskey."

He was the soberest Jody had ever heard of his being.

"A good man snake-bit," he said mournfully, "and the whole county out of whiskey."

Ma Baxter said dully, "Jody, you want somethin'?"

"I ain't hongry."

His stomach was as queasy as his father's. It seemed to him that he could feel the poison working in his own veins, attacking his heart, churning in his gizzard.

Doc said, "Blest if he ain't goin' to keep that milk down."

Penny was in a deep sleep.

Ma Baxter rocked and sipped and nibbled.

She said, "The Lord watches the sparrer's fall. Mought be He'll take a hand for the Baxters."

Jody went into the front room. Buck and Mill-wheel had lain down on the deer-skin rugs on the floor.

Jody said, "Ma and Doc's eatin'. You-all hongry?"

Buck said, "We'd jest done et when you come. Don't pay us no mind. We'll sleep here and wait-see how it comes out."

Jody crouched on his heels. He would have liked to talk with them. It would be good to talk of dogs and guns and hunting, of all the things that living men could do. Buck snored. Jody tiptoed back to the bedroom. Doc was nodding in his chair. His mother moved the candle from the bed-side and returned to her rocker. The runners swished a while and then were still. She too nodded.

It seemed to Jody that he was alone with his father. The vigil was in his hands. If he kept awake, and labored for breath with the tortured sleeper, breathing with him and for him, he could keep him alive. He drew a breath as deep as the ones his father was drawing. It made him dizzy. He was light-headed and his stomach was empty. He knew he would feel better if he should eat, but he could not swallow. He sat down on the floor and leaned his head against the side of the bed. He began to think back over the day, as though he walked a road backward. He could not help but feel a greater security here beside his father, than in the stormy night. Many things, he realized, would be terrible alone that were not terrible when he was with Penny. Only the rattlesnake had kept all its horror.

He recalled the triangular head, the lightning flash of its striking, the subsidence into alert coils. His flesh crawled. It seemed to him he should never be easy in the woods again. He recalled the coolness of his father's shot, and the fear of the dogs. He recalled the doe and the horror of her warm meat against his father's wound. He remembered the fawn. He sat upright. The fawn was alone in the night, as he had been alone. The catastrophe that might take his father, had made it motherless. It had lain hungry and bewildered through the thunder and rain and lightning, close to the devastated body of its dam, waiting for the stiff form to arise and give it warmth and food and comfort. He pressed his face into the hanging covers of the bed and cried bitterly. He was torn with hate for all death and pity for all aloneness.

Jody
Finds the Fawn

JODY MOVED through a tortuous dream. With his father beside him, he fought a nest of rattlesnakes. They crawled across his feet, trailing their rattles, clacking lightly. The nest resolved itself into one snake, gigantic, moving toward him on a level with his face. It struck and he tried to scream but could not. He looked for his father. He lay under the rattler, with his eyes open to a dark sky. His body was swollen to the size of a bear. He was dead. Jody began to move backward away from the rattler, one agonized step at a time. His feet were glued to the ground. The snake suddenly vanished and he stood alone in a vast windy place, holding the fawn in his arms. Penny was gone. A sense of sorrow filled him so that he thought his heart would break. He awakened, sobbing.

He sat up on the hard floor. Day was breaking over the clearing. A pale light lay in streaks beyond the pine trees. The room was filled with grayness. For an instant he was still conscious of the fawn against him. Then he remembered. He scrambled to his feet and looked at his father.

Penny was breathing with a greater ease. He was still swollen and fevered, but he looked no worse than when the wild honey bees had stung him. Ma Baxter was asleep in her rocker with her head thrown far back. Old Doc lay across the foot of the bed.

Jody whispered, "Doc!"

Doc grunted and lifted his head.

"What is it—what is it—what is it?"

"Doc! Look at Pa!"

Doc shifted his body and eased himself on one elbow. He blinked and rubbed his eyes. He sat up. He leaned over Penny.

"King o' the jay-birds, he's made it."

Ma Baxter said, "Eh?"

She sat upright.

"He dead?"

"Not by a long sight."

She burst out crying.

Doc said, "You sound like you're sorry."

She said, "You jest don't know what 'twould mean, him leavin' us here."

Jody had never heard her speak so gently.

Doc said, "Why, you got you another man here. Look at Jody, now. Big enough to plow and reap and do the huntin'."

She said, "Jody's a'right, but he ain't a thing but boy. Got his mind on nothin' but prowlin' and playin'."

He hung his head. It was true.

She said, "His Pa encourages him."

Doc said, "Well, boy, be glad you got encouragement. Most of us live our lives without it. Now, Ma'am, let's get some more milk down this feller, time he wakes."

Jody said eagerly, "I'll go milk, Ma."

She said with satisfaction, "About time."

He passed through the front room. Buck was sitting up on the floor, rubbing his head sleepily. Mill-wheel was still asleep.

Jody said, "Doc says Pa's done made it."

"I be dogged. I woked up, fixin' to go he'p bury him."

Jody went around the side of the house and took down the milk-gourd from the wall. He felt as light as the gourd. It seemed to him in his liberation that he might spread his arms and float over the gate like a feather. The dawn was still nebulous. A mocking-bird made a thin metallic sound in the chinaberry. The Dominick rooster crowed uncertainly. This was the hour at which Penny arose, allowing Jody to sleep a little later. The morning was still, with a faint fluttering of breeze through the tops of the tall pine trees. The sunrise reached long fingers into the clearing. As he clicked the lot-gate, doves flew from the pines with a whistling of wings.

He called exultantly after them, "Hey, doves!"

Trixie lowed, hearing him. He climbed into the loft for fodder for her. She was very patient, he thought, giving her milk in return for so poor a feeding. She munched hungrily. She lifted a hind leg once in threat when he was clumsy with the milking. He stripped two teats carefully, then turned the calf in with her to nurse on the other two. There was not as much milk as his father would have gotten from her. He decided that he would drink none himself so that his father might have all of it until he was well again.

The calf butted the sagging udder and sucked noisily. It was too big still to be nursing. The thought of the fawn returned to him. A leaden feeling came over him again. It would be desperate with hunger this morning. He wondered if it would try to nurse the cold teats of the doe. The open flesh of the dead deer would attract the wolves. Perhaps they had found the fawn and had torn its soft body to ribbons. His joy in the morning, in his father's living, was darkened and tainted. His mind followed the fawn and would not be comforted.

His mother took the milk-gourd without comment on the quantity. She strained the milk and poured a cupful and took it to the sick room. He followed her. Penny was awake. He smiled weakly.

He whispered thickly, "Ol' Death got to wait a while on me."

Doc said, "You belong to be kin to the rattlesnakes, man. How you done it without whiskey, I don't know."

Penny whispered, "Why, Doc, I'm a king snake. You know a rattler cain't kill a king snake."

Buck and Mill-wheel came into the room. They grinned.

Buck said, "You ain't purty, Penny, but you're alive."

Doc held the milk to Penny's lips. He swallowed thirstily.

Doc said, "I can't take much credit for savin' you. Your time just hadn't come to make a die of it."

Penny closed his eyes.

He said, "I could sleep a week."

Doc said, "That's what I want you to do. I can't do no more for you."

He stood up and stretched his legs.

Ma Baxter said, "Who'll do the farmin' and him asleep?"

Buck said, "What's he got, belongs to be done?"

"Mostly the corn, needs another workin' to be laid by. The 'taters needs hoein', but Jody's right good at hoein', do he choose to stick to it."

"I'll stick, Ma."

Buck said, "I'll stay and work the corn and sich."

She was flustered.

She said stiffly, "I hates to be beholden to you."

"Now, Ma'am, they ain't too many of us shiftin' for a livin' out here. I'd be a pore man, didn't I not stay."

She said meekly, "I'm shore obliged. If the corn don't make, we jest as good all three to die o' snake-bite."

Doc said, "This is the soberest I've waked up since my wife died. I'd be proud to eat breakfast before I go."

She bustled to the kitchen. Jody went to build up the fire.

She said, "I never figgered I'd be beholden to a Forrester."

"Buck ain't exactly a Forrester, Ma. Buck's a friend."

"Hit do look that-a-way."

She filled the coffee-pot with water and added fresh coffee to the grounds.

She said, "Go to the smoke-house and git that last side o' bacon. I'll not be out-done."

He brought it proudly. She allowed him to slice the meat.

He said, "Ma, Pa shot a doe and used the liver to draw out the pizen. He bled hisself and then laid on the liver."

"You should of carried back a haunch o' the meat."

"There wasn't no time to figger on sich as that."

"That's right too."

"Ma, the doe had a fawn."

"Well, most does has fawns."

"This un was right young. Nigh about new-borned."

"Well, what about it? Go set the table. Lay out the brier-berry jelly. The butter's right strong but it's yit butter. Lay it out, too."

She was stirring up a corn pone. The fat was sizzling in the skillet. She poured in the batter. The bacon crackled in the pan. She turned and flattened the slices, so that they would brown evenly. He wondered if they would ever be able to fill up Buck and Mill-wheel, accustomed to the copiousness of Forrester victuals.

He said, "Make a heap o' gravy, Ma."

"Iffen you'll do without your milk, I'll make milk-gravy."

The sacrifice was nothing.

He said, "We could of kilt a chicken."

"I studied on it, but they're all too young or too old."

She turned the corn pone. The coffee began to boil.

He said, "I could of shot some doves or some squirrels this mornin'."

"A fine time to think of it. Go tell the men-folks to wash theirselves and come to table."

He called them. The three men went outside to the watershelf and slapped water over their faces, dabbled their hands. He brought them a clean towel.

Doc said, "Blest if I don't get hungry when I'm sober."

Mill-wheel said, "Whiskey's a food. I could live on whiskey."

Doc said, "I've near about done it. Twenty years. Since my wife died."

Jody was proud of the table. There were not as many different dishes as the Forresters served, but there was enough of everything. The men ate greedily. At last they pushed away their plates and lit their pipes.

Mill-wheel said, "Seems like Sunday, don't it?"

Ma Baxter said, "Sickness allus do seem like Sunday, someway. Folks settin' around, and the men not goin' to the field."

Jody had never seen her so amiable. She had waited to eat until the men were done, for fear of their not having plenty. She sat now eating with relish. The men chatted idly. Jody allowed his thoughts to drift back to the fawn. He could not keep it out of his mind. It stood in the back of it as close as he had held it, in his dreaming, in his arms. He slipped from the table and went to his father's bedside. Penny lay at rest. His eyes were open and clear, but the pupils were still dark and dilated.

Jody said, "How you comin', Pa?"

"Jest fine, son. Ol' Death gone thievin' elsewhere. But wa'n't it a close squeak!"

"I mean."

Penny said, "I'm proud of you, boy, the way you kept your head and done what was needed."

"Pa——"

"Yes, son."

"Pa, you recollect the doe and the fawn?"

"I cain't never forget 'em. The pore doe saved me, and that's certain."

"Pa, the fawn may be out there yit. Hit's hongry, and likely mighty skeert."

"I reckon so."

"Pa, I'm about growed and don't need no milk. How about me goin' out and seein' kin I find the fawn?"

"And tote it here?"

"And raise it."

Penny lay quiet, staring at the ceiling.

"Boy, you got me hemmed in."

"Hit won't take much to raise it, Pa. Hit'll soon git to where it kin make out on leaves and acorns."

"Dogged if you don't figger the farrest of ary young un I've ever knowed."

"We takened its mammy, and it wa'n't no-ways to blame."

"Shore don't seem grateful to leave it starve, do it? Son, I ain't got it in my heart to say 'No' to you. I never figgered I'd see daylight, come dawn today."

"Kin I ride back with Mill-wheel and see kin I find it?"

"Tell your Ma I said you're to go."

He sidled back to the table and sat down. His mother was pouring coffee for every one.

He said, "Ma, Pa says I kin go bring back the fawn."

She held the coffee-pot in mid-air.

"What fawn?"

"The fawn belonged to the doe we kilt, to use the liver to draw out the pizen and save Pa."

She gasped.

"Well, for pity sake——"

"Pa says hit'd not be grateful, to leave it starve."

Doc Wilson said, "That's right, Ma'am. Nothing in the world don't ever come quite free. The boy's right and his daddy's right."

Mill-wheel said, "He kin ride back with me. I'll he'p him find it."

She set down the pot helplessly.

"Well, if you'll give it your milk— We got nothin' else to feed it."

"That's what I aim to do. Hit'll be no time, and it not needin' nothin'."

The men rose from the table.

Doc said, "I don't look for nothing but progress, Ma'am, but if he takes a turn for the worse, you know where to find me."

She said, "Well. What do we owe you, Doc? We cain't pay right now, but time the crops is made——"

"Pay for what? I've done nothing. He was safe before I got here. I've had a night's lodging and a good breakfast. Send me some syrup when your cane's ground."

"You're mighty good, Doc. We been scramblin' so, I didn't know folks could be so good."

"Hush, woman. You got a good man there. Why wouldn't folks be good to him?"

Buck said, "You reckon that ol' horse o' Penny's kin keep ahead o' me at the plow? I'm like to run him down."

Doc said, "Get as much milk down Penny as he'll take. Then give him greens and fresh meat, if you can get it."

Buck said, "Me and Jody'll tend to that."

Mill-wheel said, "Come on, boy. We got to git ridin'."

Ma Baxter asked anxiously, "You'll not be gone long?"

Jody said, "I'll be back shore, before dinner."

"Reckon you'd not git home a-tall," she said, "if 'twasn't for dinner-time."

Doc said, "That's man-nature, Ma'am. Three things bring a man home again—his bed, his woman, and his dinner."

Buck and Mill-wheel guffawed. Doc's eye caught the cream-colored 'coonskin knapsack.

"Now ain't that a pretty something? Wouldn't I like such as that to tote my medicines?"

Jody had never before possessed a thing that was worth giving away. He took it from its nail, and put it in Doc's hands.

"Hit's mine," he said. "Take it."

"Why, I'd not rob you, boy."

"I got no use for it," he said loftily. "I kin git me another."

"Now I thank you. Every trip I make, I'll think, 'Thank you, Jody Baxter.'"

He was proud with old Doc's pleasure. They went outside to water the horses and feed them from the scanty stock of hay in the Baxter barn.

Buck said to Jody, "You Baxters is makin' out and that's about all, ain't it?"

Doc said, "Baxter's had to carry the work alone. Time the boy here gits some size to him, they'll prosper."

Buck said, "Size don't seem to mean much to a Baxter."

Mill-wheel mounted his horse and pulled Jody up behind him. Doc mounted and turned away in the opposite direction. Jody waved after him. His heart was light.

He said to Mill-wheel, "You reckon the fawn's yit there? Will you he'p me find him?"

"We'll find him, do he be alive. How you know it's a he?"

"The spots was all in a line. On a doe-fawn, Pa says the spots is ever' which-a-way."

"That's the female of it."

"What you mean?"

"Why, females is on-accountable."

Mill-wheel slapped the horse's flank and they broke into a trot.

"This female business. How come you and your Pa to pitch into us, when we was fightin' Oliver Hutto?"

"Oliver was gittin' the wust of it. Hit didn't seem right, a hull passel o' you-all whoppin' Oliver."

"You right. Hit were Lem's gal and Oliver's gal. They should of fit it out alone."

"But a gal cain't belong to two fellers at oncet."

"You jest don't know gals."

"I hate Twink Weatherby."

"I'd not look at her, neither. I got a widder-woman at Fort Gates, knows how to be faithful."

The matter was too complicated. Jody gave himself over to thoughts of the fawn. They passed the abandoned clearing.

He said, "Cut to the north, Mill-wheel. Hit were up here Pa got snake-bit and kilt the doe and I seed the fawn."

"What was you and your daddy doin' up this road?"

Jody hesitated.

"We was huntin' our hogs."

"Oh— Huntin' your hogs, eh? Well, don't fret about them hogs. I jest got a idee they'll be home by sundown."

"Ma and Pa'll shore be proud to see 'em come in."

"I had no idee, you-all was runnin' so tight."

"We ain't runnin' tight. We're all right."

"You Baxters has got guts, I'll say that."

"You reckon Pa'll not die?"

"Not him. His chitlin's is made o' iron."

Jody said, "Tell me about Fodder-wing. Is he shore enough ailin'? Or didn't Lem want I should see him?"

"He's purely ailin'. He ain't like the rest of us. He ain't like nobody. Seems like he drinks air 'stead o' water, and feeds on what the wild creeturs feeds on, 'stead o' bacon."

"He sees things ain't so, don't he? Spaniards and sich."

"He do, but dogged if they ain't times he'll make you think he do see 'em."

"You reckon Lem'll leave me come see him?"

"I'd not risk it yit. I'll git word to you one day when mebbe Lem's gone off, see?"

"I shore crave to see Fodder-wing."

"You'll see him. Now whereabouts you want to go, huntin' that fawn? Hit's gittin' right thick up this trail."

Suddenly Jody was unwilling to have Mill-wheel with him. If

the fawn was dead, or could not be found, he could not have his disappointment seen. And if the fawn was there, the meeting would be so lovely and so secret that he could not endure to share it.

He said, "Hit's not fur now, but hit's powerful thick for a horse. I kin make it a-foot."

"But I'm daresome to leave you, boy. Suppose you was to git lost, or snake-bit, too?"

"I'll take keer. Hit'll take me likely a long time to find the fawn, if he's wandered. Leave me off right here."

"All right, but you go mighty easy now, pokin' in them pal-meeters. This is rattlesnake Heaven in these parts. You know north here, and east?"

"There, and there. That fur tall pine makes a bearin'."

"That's right. Now do things go wrong again, you or Buck, one, ride back for me. So long."

"So long, Mill-wheel. I'm shore obliged."

He waved after him. He waited for the sound of the hooves to end, then cut to the right. The scrub was still. Only his own crackling of twigs sounded across the silence. He was eager almost past caution, but he broke a bough and pushed it ahead of him where the growth was thick and the ground invisible. Rattlers got out of the way when they had a chance. Penny had gone farther into the oak thicket than he remembered. He wondered for an instant if he had mistaken his direction. Then a buzzard rose in front of him and flapped into the air. He came into the clearing under the oaks. Buzzards sat in a circle around the carcass of the doe. They turned their heads on their long scrawny necks and hissed at him. He threw his bough at them and they flew into an adjacent tree. Their wings creaked and whistled like rusty pump-handles. The sand showed large cat-prints, he could not tell whether of wild-cat or of panther. But the big cats killed fresh, and they had left the doe to the carrion birds. He asked himself whether the sweeter meat of the fawn had scented the air for the curled nostrils.

He skirted the carcass and parted the grass at the place where he had seen the fawn. It did not seem possible that it was only yesterday. The fawn was not there. He circled the clearing. There was no sound, no sign. The buzzards clacked their wings, impatient to return to their business. He returned to the spot where the fawn had emerged and dropped to all fours, studying the sand for the small hoof-prints. The night's rain had washed away all tracks except those of cat and buzzards. But the cat-sign had not been made in this direction. Under a scrub palmetto he was able to make out a track, pointed and dainty as the mark of a ground-dove. He crawled past the palmetto.

Movement directly in front of him startled him so that he tumbled backward. The fawn lifted its face to his. It turned its head with a wide, wondering motion and shook him through with the stare of its liquid eyes. It was quivering. It made no effort to rise or run. Jody could not trust himself to move.

He whispered, "It's me."

The fawn lifted its nose, scenting him. He reached out one hand and laid it on the soft neck. The touch made him delirious. He moved forward on all fours until he was close beside it. He put his arms around its body. A light convulsion passed over it but it did not stir. He stroked its sides as gently as though the fawn were a china deer and he might break it. Its skin was softer than the white 'coonskin knapsack. It was sleek and clean and had a sweet scent of grass. He rose slowly and lifted the fawn from the ground. It was no heavier than old Julia. Its legs hung limply. They were surprisingly long and he had to hoist the fawn as high as possible under his arm.

He was afraid that it might kick and bleat at sight and smell of its mother. He skirted the clearing and pushed his way into the thicket. It was difficult to fight through with his burden. The fawn's legs caught in the bushes and he could not lift his own with freedom. He tried to shield its face from prickling vines. Its head bobbed with his stride. His heart thumped with the marvel of its acceptance of him. He reached the trail and walked as fast as he could until he came to the intersection with the road home. He stopped to rest and set the fawn down on its dangling legs. It wavered on them. It looked at him and bleated.

He said, enchanted, "I'll tote you time I git my breath."

He remembered his father's saying that a fawn would follow that had been first carried. He started away slowly. The fawn stared after him. He came back to it and stroked it and walked away again. It took a few wobbling steps toward him and cried piteously. It was willing to follow him. It belonged to him. It was his own. He was light-headed with his joy. He wanted to fondle it, to run and romp with it, to call to it to come to him. He dared not alarm it. He picked it up and carried it in front of him over his two arms. It seemed to him that he walked without effort. He had the strength of a Forrester.

His arms began to ache and he was forced to stop again. When he walked on, the fawn followed him at once. He allowed it to walk a little distance, then picked it up again. The distance home was nothing. He could have walked all day and into the night, carrying it and watching it follow. He was wet with sweat but a light breeze blew through the June morning, cooling him. The sky was as clear as spring water in a blue china cup. He came to the clearing. It was fresh and green after the night's rain. He could see Buck Forrester following old Cæsar at the plow in the cornfield. He thought he heard him curse the horse's slowness. He fumbled with the gate latch and was finally obliged to set down the fawn to manage it. It came to him that he would walk into the house, into Penny's bedroom, with the fawn walking behind him. But at the steps, the fawn balked and refused to climb them. He picked it up and went to his father. Penny lay with closed eyes.

Jody called, "Pa! Lookit!"

Penny turned his head. Jody stood beside him, the fawn clutched hard against him. It seemed to Penny that the boy's eyes were as bright as the fawn's. His face lightened, seeing them together.

He said, "I'm proud you found him."

"Pa, he wa'n't skeert o' me. He were layin' up right where his mammy had made his bed."

"The does learns 'em that, time they're borned. You kin step on a fawn, times, they lay so still."

"Pa, I toted him, and when I set him down, right off he follered me. Like a dog, Pa."

"Ain't that fine? Let's see him better."

Jody lifted the fawn high. Penny reached out a hand and touched its nose. It bleated and reached hopefully for his fingers.

He said, "Well, leetle feller. I'm sorry I had to take away your mammy."

"You reckon he misses her?"

"No. He misses his rations and he knows that. He misses somethin' else but he don't know jest what."

Ma Baxter came into the room.

"Look, Ma, I found him."

"I see."

"Ain't he purty, Ma? Lookit them spots all in rows. Lookit them big eyes. Ain't he purty?"

"He's powerful young. Hit'll take milk for him a long whiles. I don't know as I'd of give my consent, if I'd knowed he was so young."

Penny said, "Ory, I got one thing to say, and I'm sayin' it now, and then I'll have no more talk of it. The leetle fawn's as welcome in this house as Jody. It's hissen. We'll raise it without grudgment o' milk or meal. You got me to answer to, do I ever hear you quarrelin' about it. This is Jody's fawn jest like Julia's my dog."

Jody had never heard his father speak to her so sternly. The tone must hold familiarity for his mother, however, for she opened and shut her mouth and blinked her eyes.

She said, "I only said it was young."

"All right. So it is."

He closed his eyes.

He said, "If ever'body's satisfied now, I'd thank you to leave me rest. Hit puts my heart to jerkin', to talk."

Jody said, "I'll fix its milk, Ma. No need you should bother."

She was silent. He went to the kitchen. The fawn wobbled after him. A pan of morning's milk stood in the kitchen safe. The cream had risen on it. He skimmed the cream into a jug and used his shirt sleeve to wipe up the few drops he could not keep from spilling. If he could keep the fawn from being any trouble to his mother, she would mind it less. He poured milk into a small gourd. He held it out to the fawn. It butted it suddenly, smelling the milk. He saved it precariously from spilling over the floor. He led the fawn outside to the yard and began again. It could make nothing of the milk in the gourd.

He dipped his fingers in the milk and thrust them into the fawn's soft wet mouth. It sucked greedily. When he withdrew them, it bleated frantically and butted him. He dipped his fingers again and as the fawn sucked, he lowered them slowly into the milk. The fawn blew and sucked and snorted. It stamped its small hooves impatiently. As long as he held his fingers below the level of the milk, the fawn was content. It closed its eyes dreamily. It was ecstasy to feel its tongue against his hand. Its small tail flicked back and forth. The last of the milk vanished in a swirl of foam and gurgling. The fawn bleated and butted but its frenzy was appeased. Jody was tempted to go for more milk, but even with his father's backing he was afraid to press his advantage too far. A doe's bag was as small as a yearling heifer's. Surely the fawn had had as much as its mother could have given it. It lay down suddenly, exhausted and replete.

He gave his attention to a bed for it. It would be too much to ask, to bring it into the house. He went to the shed behind the house and cleaned out a corner down to the sand. He went to the live oaks at the north end of the yard and pulled down armfuls of Spanish moss. He made a thick bed in the shed. A hen was on a nest close by. Her bright beady eyes watched him dubiously. She finished her laying and flew through the door, cackling. The nest was a new one, with six eggs in it. Jody gathered them carefully and took them to his mother in the kitchen.

He said, "You'll be proud to git these, Ma. Extry eggs."

"Hit's a good thing they's somethin' extry around to eat."

He ignored the comment.

He said, "The new nest is right next to where I fixed the fawn's bed. In the shed, where it'll not bother nobody."

She did not answer and he went outside where the fawn lay under a mulberry tree. He gathered it up and carried it to its bed in the dark shed.

"Now you belong to do whatever I tell you," he said. "Like as if I was your mammy. I tell you to lay here 'til I come git you agin."

The fawn blinked its eyelids. It groaned comfortably and dropped its head. He tiptoed from the shed. No dog, he thought, could be more biddable. He went to the wood-pile and shaved fine splinters of fatwood for kindling. He arranged the pile neatly. He gathered an armful of black-jack oak and took it to his mother's wood-box in the kitchen.

He said, "Was it all right, Ma, the way I skimmed the cream?"

"Hit was all right."

He said, "Fodder-wing's ailin'."

"Is?"

"Lem wouldn't leave me see him. Lem's the only one is mad at us, Ma. On account of Oliver's gal."

"Uh-huh."

"Mill-wheel said he'd leave me know and I could slip in some time and see Fodder-wing when Lem ain't around."

She laughed.

"You're talkified as a old woman today."

She passed him on her way to the hearth and touched his head lightly.

She said, "I feel right good, myself. I never figgered your Pa'd see daylight today."

The kitchen was filled with peace. There was a clanking of harness. Buck passed through the gate from the field and crossed the road to the lot to put up old Cæsar for the noon hour.

Jody said, "I best go he'p him."

But it was the fawn that drew him from the contentment of the house. He slipped into the shed to marvel at its existence and his possession. When he returned with Buck from the lot, chattering of the fawn, he beckoned him to follow.

He said, "Don't skeer him. There he lies——"

Buck was not as satisfying as Penny in his response. He had seen so many of Fodder-wing's pets come and go.

"He'll likely go wild and run off," he said, and went to the water-shelf to wash his hands before dinner.

A chill came over Jody. Buck was worse than his mother to take away pleasure. He lingered a moment with the fawn, stroking it. It moved its sleepy head and nuzzled his fingers. Buck could not know of the closeness. It was all the better for being secret. He left the fawn and went to the basin and washed, too. The touch of the fawn had left his hands scented with a faint grassy pungency. He hated to wash it away, but decided that his mother might not find it as pleasant.

His mother had wet and combed her hair for dinner, not with coquetry, but with pride. She wore a clean sacking apron over her brown calico.

She said to Buck, "With only Penny to do, we ain't got the rations plentiful like you folks. But we do eat clean and decent."

Jody looked quickly to see if Buck would take offense. Buck ladled grits into his plate and scooped a hole in the center for the fried eggs and gravy.

"Now, Miss Ory, don't fret about me. Jody and me'll slip off this evenin' and git you a mess o' squirrels and mebbe a turkey. I seed turkey signs the fur edge o' the pea field."

Ma Baxter filled a plate for Penny, and added a cup of milk. "You take it to him, Jody."

He went to his father. Penny shook his head at the plate.

"Hit look jest plain nasty to me, son. Set up there and feed me a spoon o' the grits, and the milk. Hit wearies me to lift my arm."

The swelling had left his face, but his arm was still three times its normal size, and his breath came heavily. He swallowed a few mouthfuls of the soft hominy and drank the milk. He motioned the plate away.

"You gittin' along all right with your baby?"

Jody reported on the moss bed.

"You picked a good place. What you fixin' to name him?"

"I jest don't know. I want a name is real special."

Buck and Ma Baxter came into the bedroom and sat down to visit. The day was hot and the sun high and there was no hurry for anything.

Penny said, "Jody's in a tight for a name for the new Baxter."

Buck said, "Tell you, Jody, when you see Fodder-wing, he'll pick a name. He's got a ear for sich things, jest like some folks has got a ear for fiddle music. He'll pick you a name is purty."

Ma Baxter said, "Go eat your dinner, Jody. That spotted fawn has takened your mind off your rations."

The opportunity was choice. He went to the kitchen and heaped a plate with food and went to the shed. The fawn was still drowsy. He sat beside it and ate his dinner. He dipped his fingers in the grease-covered grits and held them out to it, but it only snuffed and turned its head away.

He said, "You better learn somethin' besides milk."

The dirt-daubers buzzed in the rafters. He scraped his plate clean and set it aside. He lay down beside the fawn. He put one arm across its neck. It did not seem to him that he could ever be lonely again.

Hitherto Uncollected:

JESSAMINE SPRINGS
THE PELICAN'S SHADOW
THE SHELL

Jessamine
Springs

THE REVEREND THOMAS J. PRESSIKER watched the road signs abstractedly. He was lonely. His loneliness puzzled and disturbed him. God was enough for any man. God's Son was enough. He was a trifle confused in his loyalty since the night the old lady at the revival meeting had arisen and demanded to know, "If God is All, why do we have to go around worshipping two of them?"

His talk to the Kiwanis Club in Elvinsport had been a great success. He had talked on "God Is My Buddy," and the Kiwanians had understood and had slapped him afterward on his back. Yet, after they had slapped, they had turned away and formed into small, tight groups and had told stories that had evidently little to do with divinity or buddying. Their hoarse laughter was a wall shutting him off from contact with his fellow-man. He liked to laugh. When he was a little boy he had had his first taste of public acclaim, telling funny stories. Of course, they were good, clean stories, which those of the Kiwanians probably were not. Yet for all he knew, these Kiwanians' stories were as innocuous as those he had recited for public acclaim in his childhood. He had never heard one of them. Only the laughter afterward.

It seemed to him sometimes that men actually did not like him. Yet they were cordial, they were gracious, they frequently gave "a good, hot cheer for the Reverend" when he addressed them. And he liked them. He liked everybody. He had begun his storytelling, he had gone into the ministry, because he liked people and wanted them, terribly, to like him. Yet today, on this hot Florida

355

afternoon, driving his Ford from Elvinsport to Kenoha, where he would speak again on "God Is My Buddy," he sat not only behind the wheel of the car but behind a barricade. On the one side were the Kiwanians, cheering him with a sound that seemed to come from a great distance, and then going off into space to talk and laugh together. On the other side was the Reverend Pressiker, lonely, loving, and wanting to belong.

He wondered often whether the gap might not be because he was an itinerant preacher. If he had his own church, his own regular congregation, he would have a home—an earthly home, a cozy counterpart of the heavenly one, where the good and kind all gathered. His denomination was famously poor. In the small Florida villages where he filled in for the more fortunate circuit preachers, they had preaching Sunday only once or twice a month, and then had to scramble to get together a collection that would not shame them to offer and him to receive. The poverty was nothing. His text was very likely to be "Inasmuch as ye have done it unto one of the least of these my children," and he had in mind, as he preached, their poverty and their leastness. Yet even among the simple backwoods folk, with their bare, freshly washed, lifted faces, he was an alien. They shook hands with him stiffly and hurried home to their noon dinners—chicken on Sundays, unless it was hog-killing time and a fat peanut ham was on the table. He was always invited to go home to dinner with one of them, and usually he accepted. Occasionally he had to refuse after he had seen a group arguing together. He knew then that he was not wanted and that the invitation came from the unhappy combination of courtesy and pressure.

His weekday talks, he assured himself, were actually in a larger field. He put aside the thought, the knowledge, that the small-town Rotarians and Kiwanians had a time of it getting speakers for nothing. He was glad to serve. He told himself every night and every morning, kneeling by whatever hard bed was his for the moment, that he was glad to serve. All men were brothers, and as his kin listened and applauded and slapped and then went away and talked of other matters, he reminded himself that he was doing the best he could.

"Jessamine Springs. Where the County Swims."

He liked the sign and its consciousness of county. He liked the consciousness of all group formations. That was why his heart warmed and beat fast when he arose to speak in places like Elvinsport and Kenoha. He was part of a group. He belonged.

"Jessamine Springs. One Mile to the Left."

He had not had a swim since the Missionary Auxiliary at Luther had had a fish fry several years ago. He had borrowed a bathing suit and had gone in the muddy pond with the rest of them. He had said, splashing about in the warm, shallow water, "We should have a community baptizing in this fine pool." He had wondered then if he looked ridiculous in the borrowed suit, for even there, as he paddled around among them, the other swimmers had ignored him.

"Here You Are. Jessamine Springs. Everybody Welcome. 10c."

He liked that "Everybody Welcome. 10c." It was the kind of sign he would put up if he owned a swimming pool. Why, even he could go in there and swim, and nobody would know that he was any different from anyone else. His heart thumped.

A line of cars was coming out of the Springs entrance onto the highway. It was almost sunset. He turned left toward the cement-lined pool. It was fed by underground springs, and the overflow trailed off into a narrow run. There was a shed at one side. Suits could be rented. A man ahead of him was paying the dime admission fee, and another dime for a suit and towel.

The Reverend Pressiker said, "The suits are—quite sanitary, I suppose?"

"They go to the laundry," the proprietor said. "Boiled."

Pressiker pushed his change across the counter and followed his fellow-swimmer into the bathhouse marked "Men." He heard his neighbor taking off his shoes and hanging up his trousers. It was a good sound, another human's clothes being hung on the other side of the thin wall. He undressed hurriedly and arranged his own garments on the rusty nails. The cement walk seemed harsh under the soft soles of his feet. He reached the pool in time to see the man ahead of him dive from the edge. Except for the two of them, the pool was empty. He was slightly disappointed.

He had never dived, and he walked, one foot cautiously ahead of the other, down the steps into the shallow end of the pool. He splashed the water, surprisingly cold, across his chest and stomach. He stooped and gave himself to the water, spreading himself out across its receptive surface. He fluttered his legs and then stood up. The shock of the cold water was delightful. He looked about for his companion. He was swimming toward him with a lazy side stroke. The Reverend Pressiker swam to meet him. They stood up at the same moment.

The other man said, "Jeez, it's cold."

Pressiker said, "A cooling fount, indeed."

The man shook his hair back from his face. "I been meaning to stop and swim here. This is on my route."

Pressiker was delighted. He said, "And on mine also."

"You on the road?"

Pressiker was often asked this question. His businesslike briefcase and civilian clothes made him appear a travelling salesman, and it pleased him to think of himself as a travelling salesman for the Lord. Usually he said, "I am on the road on the Lord's business." Now, with his longing for simple community, he said, "Indeed, yes. On the road. On the broad highway."

"Books?"

"In a way. One book. Only one."

"Kind of limited, eh? But they say this is the age of specialization."

The man dived under the water and came up some feet away, then struck out for the deep end of the pool. The Reverend Pressiker followed, swimming with a careful breast stroke. He was a little panicky as he advanced, and headed in toward the side railing. The other man turned at the deep end and swam back and joined him.

Pressiker said, "I saw many cars departing as I entered. A multitude."

"That's why I turned in—because they were leaving. I'm not so keen about swimming with a couple of dozen Boy Scouts."

"Ah yes. The little—" he hesitated. Ordinarily he would have said, "The little ones." He said, "The little shavers."

The man said, "When I swim, I like to swim. Want to race?"

"Thank you. That's good of you. I'm afraid I might falter in a—no, not foot race. It isn't a foot race, is it? I have done very little of an athletic nature in a long, arduous life given to the—I have swum very little. I use the breast stroke. I think it develops the physique, don't you?"

"I don't know about the physique, but it's damn slow."

The man stroked away, hand over hand. Pressiker watched him, then floated into the water. He counted aloud.

"One, two, kick. One, two, kick."

"You sure haven't done much of this." The man was resting his back against the far edge of the pool.

"Indeed, no. My—my work takes my—my all."

The man submerged like a porpoise, swam the length of the pool and back again, and came up blowing.

"Headed for Kenoha?"

"Yes. Yes, Kenoha."

"Where you stopping?"

"I don't know. I have not, you might say, where to lay my head. I hope to rest with friends."

"Lucky. I got an expense account, but it don't pay for beer."

Pressiker lowered himself in the water, bounced up, and lowered himself again. He was tremendously happy. He was immersed not in water but in a fluid fellowship.

"Look not on the wine when it is red," he said gaily, "but nothing is said about beer!"

He felt devilish and free. He thought of asking the man to have a beer with him in Kenoha.

"Well, I've had enough exercise for a guy that doesn't get much," said the other man. He swung himself over the edge of the pool and shook himself like a dog. "Be seeing you, Reverend," he said.

"Be seeing you." Pressiker waved a wet arm after his friend.

The man sloshed into the bathhouse. Pressiker stood up in the shallow water and stared after him.

"Now, how could he possibly know I was a preacher?"

He hitched up the straps of the rented bathing suit and looked about the empty pool. His throat tightened as it had done when he was a little boy, trying not to cry.

The Pelican's
Shadow

THE LEMON-COLORED AWNING over the terrace swelled in the
southeasterly breeze from the ocean. Dr. Tifton had chosen
lemon so that when the hungry Florida sun had fed on the canvas
the color would still be approximately the same.

"Being practical on one's honeymoon," he had said to Elsa,
"stabilizes one's future."

At the moment she had thought it would have been nicer to say
"our" honeymoon and "our" future, but she had dismissed it as
another indication of her gift for critical analysis, which her husband considered unfortunate.

"I am the scientist of the family, my mouse," he said often. "Let
me do the analyzing. I want you to develop all your latent fem-
ininity."

Being called "my mouse" was probably part of the development.
It had seemed quite sweet at the beginning, but repetition had
made the mouse feel somehow as though the fur were being worn
off in patches.

Elsa leaned back in the long beach chair and let the magazine
containing her husband's new article drop to the rough coquina
paving of the terrace. Howard did express himself with an exquisite precision. The article was a gem, just scientific enough,
just humorous, just human enough to give the impression of a
choice mind back of it. It was his semi-scientific writings that had
brought them together.

Fresh from college, she had tumbled, butter side up, into a job
as assistant to the feature editor of *Home Life*. Because of her

361

enthusiasm for the Tifton series of articles, she had been allowed
to handle the magazine's correspondence with him. He had written
her, on her letter of acceptance of "Algae and Their Human
Brothers":

MY DEAR MISS WHITTINGTON:
   Fancy a woman's editor being appealed to by my algae! Will you
have tea with me, so that my eyes, accustomed to the microscope, may
feast themselves on a *femme du monde* who recognizes not only that
science is important but that in the proper hands it may be made
important even to those little fire-lit circles of domesticity for which
your publication is the *raison d'être*!

   She had had tea with him, and he had proved as distinguished
as his articles. He was not handsome. He was, in fact, definitely
tubby. His hair was steel-gray and he wore gray tweed suits, so
that, for all his squattiness, the effect was smoothly sharp. His
age, forty-odd, was a part of his distinction. He had marriage, it
appeared, in the back of his mind. He informed her with engag-
ing frankness that his wife must be young and therefore malle-
able. His charm, his prestige, were irresistible. The "union," as
he called it, had followed quickly, and of course she had dropped
her meaningless career to give a feminine backing to his endeavors,
scientific and literary.
   "It is not enough," he said, "to be a scientist. One must also be
articulate."
   He was immensely articulate. No problem, from the simple ones
of a fresh matrimony to the involved matters of his studies and
his writings, found him without an expression.
   "Howard intellectualizes about everything," she wrote her
former editor, May Morrow, from her honeymoon. She felt a
vague disloyalty as she wrote it, for it did not convey his terrific
humanity.
   "A man is a man first," he said, "and *then* a scientist."
   His science took care of itself, in his capable hands. It was his
manhood that occupied her energies. Not his male potency—
which again took care of itself, with no particular concern for her
own needs—but all the elaborate mechanism that, to him, made up

the substance of a man's life. Hollandaise sauce, for instance. He had a passion for hollandaise, and like his microscopic studies, like his essays, it must be perfect. She looked at her wristwatch. It was his wedding gift. She would have liked something delicate and diamond-studded and feminine, something suitable for "the mouse," but he had chosen a large, plain-faced gold Hamilton of railroad accuracy. It was six o'clock. It was not time for the hollandaise, but it was time to check up on Jones, the manservant and cook. Jones had a trick of boiling the vegetables too early, so that they lay limply under the hollandaise instead of standing up firm and decisive. She stirred in the beach chair and picked up the magazine. It would seem as though she were careless, indifferent to his achievements, if he found it sprawled on the coquina instead of arranged on top of the copies of *Fortune* on the red velvet fire seat.

She gave a start. A shadow passed between the terrace and the ocean. It flapped along on the sand with a reality greater than whatever cast the shadow. She looked out from under the awning. One of those obnoxious pelicans was flapping slowly down the coast. She felt an unreasonable irritation at sight of the thick, hunched shoulders, the out-of-proportion wings, the peculiar contour of the head, lifting at the back to something of a peak. She could not understand why she so disliked the birds. They were hungry, they searched out their food, they moved and mated like every living thing. They were basically drab, like most human beings, but all that was no reason for giving a slight shudder when one passed over the lemon-colored awning and winged its self-satisfied way down the Florida coastline.

She rose from the beach chair, controlling her annoyance. Howard was not sensitive to her moods, for which she was grateful, but she had found that the inexplicable crossness which sometimes seized her made her unduly sensitive to his. As she feared, Jones had started the cauliflower ahead of time. It was only just in the boiling water, so she snatched it out and plunged it in ice water.

"Put the cauliflower in the boiling water at exactly six-thirty," she said to Jones.

As Howard so wisely pointed out, most of the trouble with servants lay in not giving exact orders.

"If servants knew as much as you do," he said, "they would not be working for you. Their minds are vague. That is why they are servants."

Whenever she caught herself being vague, she had a moment's unhappy feeling that she should probably have been a lady's maid. It would at least have been a preparation for matrimony. Turning now from the cauliflower, she wondered if marriage always laid these necessities for exactness on a woman. Perhaps all men were not concerned with domestic precision. She shook off the thought, with the sense of disloyalty that always stabbed her when she was critical. As Howard said, a household either ran smoothly, with the mechanism hidden, or it clanked and jangled. No one wanted clanking and jangling.

She went to her room to comb her hair and powder her face and freshen her lipstick. Howard liked her careful grooming. He was himself immaculate. His gray hair, smoothed back over his scientist's head that lifted to a little peak in the back, his gray suits, even his gray pajamas were incredibly neat, as smooth and trim as feathers.

She heard the car on the shell drive and went to meet him. He had brought the mail from the adjacent city, where he had the use of a laboratory.

"A ghost from the past," he said sententiously, and handed her a letter from *Home Life.*

He kissed her with a longer clinging than usual, so that she checked the date in her mind. Two weeks ago—yes, this was his evening to make love to her. Their months of marriage were marked off into two-week periods as definitely as though the / line on the typewriter cut through them. He drew off from her with disapproval if she showed fondness between a / and a /. She went to the living room to read her letter from May Morrow.

Dear Elsa:
Your beach house sounds altogether too idyllic. What previous incarnated suffering has licenced you to drop into an idyll? And so young in life. Well, maybe I'll get mine next time.

As you can imagine, there have been a hundred people after your job. The Collins girl that I rushed into it temporarily didn't work out at all, and I was beginning to despair when Jane Maxe, from *Woman's Outlook*, gave me a ring and said she was fed up with their politics and would come to us if the job was permanent. I assured her that it was hers until she had to be carried out on her shield. You see, I know your young type. You've burned your bridges and set out to be A Good Wife, and hell will freeze before you quit anything you tackle.

Glad the Distinguished Spouse proves as clever in daily conversation as in print. Have you had time to notice that trick writers have of saying something neat, recognizing it at once as a precious nut to be stored, then bringing it out later in the long hard winter of literary composition? You will. Drop me a line. I wonder about things sometimes.

MAY

She wanted to sit down at the portable at once, but Dr. Tifton came into the room.

"I'll have my shower later," he said, and rolled his round gray eyes with meaning.

His mouth, she noticed, made a long, thin line that gave the impression of a perpetual half-smile. She mixed the Martinis and he sipped his with appreciation. He had a smug expectancy that she recognized from her brief dealings with established authors. He was waiting for her favorable comment on his article.

"Your article was grand," she said. "If I were still an editor, I'd have grabbed it."

He lifted his eyebrows. "Of course," he said, "editors were grabbing my articles before I knew you." He added complacently, "And after."

"I mean," she said uncomfortably, "that an editor can only judge things by her own acceptance."

"An editor?" He looked sideways at her. His eye seemed to have the ability to focus backward. "And what does a wife think of my article?"

She laughed. "Oh, a wife thinks that anything you do is perfect." She added, "Isn't that what wives are for?"

She regretted the comment immediately, but he was bland.

"I really think I gave the effect I wanted," he said. "Science is of no use to the layman unless it's humanized."

They sipped the Martinis.

"I'd like to have you read it aloud," he said, studying his glass casually. "One learns things from another's reading."

She picked up the magazine gratefully. The reading would fill nicely the time between cocktails and dinner.

"It really gives the effect, doesn't it?" he said when she had finished. "I think anyone would get the connection, of which I am always conscious, between the lower forms of life and the human."

"It's a swell job," she said.

Dinner began successfully. The donac broth was strong enough. She had gone out in her bathing suit to gather the tiny clams just before high tide. The broiled pompano was delicately brown and flaky. The cauliflower was all right, after all. The hollandaise, unfortunately, was thin. She had so frightened Jones about the heinousness of cooking it too long that he had taken it off the fire before it had quite thickened.

"My dear," Dr. Tifton said, laying down his fork, "surely it is not too much to ask of an intelligent woman to teach a servant to make a simple sauce."

She felt a little hysterical. "Maybe I'm not intelligent," she said.

"Of course you are," he said soothingly. "Don't misunderstand me. I am not questioning your intelligence. You just do not realize the importance of being exact with an inferior."

He took a large mouthful of the cauliflower and hollandaise. The flavor was beyond reproach, and he weakened.

"I know," he said, swallowing and scooping generously again, "I know that I am a perfectionist. It's a bit of a bother sometimes, but of course it is the quality that makes me a scientist. A literary—shall I say literate?—no, articulate scientist."

He helped himself to a large pat of curled butter for his roll. The salad, the pineapple mousse, the after-dinner coffee and liqueur went off acceptably. He smacked his lips ever so faintly.

"Excuse me a moment, my mouse," he said. His digestion was rapid and perfect.

Now that he was in the bathroom, it had evidently occurred to him to take his shower and get into his dressing gown. She heard the water running and the satisfied humming he emitted when all was well. She would have time, for he was meticulous with his fortnightly special toilet, to begin a letter to May Morrow. She took the portable typewriter out to a glass-covered table on the terrace. The setting sun reached benignly under the awning. She drew a deep breath. It was a little difficult to begin. May had almost sounded as though she did not put full credence in the idyll. She wanted to write enthusiastically but judiciously, so May would understand that she, Elsa, was indeed a fortunate young woman, wed irrevocably, by her own deliberate, intelligent choice, to a brilliant man—a real man, second only in scientific and literary rating to Dr. Beebe.

DEAR MAY:

It was grand to hear from you. I'm thrilled about Jane Maxe. What a scoop! I could almost be jealous of both of you if my lines hadn't fallen into such gloriously pleasant places.

I am, of course, supremely happy—

She leaned back. She was writing gushily. Married women had the damndest way, she had always noticed, of gushing. Perhaps the true feminine nature was sloppy, after all. She deleted "gloriously," crossed out "supremely," and inserted "tremendously." She would have to copy the letter.

A shadow passed between the terrace and the ocean. She looked up. One of those beastly pelicans was flapping down the coast over the sand dunes. He had already fed, or he would be flapping, in that same sure way of finding what he wanted, over the surf. It was ridiculous to be disturbed by him. Yet somewhere she suspected there must be an association of thoughts that had its base in an unrecognized antipathy. Something about the pelican's shadow, darkening her heart and mind with that absurd desperation, must be connected with some profound and secret dread, but she could not seem to put her finger on it.

She looked out from under the lemon-colored awning. The pelican had turned and was flapping back again. She had a good look at him. He was neatly gray, objectionably neat for a creature with such greedy habits. His round head, lifted to a peak, was sunk against his heavy shoulders. His round gray eye looked down below him, a little behind him, with a cold, pleased, superior expression. His long, thin mouth was unbearably smug, with the expression of a partial smile.

"Oh, go on about your business!" she shouted at him.

The
Shell

AFTER THE MESSAGE came, she spent most of the time on the
beach picking up sea shells. Sometimes she made piles of
all kinds. Sometimes she passed by the common shells and picked
up only the rare ones. She waited for three days, as though the
mere passage of time would make the message clear. Then she
remembered that Bill had told her to get on the beach bus and
go to the Red Cross in the city if she was in trouble. The message
seemed to be trouble, so she walked from the cottage on the dune
to the coastal highway and stood there with her hands folded over
her purse, and a bus stopped for her, as Bill had said it would do.
She was so young and so pretty that people on the bus smiled at
her, and she smiled back, like a shy but amiable child. She got off
the bus at the terminal. She stood still. The driver passed her on
his way to the office and turned back.

He asked, "Where did you want to go?"

"I want to go to the Red Cross."

"It's right across the street. There."

Inside the office she stood in front of a desk while many people
came and went and talked with a plain, capable woman. After a
long time the woman said, without looking up, "Can I do something for you?"

"Please, can you tell me what it means when it says he is
missing?"

The woman looked up in amazement. She hardened before the
gentle face with china-blue eyes, loose blond hair, and an infuri-
ating innocence.

She said, "Really now, just what do you think it means?"

"I think it means they don't know where he is. Not right now."

"Not right now?"

"No, not the same as lost. I thought maybe you'd know how long it will take them to find him, if it isn't the same as lost."

"Really! I can assure you it is the same as lost. It means he may possibly be found but that probably he won't."

"Probably he won't?"

"Almost certainly not. Is it someone close to you?"

"Oh, no. He's a long way away. He said it would be a long way."

"Is there anything we can do for you?"

"I don't know."

She returned to the bus station and stood until the same driver asked her if she wanted to go back to the beach. When she opened her purse to pay her fare, she saw Bill's picture and took it out. It was not the same as when she looked at him, himself, but it was tangible, and she held it in her lap as a child holds a doll. She remembered with pleasure that Bill had her picture, too, and had written her—she had had to ask the colored girl to explain only a few of the words—that he had showed it to the men on his ship and they had said she was very pretty. He knew that it pleased her to be told she was pretty, though she was without vanity, and she kept her silky hair brushed and her dainty body neat and clean as instinctively as a kitten washes its fur. She understood Bill's showing the picture, but she would not have understood what followed.

Even in the picture, the exquisite wistful face was entirely vacuous. One man had said maliciously, "Smart, too?"

Bill had eyed the questioner. "My wife," he said gravely, "is a moron. She's a moron the way a wild rose is a moron."

The man, shocked, had said gruffly, "She got anybody to look out for her while you're over?"

"A colored girl I've had several years. She understands. She'll take care of her until I get back. We don't either of us have any family."

On the bus, forgetting to watch for her stop, she thought about
the colored girl. The girl had left a week before the message came.
She had cooked a great many things and filled the icebox and
said, "I hates to fail you. I hates to fail him, when I promised.
But I cain't live this lonesome life no more. It was all right, summers, when we had gas to go and he took me back'ards and
fo'wards. Nobody cain't come to see me, I cain't git no place,
excusin' goin' on the bus oncet a week marketin'. My boy friend
he said he couldn't fool with me no more, didn't I git to town. He
hadn't ought to of left you in this lonesome place."

He had left her in the cottage on the dune because she was
happy at the seashore in the summer. The shells kept her occupied for hours at a time. And too, he would be on the ocean most
of the time, he told her, and she might look at it and know that
somewhere he was there. The rent on the cottage was paid, and
the rent on the small apartment in the city for the winter, and the
colored girl understood that they were to move to the city when
the fall storms began.

She did not notice her stop, but the bus driver remembered, and
when he stopped the bus and looked back at her she got off and
walked up to the cottage. She felt hungry and went to the icebox.
There did not seem to be very much left in it, and it occurred to
her that she should have bought something while she was in the
city. She had used most of her money, but there were two government checks in her purse. The colored girl had cashed the
previous ones for her, since she found the bank confusing, although everyone was always kind and helpful. She ate some
crackers and peanut butter and walked automatically down to the
beach.

The tide was low and the sea calm. She wished she had put on
her bathing suit, even though she understood that she was not to
go out in the water any deeper than her knees. A fisherman had
told the colored girl that the sharks were bad. They were seldom
seen so far north on the coast, but the colored girl explained to
her that the sinking of ships had disposed dead bodies of sailors
through the water and the sharks had followed. One day she had

found a pair of blue dungarees on the beach, the cuffs tied with string. She stared at them a long time, since she thought there was probably a dead sailor in them. On approaching closer she saw that they were empty.

Now she gathered a few shells idly and sat down on the sand and arranged them in a circular pattern. She tried to think. Bill had often urged her, "Try to think, honey. Try real hard." She asked herself what she should think about, and the answer came easily, "About Bill." She could remember a great deal, although it was spread in a diffused fog, with only the memory of his smile and his always being there standing clear. There had been perhaps a few years when she had not known him, but they were lost in the haze that veiled the same years when her mother and father were alive. She had been six years old when she went to live with her older sister. Long after she and Bill were married and the sister had moved somewhere across the country, she had heard Bill say, "I don't know whether she was born like that, or whether her sister did it to her. Her sister hated her because she was so pretty, and because she didn't want her, and she beat her as I wouldn't beat a dog. It seems to me you can hurt a child's mind that way. But I don't know."

She had known Bill was talking about her, but she had felt no special interest. The beatings had faded into the fog, too. But she remembered Bill in the first grade at school. She remembered standing in the center of a ring of children who were jostling her as animals jostle the unnatural or injured before they attack, and then Bill came into the ring and the animal-children melted away. After that, down the years, there was only Bill. He walked with her to and from school, carrying her books and her lunch basket. The lunch basket usually had cruelly little in it, and he shared his with her, sitting in the play yard beside her. When he found that she did not understand the lessons, and turned in blank copybooks for her homework, he wrote out her lessons. He was unable to protect her in the classroom, where she only smiled and shook her head when called on. He managed the homework cleverly, and in a different handwriting, so that only one of the teachers guessed the strange condition, the strange protection, the strange love, and her he bearded, telling her that what she took for stupidity was a great shyness, because of the beatings at home. The disparity between the homework and the class lessons puzzled the teachers, but they passed her from grade to grade until the eighth grade was done and she could read and write a little, and Bill could carry her no further. He went on to high school alone, working in the afternoons and late at night, saving his money. Although he was offered a scholarship, he would not go to college but took a job and married her, and all the years had been as sweet as a south wind blowing over wild roses.

There were not many shells on the beach, for the last high tide had been a gentle one and there was no debris, either from the sea or the lands beyond the sea. She walked a way and gathered a few angel's wings and a mossy conch. Then she saw the little shell, a shell for a doll house, minute, white, turned in lovely spirals. She picked it up and spoke to it, and saw that it was broken and imperfect. It was too small and fragile, now that it was empty, to have survived the buffeting of great forces. There were tiny holes along its infinitesimal length, where the roaring seas had pounded it against the implacable sands. She nestled it against her face and when it pricked her looked closely again and saw that the tip was sharp and pointed. It was a fine pencil to write with, and she sat down and in the sand began to draw loops and circles with delight. A memory touched her and she drew a heart, as Bill had taught her, and she put inside the heart their initials, as he had also showed her.

She laughed. She looked up with surprise when a ripple of water washed over the curve of the heart. The tide was coming in. The wind was from the east and against the sky the ocean heaved and formed breakers that rolled in from a long way away. That was where Bill was, she thought, a long way away, beyond the breakers. A paw of water slapped in and wiped out half the heart on the sand. Bill was lost, he was missing, and this was what it meant. He would almost certainly not come back, for the lady had said so. But certainly he could not be altogether lost; he was only out there against the horizon. He had told her to watch the sea, for he would be there. If no one was looking for him to find him, she might look for him. "Try to think, honey. Try real hard." Oh, she would try, and she would find him, for he had never been far away.

She stood up, clutching the shell, and waded into the cool water. He could not possibly be so far away that she could not find him. The tide surged about her waist and above her small breasts. A wave washed over her face. The undertow lifted her feet and there was under her no more the earth but a fluid force of great power, swaying her like seaweed. A smooth body brushed past her, nudging her with a hard nose, and then another. She opened her hand and the little empty shell dropped from it and spiralled down and through the water, to reach the sand and be thrown by the tide on the beach again, still further to be broken. The shell was worthless, and had been even when there was life within it. But it was a pretty little thing and it was a pity that it should be quite destroyed.

from
WHEN THE WHIPPOORWILL

Gal
Young Un

THE HOUSE was invisible from the road which wound, almost untraveled, through the flat-woods. Once every five days a turpentine wagon creaked down the ruts, and Negroes moved like shadows among the pines. A few hunters in season came upon them chipping boxes, scraping aromatic gum from red pots into encrusted buckets; inquired the way and whether quail or squirrel or turkey had been seen. Then hunters and turpentiners moved again along the road, stepping on violets and yellow pitcher-plants that rimmed the edges.

The Negroes were aware of the house. It stood a few hundred yards away, hidden behind two live oaks, isolated and remote in a patch of hammock. It was a tall square two-stories. The woman who gave them water from her well when the near-by branch was dry looked to them like the house, tall and bare and lonely, weathered gray, like its unpainted cypress. She seemed forgotten.

The two white men, hunting lazily down the road, did not remember—if they had ever known—that a dwelling stood here. Flushing a covey of quail that flung themselves like feathered bronze discs at the cover of the hammock, their first shots flicked through the twin oaks. They followed their pointer dog on the trail of single birds and stopped short in amazement. Entering the north fringe of the hammock, they had come out on a sandy open yard. A woman was watching them from the back stoop of an old house.

"Shootin' mighty close, men," she called.

Her voice sounded unused, like a rusty iron hinge.

377

The older man whistled in the dog, ranging feverishly in the low palmettos. The younger swaggered to the porch. He pushed back the black slouch hat from his brazen eyes.

"Never knowed nobody lived in six miles o' here."

His tone was insolent. He drew a flattened package of cigarettes from his corduroy hunting jacket, lighted one, and waited for her to begin scolding. Women always quarreled with him. Middle-aged women, like this one, quarreled earnestly; young ones snapped at him playfully.

"It's a long ways from anybody, ain't it?" she agreed.

He stared at her between puffs.

"Jesus, yes."

"I don't keer about you shootin'," she said. "It's purely sociable, hearin' men-folks acrost the woods. A shot come thu a winder jest now, that's all the reason I spoke."

The intruders shifted their shotguns uneasily. The older man touched his finger to his cap.

"That's all right, ma'am."

His companion strolled to the stone curbing of an open well. He peered into its depths, shimmering where the sun of high noon struck vertically.

"Good water?"

"The finest ever. Leave me fetch you a clean cup."

She turned into the house for a white china coffee cup. The men wound up a bucket of water on creaking ropes. The older man drank politely from the proffered cup. The other guzzled directly from the bucket. He reared back his head like a satisfied hound, dripping a stream of crystal drops from his red mouth.

"Ain't your dog thirsty? Here—reckon my ol' cat won't fuss if he drinks outen his dish." The woman stroked the animal's flanks as he lapped. "Ain't he a fine feller?"

The hunters began to edge away.

"Men, I jest got common rations, bacon an' biscuit an' coffee, but you're plumb welcome to set down with me."

"No thank you, ma'am." They looked at the sun. "Got to be moseyin' home."

The younger man was already on his way, sucking a straw. The other fumbled in his game-pocket.

"Sorry we come so close up on you, lady. How 'bout a bird for your dinner?"

She reached out a large hand for the quail.

"I'd shore thank you for it. I'm a good shot on squirrel, an' turkeys when I git 'em roosted. Birds is hard without no dog to point 'em. I gits hungry for quail . . ."

Her voice trailed off as the hunters walked through the pines toward the road. She waved her hand in case they should turn around. They did not look back.

The man was hunting alone because he had been laughed at. His cronies in the Florida village, to which he had returned after a few years' wandering, knew that he detested solitude. It was alien to him, a silent void into which he sank as into quicksand. He had stopped at the general store to pick up a hunting partner. The men lounging there hours at a time were usually willing to go with him. This time none was ready.

"Come go with me, Willy," he insisted. "I cain't go by myself."

The storekeeper called over his shoulder, weighing out a quarter's worth of water-ground meal for a Negro.

"You'll git ketched out alone in the woods sometime, Trax, an' nobody won't know who 'tis."

The men guffawed.

"Trax always got to git him a buddy."

His smoldering eyes flared at them. He spat furiously across the rough pine floor of the store.

"I ain't got to git me none o' these sorry catbirds."

He had clattered down the wooden steps, spitting angrily every few feet. They were jealous, he thought, because he had been over on the east coast. He had turned instinctively down the south road out of the village. Old man Blaine had brought him this way last week. He hunted carelessly for two or three hours, taking pot shots at several coveys that rose under his feet. His anger made him miss the birds widely. It was poor sport without a companion and a dog.

Now he realized that he was lost. As a boy he had hunted these woods, but always with other boys and men. He had gone through them unseeing, stretching his young muscles luxuriously, absorbing lazily the rich Florida sun, cooling his face at every running branch. His shooting had been careless, avid. He liked to see the brown birds tumble in midair. He liked to hunt with the pack, to gorge on the game dinners they cooked by lake shores under oak trees. When the group turned homeward, he followed, thinking of supper; of the 'shine his old man kept hidden in the smokehouse; of the girls he knew. Some one else knew north and south, and the cross patterns of the piney-woods roads. The lonely region was now as unfamiliar as though he had been a stranger.

It was an hour or two past noon. He leaned his 12-gauge shotgun against a pine and looked about him nervously. He knew by the sun that he had come continuously south. He had crossed and recrossed the road, and could not decide whether it now lay to the right or left. If he missed it to the right, he would come to cypress swamps. He licked his lips. If he picked the wrong road to the left, it would bring him out a couple of miles above the village. That would be better. He could always get a lift back. He picked up his gun and began to walk.

In a few minutes a flat gray surface flashed suddenly from a patch of hammock. He stopped short. Pleasure swept over him, cooling his hot irritation. He recognized the house where he and Blaine had drawn water. He had cursed Blaine for giving a quail to the woman. He wiped the sweat from his face. The woman would feed him and direct him out of the flat-woods. Instinctively he changed his gait from a shuffling drag to his customary swagger.

He rapped loudly on the smooth cypress front door. It had a half-moon fanlight over it. The house was old but it was capacious and good. There was, for all its bareness, an air of prosperity. Clean white curtains hung at the windows. A striped cat startled him by rearing against his legs. He kicked it away. The woman must be gone. A twig cracked in the yard beyond the high piazza. He turned. The woman was stalking around the side of the house to see before she was seen. Her gray face lightened as she recognized him. She laughed.

"Mister, if you knowed how long it's been since I heerd a rap. Don't nobody knock on my front door. The turpentine niggers calls so's I won't shoot, and the hunters comes a-talkin' to the well."

She climbed the front steps with the awkwardness of middle age. She dried a hand on her flour-sacking apron and held it out to him. He took it limply, interrupting the talk that began to flow from her. He was ugly with hunger and fatigue and boredom.

"How 'bout a mess o' them rations you was offerin' me last week?"

His impatience was tempered with the tone of casual intimacy in which he spoke to all women. It bridged time and space. The woman flushed.

"I'd be mighty well pleased——"

She opened the front door. It stuck at the sill, and she threw a strong body against it. He did not offer to help. He strolled in ahead of her. As she apologized for the moments it would take to fry bacon and make coffee, he was already staring about him at the large room. When she came to him from the kitchen half an hour later, her face red with her hurry, the room had made an impress on his mind, as roads and forests could not do. The size of the room, of the clay fireplace, the adequacy of chairs and tables of a frontier period, the luxury of a Brussels carpet, although ancient, over wood, the plenitude of polished, unused kerosene lamps—the details lay snugly in his mind like hoarded money.

Hungry, with the smell of hot food filling his breath, he took time to smooth his sleek black hair at a walnut-framed mirror on the varnished matchboard wall. He made his toilet boldly in front of the woman. A close watching of his dark face, of the quickness of his hands moving over his affectation of clipped side-burns, could only show her that he was good to look at. He walked to the kitchen with a roll, sprawling his long legs under the table.

With the first few mouthfuls of food good humor returned to him. He indulged himself in graciousness. The woman served him lavishly with fried cornbread and syrup, coffee, white bacon in thick slices, and fruits and vegetables of her own canning. His gluttony delighted her. His mouth was full, bent low over his heaped plate.

"You live fine, ma'am, for any one lives plumb alone."

She sat down opposite him, wiping back the wet gray hair from her forehead, and poured herself a convivial cup of coffee.

"Jim—that was my husband—an' Pa always did say if they was good rations in the house they'd orter be on the table. I ain't got over the habit."

"You been livin' alone quite some time?"

"Jim's fifteen year dead. Pa 'bout six."

"Don't you never go nowheres?"

"I got no way to go. I kep' up stock for two-three year after Pa died, but 'twa'n't wuth the worry. They's a family lives two mile closer to town than me, has a horse an' wagon. I take 'em my list o' things 'bout oncet a month. Seems like . . ."

He scarcely listened.

A change of atmosphere in her narrative indicated suddenly to him that she was asking him about himself.

"You a stranger?"

She was eager, leaning on the table waiting for his answer.

He finished a saucer of preserved figs, scraping at the rich syrup with relish. He tilted back in his chair luxuriously and threw the match from his cigarette in the general direction of the wood stove. He was entirely at home. His belly well filled with good food, his spirit touched with the unfailing intoxication to him of a woman's interest, he teetered and smoked and talked of his life, of his deeds, his dangers.

"You ever heerd the name o' Trax Colton?"

She shook her head. He tapped his chest significantly, nodding at her.

"That's me. You've heerd tell, if you on'y remembered, o' me leavin' here a few years back on account of a little cuttin' fuss. I been on the east coast—Daytona, Melbourne, all them places. The fuss blowed over an' I come back. Fixin' to take up business here."

He frowned importantly. He tapped a fresh cigarette on the table, as he had learned to do from his companions the past years. He thought with pleasure of all that he had learned, of the sophistication that lay over his Cracker speech and ways like a cheap bright coat.

"I'm an A-1 bootlegger, ma'am."

For the time being he was a big operator from the east coast. He told her of small sturdy boats from Cuba, of signal flares on the St. Augustine beach at midnight, of the stream of swift automobiles moving in and out just before high tide. Her eyes shone. She plucked at the throat of her brown-checked gingham dress, breathing quickly. It was fitting that this dark glamorous young man should belong to the rocket-lit world of danger. It was ecstasy painful in its sharpness, that he should be tilted back at her table, flicking his fragrant ashes on her clean, lonely floor.

He was entirely amiable as he left her. Pleased with himself, he was for a moment pleased with her. She was a good woman. He laid his hand patronizingly on her shoulder. He stroked the striped cat on his way down the steps. This time he turned to lift his hand to her. She waved heartily as long as his lithe body moved in sight among the pines.

An impulse took her to the mirror where he had smoothed his hair, as though it would bring him within her vision again. She saw herself completely for the first time in many years. Isolation had taken the meaning from age. She had forgotten until this moment that she was no longer young. She turned from the mirror and washed the dishes soberly. It occurred to her that the young man had not even asked her name.

The hammock that had been always a friendly curtain about the old house was suddenly a wall. The flat-woods that had been sunny and open, populous with birds and the voice of winds, grew dense and dark. She had been solitary. She had grieved for Jim and for the old man her father. But solitude had kept her company in a warm natural way, sitting cozily at her hearth, like the cat. Now loneliness washed intolerably over her, as though she were drowning in a cold black pond.

The young man's complacency lasted a mile or two. As his feet began to drag, fact intruded on the fiction with which he had enraptured the gray-haired woman. Memories seeped back into him like a poison: memories of the lean years as ignorant hanger-on of prosperous bootleggers; of his peddling to small garages of lye-cut 'shine in ignominious pints. The world for which he considered himself fitted had evaded him. His condition was desperate. He thought of the woman who had fed him, whom he had entranced with his story. Distaste for her flooded him, as though it was her fault the story was a lie. He lifted his shotgun and blew the head from a redbird trilling in a wild plum tree.

The storekeeper in the village was the only person who recognized Mattie Syles. The store was packed with the Saturday-night buyers of rations. A layer of whites milled in front of the meat counter; a layer of blacks shifted behind them. At the far grocery counter along a side wall a wedge of Negroes had worked in toward the meal and sugar barrels, where helpers weighed out the dimes' and quarters' worth with deliberately inaccurate haste. Two white women were buying percale of the storekeeper's wife at the dry-goods counter.

The woman came in defiantly, as though the store was a shameful place where she had no business. She looked searchingly from side to side. The storekeeper's wife called, "Evenin', ma'am," and the two white women wheeled to stare and whisper after that. She advanced toward the meat counter. The Negroes parted to let her in. The storekeeper poised his knife over a pork backbone to look at her. He laid it down, wiped his hands with a flourish on his front, and shook hands across the counter.

"If this ain't a surprise! Must be four-five years since you been to town! Meat I been sendin' you by Lantrys been all right? What kin I do for you? Butchered this mornin'—got fresh beef. How 'bout a nice thin steak?"

She made her purchases slowly and moved to the staples counter. She insisted on being left until the last.

"I ain't in no hurry."

The store was almost empty and ready to close when she gathered her sacks together and climbed into the Lantrys' wagon, waiting outside the door. As Lantry clicked to his horse and they

moved off she did not notice that the man she had hoped desperately to see was just strolling into the store.

"Gimme a couple o' packs o' Camels to tide me over Sunday."

"Fifteen cents straight now, Trax."

"Jest one, then."

The storekeeper spoke across the vacant store to his wife, rolling
up the bolts of cloth.

"Edna, you have better manners with the customers, or we'll be
losing 'em. Why'n't you take up some time with Mis' Syles?"

"Who?"

"Mis' Syles—Jim Syles' widder—ol' man Terry's daughter—lives
four-five mile south, out beyond Lantry's. You knew her, Edna.
Lantry's been buyin' for her."

"I never knowed her. How'd I know her now? Why'n't you call
her by name, so's I'd of knowed?"

"Well, you better keep track of her if she's goin' to take to
comin' to town agin. She's rich."

Trax turned in the doorway.

"You talkin' about that gank-gutted woman left jest now?"

He had avoided going into the store until she left. He had not
intended to bring her volubility upon him in public, have her
refer to their meal together. He had half-guessed she had come
looking for him. Women did.

"She live alone in a two-story house you cain't see from the
road?"

"That's her," the storekeeper agreed. "That's Mis' Syles, a'right."

"She's rich?"

"I mean rich. Got her five dollars a week steady rent-money
from turpentine, an' three thousand dollars insurance in the bank
her daddy left her. An' then lives t'other end o' nowhere. Won't
leave the old house."

"'Bout time somebody was fixin' to marry all that, goin' to
waste."

"She wouldn't suit you, Trax. You didn't git a good look at her.
You been used to 'em younger an' purtier."

The man Colton was excited. He walked out of the store without the customary "Well, evenin'" of departure. He hurried to Blaine's, where he was boarding, but did not go in. It was necessary to sit alone on the bench outside and think. His luck had not deserted him. As he leaned his dark head back against the wall, the tropical stars glittering over him were the bright lights of the city streets. Here and there a fat star flickered. These were the burnished kerosene lamps of the widow Syles. The big room— the fireplace that would heat it on the coolest nights—one by one he drew out the remembered details and tucked them into his plans.

The man courted the woman with the careless impatience of his quail hunting. He intended to be done with it as quickly as possible. There was, astonishingly, a certain pleasure in her infatuation. He responded to any woman's warmth as a hound does to a grate fire, stretching comfortably before it. The maternal lavishness of her emotion for him was satisfying. Younger women, pretty women, expected something of him, coaxed and coquetted.

On his several visits to the widow before he condescended to be married to her, he sprawled in the early spring nights before the big fireplace. He made it plain that he was not one to sit around the kitchen stove. His fastidiousness charmed her. She staggered into the room with her generous arms heaped with wood: live oak and hickory, and some cedar chips, because Trax liked the smell. From his chair he directed the placing of the heavy logs. A fire must crackle constantly to please him. She learned to roll cigarettes for him, bringing them to him to lick flickeringly, like a snake, with his quick tongue. The process stirred her. When she placed the finished cigarette between his lips and lighted it with a blazing lighter'd splinter, when he puffed languidly on it and half-closed his eyes, and laid his fingers perhaps on her large-boned hand, she shivered.

The courting was needlessly protracted because she could not believe that he would have her. It was miracle enough that he should be here at all in these remote flat-woods. It was unbelievable that he should be willing to prolong the favor, to stay with her in this place forever.

She said, "Cain't be you raly wants me."

Yet she drank in his casual insistence.

"Why not? Ain't a thing the matter with you."

She understood sometimes—when she wakened with a clear mind in the middle of the night—that something strange had happened to her. She was moving in a delirium, like the haze of malaria when the fever was on. She solaced herself by thinking that Trax too might be submerged in such a delicious fog.

When he left her one night in the Blaine Ford he had borrowed, the retreating explosions of the car left behind a silence that terrified her. She ran to the beginning of the pines to listen. There was no sound but the breath of the south wind in the needles. There was no light but the endless flickering of stars. She knew that if the man did not come back again she would have to follow him. Solitude she had endured. She could not endure desolation.

When he came the next day she was ready to go to the village with him to the preacher. He laughed easily at her hurry and climbed ahead of her into the borrowed car. He drove zestfully, with abandon, bouncing the woman's big frame over the ruts of the dirt road.

As they approached the village he said casually, "I keep my money in Clark City. We'd orter do our business together. Where's yours?"

"Mine's there, too. Some's in the post office an' some in the bank."

"Supposin' we go git married there. An' reckon you kin lend me a hundred till I add up my account?"

"Don't you go spendin' no money on me, Trax, if you ain't got it real free to spend." She was alarmed for his interests. "You leave me pay for things a while."

He drew a deep breath of relief. He was tempted for a moment to get her cash and head for the east coast at once. But he had made his plans to stay. He needed the old house in the safe flatwoods to make his start. He could even use the woman.

When they came back through the village from the city she

stopped at the store for supplies. The storekeeper leaned across the fresh sausage to whisper confidentially.

" 'Tain't my business, Mis' Syles, but folks is sayin' Trax Colton is sort o' courtin' you. You come of good stock, an' you'd orter step easy. Trax is purely trash, Mis' Syles."

She looked at him without comprehension.

She said, "Me an' Trax is married."

The gray of the house was overlaid with the tenderness of the April sun. The walls were washed with its thin gold. The ferns and lichens of the shingled roof were shot through with light, and the wren's nest under the eaves was luminous. The striped cat sprawled flattened on the rear stoop, exposing his belly to the soft warmth. The woman moved quietly at her work, for fear of awakening the man. She was washing. When she drew a bucket of water from the well she steadied it with one hand as it swung to the coping, so that there should be no sound.

Near the well stood bamboo and oleander. She left her bucket to draw her fingers along the satin stoutness of the fresh green bamboo shoots, to press apart the new buds of the oleander in search of the pale pinkness of the first blossoms. The sun lay like a friendly arm across her square shoulders. It seemed to her that she had been chilled, year on year, and that now for the first time she was warmed through to her marrow. Spring after the snapping viciousness of February; Trax sleeping in the bed after her solitude . . . When she finished her washing she slipped in to look at him. A boyish quiet wiped out the nervous shiftiness of his waking expression. She wanted to gather him up, sleeping, in her strong arms and hold him against her capacious breast.

When his breakfast was almost ready, she made a light clatter in the kitchen. It irritated him to be called. He liked to get up of his own accord and find breakfast smoking, waiting for him. He came out gaping, washed his face and hands in the granite basin on the water-shelf, combed his hair leisurely at the kitchen mirror, turning his face this way and that. Matt stood watching him, twisting her apron. When he was quite through, she came to him and laid her cheek against his.

"Mornin', Trax-honey."

Her voice was vibrant.

"Mornin'."

He yawned again as he dropped into his chair. He beat lightly on his down-turned plate with his knife and surveyed the table. He scowled.

"Where's the bacon?"

"Honey, I didn't think you'd want none with the squirrel an' eggs an' fish."

"My God, I cain't eat breakfast without bacon."

"I'm sorry, Trax. 'Twon't take me but a minute now."

She was miserable because she had not fried bacon and he wanted it.

He slid eggs and meat and biscuits to his plate, poured coffee with an angry jerk so that it spilled on the table, shoveled the food in, chewing with his mouth open. When Matt put the crisp thick slices of white bacon before him, he did not touch them. He lighted a cigarette and strolled to the stoop, pushing off the cat so that he might sit down. He leaned back and absorbed the sun. This was fine.

He had deliberately allowed himself these few idle weeks. He had gone long without comfort. His body needed it. His swaggering spirit needed it. The woman's adoration fed him. He could have had no greater sense of well-being, of affluence, if she had been a Negro servant. Now he was ready for business. His weasel mind was gnawing its hole into the world he longed for.

"Matt!"

She left the dishes and came to stand over him.

"Matt, you're goin' in business with me. I want you should git me three hundred dollars. I want to set up a eight-barrel still back o' the house, down by the branch."

Trax had crashed like a meteor into the flat-woods. It had not occurred to her that his world must follow him. That was detached from him, only a strange story that he had told. She had a sensation of dismay that any thing, any person, must intrude on her ecstasy.

She said anxiously, "I got enough to make out on, Trax. You don't need to go startin' up nothin' like that."

"All right—if you want I should put my outfit some'eres else——"

"No, no. Don't you do that. Don't you go 'way. I didn't know you was studyin' on nothin' like that—you jest go ahead an' put it clost as you like."

"Down by the branch, like I said."

He visioned the layout for her. She listened, distraught. The platform here, for the barrels of mash. There, the woodpile for the slow fire. Here again, the copper still itself. The cover was dense, utterly concealing. The location was remote.

"The idee, Matt," he was hunched forward, glowing, "is to sell your own stuff what they call retail, see? It costs fifty, seventy-five cents a gallon to make. You sell by the five-gallon jug for seven dollars, like they're doin' now, you don't make nothin'. That's nigger pay. But what do you git for it by the drink? A quarter. A quarter a drink an' a dollar a pint. You let people know they kin git 'em a drink out here ary time to Trax Colton's, you got 'em comin' in from two-three counties for it. You git twenty-gallons ahead an' color some up, cook it a whiles underground to darken it, an' you take it to places like Jacksonville an' Miami— you get you real money."

It was as though thunder and lightning threatened over the flat-woods. The darkness of impending violence filled them. She stared at him.

" 'Course, if you don't want to invest in my business with me, I got to be gittin' back where I come from."

The smoke from his cigarette drifted across her.

"No, no! It's all right!"

His glamorousness enfolded her like the April sun.

"Honey, anything you want to do's all right."

Setting up the still was a week's work. Men began to come and go. Where there had been, once in five days, the silent tur-pentiners, once in a while the winter hunters, there were now Negroes bringing in cut wood; a local mason putting together brick and mortar; a hack carpenter building a platform with a roof; men in trucks bringing in sacks of meal and sugar, glass demijohns and oak kegs.

The storekeeper brought five hundred pounds of sugar.

"Howdy, Mis' Colton. Reckon you never figgered you'd be 'shinin'."

"No."

"But you couldn't git you no better place for it."

Her square face brightened.

"That's jest what Trax says."

That night she approached him.

"Trax, all these here men knowin' what you're doin'—reckon it's safe?"

"They got no reason to say nothin'. The only reason anybody'd turn anybody else up was if he'd done somethin' to him. Then they'd git at him that-a-way. Git his still, see? Git him tore up. That way they'd git him."

She made no further comment. Her silence made its way through the wall of his egotism.

"You don't talk as much as you did, Matt. Else I got used to it."

"I was alone so long, honey. Seemed like I had to git caught up."

But the spring warmth was no longer so loosening to the tongue. The alien life the man was bringing in chilled the exuberance that had made her voluble.

"I'm fixin' to learn you to make the whiskey, Matt."

She stared at him.

"Less help we have, knowin' how much I got an' where 'tis, better it suits me, see?"

She said finally, "I kin learn."

The work seemed strange, when all her folk had farmed and timbered. But her closest contact with Trax was over the sour, seething mash. When they walked together back of the house, down to the running branch, their bodies pushing side by side through the low palmettos, they were a unit. Except to curse her briefly when she was clumsy, he was good-natured at his work. Crouching by the fire burning under the copper drum, the slow dripping from the coils, of the distillate, the only sound except for small woods life, she felt themselves man and wife. At other times his lovely body and unlovely spirit both evaded her.

He was ready to sell his wares. He drove to the village and to neighboring towns and cities, inviting friends and acquaintances to have a drink from one of the gallon jugs under the rear seat of the borrowed car. They pronounced it good 'shine. To the favored few financially able to indulge themselves he gave a drink of the "aged" liquor. Accustomed to the water-clear, scalding rawness of fresh 'shine, they agreed gravely that no better whiskey ever came in from Cuba. He let it be known that both brands would be available at any time, day or night, at the old Terry house four miles south of the village. He made a profound impression. Most bootleggers sold stuff whose origin and maker were unknown. Most 'shiners had always made it, or drifted into it aimlessly. Trax brought a pomp and ceremony to the local business.

Men found their way out the deep-rutted road. They left their cars among the pines and stumbled through the hammock to the house. They gathered in the big room Trax had recognized as suitable for his purposes. The long trenchered table old man Terry had sliced from red bay held the china pitcher of "corn" and the jelly glasses from which they drank. Their bird-dogs and hounds padded across the piazza and lay before the fire. Trax drank with them, keying their gatherings to hilarity. He was a convivial host. Sometimes Blaine brought along his guitar, and Trax clapped his hands and beat his feet on the floor as the old man picked the strings. But he was uneasy when a quarrel developed. Then he moved, white-faced among the men, urging some one else to stop it.

At first the woman tried to meet them hospitably. When, deep in the hammock at the still, she heard the vibration of a motor, she hurried up to the house to greet the guests. She smoothed back the gray hair from her worn face and presented her middle-aged bulk in a clean apron. If there was one man alone, Trax introduced her casually, insolently.

"This is my old woman."

When a group of men came together, he ignored her. She stood in the doorway, smiling vaguely. He continued his talk as though she were not there. Sometimes one of the group, embarrassed, acknowledged her presence.

"How do, ma'am."

For the most part they took their cue from Trax and did not see her. Once, on her withdrawal to the kitchen, a stranger had followed for a match.

"Don't you mind workin' way out here in the wood?"

But she decided that Trax was too delicate to want his wife mixing with men who came to drink. At night he sometimes invited her into the big room with conspicuous courtesy. That was when one or two women had come with the men. Her dignity established the place as one where they might safely come. She sat miserably in their midst while they made banal jokes and drank from the thick glasses. They were intruders. Their laughter was alien among the pine trees. She stayed at the still most of the time. The labor was heavy and exacting. The run must be made when the mash was ready, whether it was day or night. It was better for Trax to stay at the house to take care of the customers.

In the early fall he was ready to expand. Matt was alone, scrubbing the floors between runs of whiskey. She heard a powerful car throbbing down the dirt road. It blew a horn constantly in a minor key. Men usually came into this place silently. She went to the piazza, wet brush in hand. With the autumnal drying of foliage, the road was discernible. The scent of wild vanilla filled the flat-woods. She drew in the sweetness, craning her neck to see.

A large blue sedan of expensive make swerved and rounded into the tracks other cars had made to the house. Trax was driving. He swung past the twin live oaks and into the sandy yard. He slammed the door behind him as he stepped out. He had bought the car with the remainder of Matt's three thousand and most of the summer's profits. He was ready to flash across his old haunts, a big operator from the interior.

"I kin sell that hundred gallons of aged stuff now for what it's worth."

He nodded wisely. He sauntered into the house, humming under his breath.

"Hi-diddy-um-tum—" He was vibrant with an expectancy in which she had no part.

She heard him curse because the floor was wet. The cat crossed his path. He lifted it by the tail and slid it along the slippery boards. The animal came to her on the piazza. She drew it into her lap and sat on her haunches a long time, stroking the smooth hard head.

Life was a bad dream. Trax was away a week at a time. He hired the two Lantry boys to take his place. Matt worked with them, for the boys unwatched would let the mash ferment too long. Trax returned to the flat-woods only for fresh supplies of liquor and of clean clothes. It pleased him to dress in blues that harmonized not too subtly with the blue sedan. He wore light-blue shirts and a red necktie that was a challenging fire under the dark insolent face. Matt spent hours each week washing and ironing the blue shirts. She protested his increasing absences.

"Trax, you jest ain't here at all. I hardly got the heart for makin' the runs, an' you gone."

He smiled.

"Ary time it don't suit you, I kin move my outfit to the east coast."

He laid the threat across her like a whip.

The young Lantrys too saw Trax glamorously. They talked of him to Matt as they mixed the mash, fired, and kept their vigils. This seemed all she had these days of the man: talk of him with the boys beside the still. She was frustrated, filled, not with resentment, but with despair. Yet she could not put her finger on the injustice. She flailed herself with his words, "Ary time you don't like it, I kin move."

She waited on Trax's old customers as best she could, running up the slight incline from the still-site to the house when she heard a car. Her strong body was exhausted at the end of the week. Yet when she had finished her elaborate baking on Saturday night she built up a roaring fire in the front room, hung the hot-water kettle close to it for his bath, and sat down to wait for him.

Sometimes she sat by the fire almost all night. Sometimes he did not come at all. Men learned they could get a drink at Colton's any hour of the night on Saturday. When the square dance at Trimtree's was done, they came out to the flat-woods at two or three o'clock in the morning. The woman was always awake. They stepped up on the piazza and saw her through the window. She sat brooding by the fire, the striped cat curled in her lap. Around her bony shoulders she hugged the corduroy hunting jacket Trax had worn when he came to her.

She existed for the Saturday nights when the throb of the blue sedan came close; the Sunday mornings when he slept late and arose, sulky, for a lavish breakfast and dinner. Then he was gone again, and she was waving after him down the road. She thought that her love and knowledge of him had been always nothing but this watching through the pine trees as he went away.

The village saw more of him. Occasionally he loitered there a day to show off before he headed for the coast. At times he returned in the middle of the week and picked up fifteen or twenty gallons cached at Blaine's and did not go out to the flat-woods at all. On these occasions he had invariably a girl or woman with him; cheap pretty things whose lightness brought them no more than their shoddy clothes. The storekeeper, delivering meal and sugar to Matt, lingered one day. The still needed her, but she could not with courtesy dismiss him. At last he drew courage.

"Mis' Matt, dogged if I don't hate to complain on Trax to you, but folks thinks you don't know how he's a-doin' you. You're workin' like a dog, an' he ain't never home."

"I know."

"You work at 'shinin', somethin' you nor your folks never done—not that it ain't all right—an' Trax off in that big fine car spendin' the money fast as he turns it over."

"I know."

"The Klan talks some o' givin' him down the country for it."

" 'Tain't nobody's business but his an' mine."

"Mis' Matt"—he scuffled in the sand—"I promised I'd speak of it. D'you know Trax has got him women goin' 'round with him?"

"No. I didn't know that."

"Ev'ybody figgered you didn't know that." He mopped his forehead. "The day you an' Trax was married, I was fixin' to tell you 'twa'n't nothin' but your money an' place he wanted to git him set up."

"That's my business, too," she said stonily.

He dropped his eyes before the cold face and moved to his truck. She called after him defiantly.

"What else did I have he'd want anyway!"

She went into the house. She understood the quality of her betrayal. The injustice was clear. It was only this: Trax had taken what he had not wanted. If he had said, "Give me the money and for the time, the house," it would have been pleasant to give, solely because he wanted. This was the humiliation: that she had been thrown in on the deal, like an old mare traded in with a farm.

The Lantry boys called unanswered from the palmettos.

She had known. There was no need of pretense. There was no difference between today and yesterday. There was only the dissipation of a haze, as though a sheet had been lifted from a dead body, so that instead of knowing, she saw.

The man came home late Saturday afternoon. Startled, Matt heard the purr of the motor and hurried to the house from the still. She thought the woman with him had come for liquor. She came to meet them, wiping her hands on her brown gingham apron. Trax walked ahead of his companion, carrying his own shiny patent leather bag and a smaller shabby one. As they came into the house, she saw that it was not a woman, but a girl.

The girl was close on his heels, like a dog. She was painted crudely, as with a haphazard conception of how it should be done. Stiff blond curls were bunched under a tilted hat. A flimsy silk dress hung loosely on an immature frame. Cheap silk stockings bagged on thin legs. She rocked, rather than walked, on incredibly spiked heels. Her shoes absorbed Matt's attention. They were pumps of blue kid, the precise blue of the sedan.

"I mean, things got hot for me on the east coast." Trax was voluble. "Used that coastal highway oncet too often. First thing I knowed, down below New Smyrna, I seed a feller at a garage give the high sign, an' I'm lookin' into the end of a .45." He flushed. "I jest did get away. It'll pay me to work this territory a whiles, till they git where they don't pay me no mind over there agin."

The girl was watching Matt with solemn blue eyes. Beside the gray bulk of the older woman, she was like a small gaudy doll. Trax indicated her to Matt with his thumb.

"Elly here'll be stayin' at the house a while."

He picked up the shabby bag and started up the stairs.

"Long as you an' me is usin' the downstairs, Matt, she kin sleep upstairs in that back room got a bed in it."

She pushed past the girl and caught him by the sleeve.

"Trax! What's this gal?"

"Ain't no harm to her." He laughed comfortably. He tweaked a wisp of her gray hair.

"She's jest a little gal young un," he said blandly, " 's got no place to go."

He drew the girl after him. The woman stared at the high-heeled blue slippers clicking on every step.

A warm winter rain thrummed on the roof. The light rush of water sank muffled into the moss that padded the shingles. The sharpest sound was a gurgling in the gutter over the rain-barrel. There had been no visible rising of the sun. Only the gray day-light had protracted itself, so that it was no longer dawn, but day. Matt sat close to the kitchen stove, her bulk shadowy in the dimness. Now and then she opened the door of the fire-box to push in a stick of pine, and the light of the flames flickered over her drawn face.

She could not tell how much of the night she had sat crouched by the range. She had lain long hours unsleeping, while Trax breathed regularly beside her. When the rain began, she left the bed and dressed by the fresh-kindled fire. The heat did not warm her. Her mouth was dry; yet every few minutes an uncontrollable chill shook her body. It would be easy to walk up the unused stairs, down the dusty hall to the back room with the rough pine bed in it, to open the door and look in, to see if anyone was there. Yet if she continued to sit by the fire, moving back the coffee-pot when it boiled, surely Trax would come to the kitchen alone, and she would know that yesterday no woman had come home with him. Through the long days her distraught mind had been busy with imaginings. They might easily have materialized, for a moment, in a painted girl, small and very young, in blue kid slippers.

Trax was moving about. She put the frying pan on the stove, sliced bacon into it, stirred up cornmeal into a pone with soda and salt and water. Trax called someone. He came into the kitchen, warmed his hands at the stove. He poured water into the wash basin and soused his face in it. Matt set the coffee pot on the table. The girl pushed open the door a little way and came through. She came to the table uncertainly as though she expected to be ordered away. Matt did not speak.

Trax said, "How's my gal?"

The girl brought her wide eyes to him and took a few steps to his chair.

"Where's your shoes, honey?"

She looked down at her stockinged feet.

"I gotta be keerful of 'em."

He laughed indulgently.

"You kin have more when them's gone. Matt, give the young un somethin' to eat."

The thought struck the woman like the warning whir of a rattler that if she looked at the girl in this moment she would be compelled to lift her in her hands and drop her like a scorpion on the hot stove. She thought, "I can't do such as that." She kept her back turned until the impulse passed and she could control her trembling. Her body was of metal and wood. It moved of itself, in jerks. A stiff wooden head creaked above a frame so heavy it seemed immovable. Her stomach weighed her down. Her ample breasts hurt her ribs, as though they were of lead. She thought, "I got to settle this now."

She said aloud slowly, "I'll not wait on her nor no other woman."

The girl twisted one foot over the other.

She said, "I ain't hungry."

Trax stood up. His mouth was thin. He said to Matt, "You'll wait on her, old lady, or you'll git along without my comp'ny."

She thought, "I got to settle it. I got to say it."

But she could not speak.

The girl repeated eagerly, "I ain't a bit hungry."

Trax picked up a plate from the table. He held it out to his wife.

She thought, "Anyway, cornbread and bacon's got nothing to do with it."

She dished out meat and bread. Trax held out a cup. She filled it with coffee. The man sat down complacently. The girl sat beside him and pecked at the food. Her eyes were lowered. Between mouthfuls, she twisted her fingers in her lap or leaned over to inspect her unshod feet.

Matt thought, "Reminding me."

The paint had been rubbed from the round face. The hair was yellow, like allamanda blooms. The artificial curls that had protruded from the pert hat had flattened out during the damp night, and hung in loose waves on the slim neck. She wore the blue silk dress in which she had arrived.

Trax said, "You eat up good, Elly. May be night 'fore we git back to eat agin." He turned to Matt. "Lantry boys been doin' all right?"

"They been doin' all right. Them's good boys. I heerd 'em come in a hour back. But they needs watchin' right on. They'll let the mash go too long, spite of everything, if I ain't right on top of 'em."

She hardened herself.

"You jest as good to stay home an' do the work yourself. I ain't goin' near the outfit."

"They kin make out by theirselves," he said easily.

He rose from the table, picking his teeth.

"Come on, Elly."

The girl turned her large eyes to the older woman, as though she were the logical recipient of her confession.

"I forgot to wash my hands an' face," she said.

Trax spoke curtly.

"Well, do it now, an' be quick."

He poured warm water in the basin for her and stood behind her, waiting. She washed slowly, with neat, small motions, like a cat. Trax handed her the clean end of the towel. They went upstairs together. Trax' voice was low and muffled. It dripped through the ceiling like thick syrup. Suddenly Matt heard the girl laugh.

She thought, "I figgered all that owl face didn't let on no more'n she meant it to."

In a few minutes they came down again. Trax called from the front room.

"Best to cook dinner tonight, Matt. We're like not to git back at noon."

They ran from the porch through the rain.

She walked after them. She was in time to see them step in the blue sedan. The high-heeled slippers flickered across the running-board. The car roared through the live oaks, down the tracks among the pines. Matt closed her eyes against the sight of it.

She thought, "Maybe she takened her satchel and I just didn't see it. Maybe she ain't coming back."

She forced herself to go to the upstairs bedroom. The drumming on the roof sounded close and louder. The bed was awkwardly made. The shabby handbag stood open in a hickory rocker, exposing its sparse contents. A sound startled her. The cat had followed, and was sniffing the unfamiliar garments in the chair. The woman gathered the animal in her arms.

She thought of the Lantry boys under the palmettos. They were careless when they were cold and wet. They might not put the last five hundred pounds of sugar under cover. Shivering in the drizzle, they might use muddy water from the bank of the branch, instead of going a few yards upstream where it ran deep and clear. She threw Trax's corduroy jacket about her and went down the incline behind the house to oversee the work.

She decided not to cook anything for the evening. But when the mist lifted in late afternoon, and the sun struck slantwise through the wet dark trees, she left the Lantry boys to finish and went to the house. She fried ham and baked soda biscuit and sweet potatoes. The meal was ready and waiting and she stirred up a quick ginger cake and put it in the oven.

She said aloud, desperately, "Might be he'll be back alone."

Yet when the dark gathered the bare house into its loneliness, as she had gathered the cat, and she lighted kerosene lamps in the long front room and a fire, the man and girl came together as she had known they would. Where she had felt only despair, suddenly she was able to hate. She picked up her anger like a stone and hurled it after the blue heels.

"Go eat your dinner."

She spoke to them as she would to Negro field hands. Trax stared at her. He herded Elly nervously ahead of him, as though to protect her from an obscure violence. Matt watched them, standing solidly on big feet. She had not been whole. She had charred herself against the man's youth and beauty. Her hate was healthful. It waked her from a drugged sleep, and she stirred faculties hurt and long unused.

She sat by the clay fireplace in the front room while the pair ate. They spoke in whispers, shot through by the sudden laugh of the girl. It was a single high sound, like the one note of the thrush. Hearing it, Matt twisted her mouth. When the casual clatter of plates subsided, she went to the kitchen and began scraping the dishes to wash them. Trax sat warily in his place. The girl made an effort to hand Matt odds and ends from the table. The woman ignored her.

Trax said to Elly, "Le's go by the fire."

Matt cleaned up the kitchen and fed the cat. She stroked its arching back as it chewed sideways on scraps of meat and potato. She took off her apron, listened at the open door for sounds from the Lantrys, bolted the door, and walked to the front room to sit stiff and defiant by the blazing pine fire. The girl sat with thin legs tucked under her chair. She looked from the man to the woman and back again. Trax stretched and yawned.

He said, "Guess I'll go down back an' give the boys a hand. I ain't any too sure they run one batch soon enough. I got to keep up my stuff. I got high-class trade. Ain't I, Elly?" He touched her face with his finger as he passed her.

The woman and the girl sat silently after his going. The cat padded in and sat between them.

The girl called timidly, "Kitty!"

Matt turned savagely.

"Keep your hands off him."

The girl laced her fingers and studied the animal.

"Do he scratch?"

Matt did not answer. She loosened her gray hair and combed it by the fire with a side-comb, plaiting it into two thin braids over her shoulders. Inside the childish hairdressing her face was bony and haggard. She went into the adjoining bedroom, undressed and got into bed. She lay reared up on one elbow, straining for every sound. The fire popped and crackled. Once the juice oozed from a pine log faster than it could burn. It made a sizzling, like boiling fat. A chair scraped and Elly went up to the back bedroom. Her high heels clicked overhead. Matt thought with satisfaction that the girl had no light. She was floundering around in the dark in the unfamiliar house.

In a little while the front door opened and closed softly. Matt heard Trax creak cautiously up the stairs to the back room.

Trax was sleeping away the bright March morning. Matt made no effort to be silent about her washing. She dipped noisily into the rain barrel. When the soft water was gone she drew from the well, rattling galvanized buckets. Elly sat on the bottom step of the rear stoop, scuffling her bare toes in the sand. She wore the blue silk dress. Beside her was a handful of her own garments in need of washing, a pair of silk stockings and two or three pieces of underwear. Matt passed in front of her to go to the clothes line.

Elly said, "Trax give me this dress."

The woman did not seem to hear.

Elly continued. "Reckon it'll wash? It's spotted."

Matt did not answer. She hung flour-sacking towels on the line. The girl picked up her small pile, looked uncertainly at the tub of soapsuds, laid down the clothes. She went to the tub and began rubbing on the first garment she drew from the suds. It was one of Matt's gingham aprons. She rubbed with energy, and Matt towered over her before she noticed that the woman had left the line.

"Take your dirty hands out o' my tub."

The girl drew back, dripping suds from her thin arms. She turned her hands back and forth.

"They ain't dirty," she protested.

Matt laughed shortly. "Mighty simple, ain't you?"

An obscured doubt brushed her, like a dove that wavers to a perch and is gone again without lighting.

"Who do you figger I am?"

The girl faced her across the wash-tub. She said gravely, "The lady lives in Trax' house."

"Trax' house? Well, he lives in mine. Never heerd tell o' no sich thing as his wife, eh?"

The girl hesitated. "Trax jest said the old woman."

Matt breathed heavily. The girl took her silence and her questions for a mark of interest.

"Trax said you'd romp on me," she offered confidentially, "but you ain't." She wrapped one bare leg around the other. "I been romped on," she went on brightly. "Pa romped on me reg'lar."

"You got folks then!"

"Yessum, but I don't know where he is. He run a blacksmith shop an' garage offen the hard road, but he closed up an' goed to Georgia with a lady. Then I lived with another lady down the road a piece. Trax sold her liquor, that's how come him to know me. She moved off, an' he takened me with him from there. Now I'm gonna live with him," she finished, adding with studied tact "—and you."

Trax came yawning to the rear stoop in time to see Matt walk toward the girl. Elly stared uncomprehending. He jumped to the sand and caught the woman's muscular arms from behind.

"Don't you touch her." He cracked his familiar whip over her. "You hurt that gal young un an' you've seed the last o' me."

The woman shook free from him in the strength of her rage.

"You git out o' here before I hurts her an' you, too. You take your gal young un an' git."

He adjusted his mind slowly. Inconceivably, he had gone too

far. Bringing the girl to the flat-woods had been dangerously brazen. It was done now. He understood that his hold on this place had become suddenly precarious. He had the car and he could move the still. Yet the layout suited his needs too exactly to be relinquished. He could not give it up. If the gray-headed woman was done with her infatuation, he was in trouble.

He said boldly, "I got no idee o' goin'. Me an' Elly'll be here right on."

She said, "I kin break ary one o' you in two with my hands."

"Not me, you cain't. Leave me tell you, ol' woman, I'm too quick for you. An' if you hurt Elly"—his dark face nodded at her —"if you crack down on her—with them big hands o' yourn—if you got any notion o' knifin' "—he paused for emphasis—"I'll git you sent to the chair, or up for life—an' I'll be here in these flat-woods—in this house—right on."

He pushed the girl ahead of him and walked into the house, lighting a cigarette. He said over his shoulder, thickly between puffs, "An' that'd suit me jest fine."

She turned blindly to the wash-tub. She soaped the blue shirts without seeing them, rubbing them up and down automatically. Her life that had run like the flat-woods road, straight and un-traveled, was now a maze, doubling back on itself darkly, twisted with confusion. The man stood with his neat trap at the end of every path; the girl with her yellow hair and big eyes, at the beginning.

She thought, "I got to settle it."

Trax and Elly came and went like a pair of bright birds. The blue kid slippers, scuffed by the sand, flashed in and out of the old house. Matt watched the comings and goings heavily, stand-ing solidly on the hand-hewn pine-board floors.

She did not go near the still. Her absence did not make the dif-ference she had imagined. The Lantrys had the work well in hand. Trax paid their wages, and their product was satisfactory. Often she did not hear them come to their work through the pines and past the hammock. A northwest wind sometimes brought the scent of the mash to her nose. The storekeeper brought in sugar and meal by a lower trail, and she seldom saw him. Trax was selling all his liquor at a high urban price, and local patronage dwindled away. The woods were quiet day and night.

Then Trax and Elly were back again, talking of hotels and highways, of new business, the talk pierced through now and again by the girl's single-noted laughter. She eyed Matt gravely, but the woman felt that the girl, oddly, had no fear. Trax was insolent, as always, his eyes narrow and his ways wary. Matt cut down on the table. She cooked scarcely enough for the three to eat. Elly ate with her catlike slowness, taking twice as long at her meager plate as the others. Matt took to rising and clearing the table as soon as she and Trax had finished. She picked up the plates casually, as though unaware that the third one still showed half its food uneaten. Trax did not seem to notice. The girl sometimes looked hungrily after the vanishing portion. She made no protest. Once Matt found her in the kitchen between meals, eating cold cornbread. Trax backed her up in her curt order to Elly to keep out.

It enraged Matt to see Elly feed the cat. Elly saved bits from her sparse helpings and held them under the table when she thought herself unobserved. Occasionally when the girl held the animal in her lap, and Matt ignored it, Trax stroked him too, because it was Elly who held him. Matt knew they sometimes had food in Elly's room at night. She began to hear a soft padding up the stairs and on the bare floor overhead, and knew the cat went up to join them. In the morning he was smug, washing his whiskers enigmatically. His desertion was intolerable. She shut him out at night. He wailed for hours at the door, accustomed to sleeping snugly inside the house.

Suddenly Trax was not taking Elly with him any more. The village had become accustomed to the grave childish face beside him when it disappeared. Casually he left her behind with Matt in the flat-woods. He drove away one morning and did not come back that night or the next.

Matt took it for a taunt. It seemed to her that he was daring her to trap herself. Elly watched the road anxiously the first day. She accepted, hours before Matt, his solitary departure.

At their first breakfast alone together, she said hesitantly, "I had a idee Trax was fixin' to go off alone."

Matt thought, "The fool don't know enough to keep quiet about it."

After the second day, Elly devoted herself to exploring outside the house. Trax had kept her close to him, and the hammock had been only a cluster of shrubs and great trees through which they came and went. The Spanish moss was hazed with green by the early spring, and she discovered that the gray strands were alive with infinitesimal rosy blossoms. Matt saw her sitting at the far edge of the hammock, pulling the stuff apart.

The woman thought, "She better get herself out of my sight."

Elly roamed through the pines as far as the road, staring up and down its silent winding, then scampered back toward the house like an alarmed squirrel. She walked stealthily to the palmettos where the Lantrys worked the still, and watched them for hours unseen. Except when Matt stared directly at her, her round-eyed gravity lifted into a certain lightness, as though she felt newly free to move about in the sunlight. She seemed content.

On a rainy afternoon Matt, ironing in the kitchen, heard a steady snipping from the front room. She stole to the door and peered through a crack. Elly was cutting pictures from an old magazine and making an arrangement of rooms and figures of men and women and children. She was talking to herself and occasionally to them. The cat was curled in her lap, shifting lazily as she moved forward or back.

Their meals together were silent. Matt became aware at dinner one day that the pink oleanders in a jelly glass were not of her picking and placing. She had always a spray of flowers or greenery on the table. Because Elly had brought in the blooms, she snatched them from the water and stuffed them in the stove.

She allowed the girl a minimum of food. Once when she took away the plates before Elly had fairly begun, the girl reached after her desperately and said, "Matt!" Again, when Matt moved from the table, leaving a plate of biscuits behind, Elly pounced on the largest and crammed it into her mouth. She began to laugh, poking in the crumbs.

She said, "You ain't romped on me yet."

Matt decided that Trax had put Elly up to goading her. She spoke for the first time in days.

"Don't you let Trax put no notions in your head. I got no idee o' rompin' on you. That ain't what I'm fixin' to do."

For the most part, the girl was uncomplaining and strangely satisfied. The immature body, however, was becoming emaciated.

Trax was gone two weeks. He came in for an afternoon and loaded up with twenty gallon-jugs concealed under the large rear seat, and went hurriedly away. He called to the two women who stood watching on the piazza.

"Got a order."

Matt nodded grimly after him. She thought, "You got you one more chance, too, if you only knowed it." She turned to observe the girl beside her. There was apparent on the young face a faint wistfulness and no surprise. Matt thought, "She's got her orders just to set tight."

Trax came home for the following weekend. He slept most of the time and was sulky. He paid no more attention to Elly than to the older woman. At no time in the two days or nights did he go to the upstairs room. When he was about, Elly followed him a few steps. Then, as he continued to ignore her, she dropped behind and took up her own simple affairs. Matt told herself that if he left this time without the girl, she was ready. On Monday morning, after loading, he went alone to the car.

She said carelessly, "I might take a notion to go some'eres or do somethin'. When you comin' back this time?"

He laughed insolently. "Steppin' out, Matt?" He was sure of himself. He was too quick for her. Whatever futilities she was planning, it would surprise her most to return on the day he named.

"Be back Sat'day."

He drove off smiling.

Matt was nervous all week. On Saturday morning she surprised the Lantry boys by appearing at the still. They had come and gone without contact with her for some weeks.

She said, "Boys, I jest got word the Pro-hi's is comin' lookin' for Trax' outfit. Now I ain't quick as you-all, an' I want each one o' you should go down the road a good piece an' stay there all day, watchin', one to the north an' t'other to the south. I'll tend the outfit, an' if I hears a whistle I'll know what it means an' it'll give me time to smash the jugs an' git to the house."

The boys were in instant alarm.

"Must be somebody's turned Trax up," they said.

Matt said, "Mighty likely. Somebody's likely got it in for him. Trax hisself done tol' me a long ways back, if anybody had it in for a man, that was the way they'd git at him."

They nodded in agreement.

"That's about it, Mis' Matt. Git him tore up an' git at him that-a-way."

They hid several demijohns in near-by cover and hurried anxiously the two ways of the road. They reported later in the village that they heard no sound for an hour or so. Toward noon their straining ears caught the crash of an axe on metal. There was the high thin splintering of glass. The isolated crashes settled into a steady shattering of wood and iron and copper. A column of smoke began to rise from the vicinity of the still. The Lantry to the south skirted the road through the pines and joined his brother. They cut through the woods to the village and announced that the Pro-hi's had come in from the west and were tearing up Colton's outfit. The word went out to avoid the flat-woods road.

The Lantrys were waiting for Trax when he came through in late afternoon. They flagged him down. They drove with him as far as their own place, telling him what they knew.

"When we lit out we could hear 'em maulin' on the barrels an' purely see the smoke. Things is tore up an' burnt up all right."

They conjectured who, of his numerous enemies, might have betrayed him. He drove at a spring-breaking clip over the root-filled ruts of the sand road. His face was black and frightened.

When he let the boys out of the car he had said nothing about the week's wages. They looked at each other.

One said, "How 'bout us gittin' ten dollars, anyway, Trax?"

"That's it. I ain't got it. I on'y got five myself. I was fixin' to turn over this lot quick."

"We hid out 'bout twenty gallons, if they ain't found it," they informed him eagerly. He listened tensely to a description of the location and was gone.

He drove into the yard and stopped the car in gear with a jerk. No one was in sight. He ran back of the house to the palmettos. A ring of fire had blackened palms and oaks and myrtle for a hundred feet around. A smoldering pile of bricks and barrel hoops and twisted metal in the center marked the site of the still. He began a frenzied search for the hidden jugs.

Matt peered from a window in the front room. She ordered Elly upstairs.

"You stay there 'til I tell you different."

The woman hurried into the yard with a jug of kerosene and a handful of papers. The sedan was twenty-five feet from the house, but the direction of the wind was safe. She soaked the hood and seats of the car with oil and piled papers on the floor. She tied a bundle of oil-soaked paper on the end of her longest clothes prop; touched a match to it. She lowered the pole to the machine. The oil caught fire. When the blaze reached the gas tank, the explosion disintegrated an already charring mass.

Trax heard the muffled roar up the incline behind him. The demijohns were where the Lantry boys had indicated. They were broken. He left the stench of overturned mash and spilled alcohol and ran to the house. He could not for a moment comprehend that the twisting mass of metal and flame was the blue sedan.

Matt stood on the rear stoop. He looked at her in bewilderment. His stare dropped from her straggling gray hair down the length of her frame. Her apron was smudged and torn. Her hands were black and raw. He came back to her implacable cold eyes. He choked.

"You done it yourself!"

He burst into spasmodic curses, then broke off, overcome by their futility. The sweat ran into his eyes. He wiped it out and gaped about him in loose-mouthed confusion. He shuffled a few feet to the stoop and sank down on the bottom step. The woman looked down at him.

"Better git goin'."

He rose, swaying.

"You ol' . . ."

His obscenities fell away from her as rain washed from the weathered shingles of the old house. She towered over him. The tall house towered over him. He was as alien as on the bright day when he had first come hunting here.

He plunged up the steps toward her, his head low between his shoulders.

"Better git back."

His outstretched fists dropped at his sides. The fingers fell open. The woman lifted the shotgun.

"Better git——"

He shook his head, unbelieving. His eyes clung to the dark cavities of the pitted steel. He moved one foot slowly to the next step.

The woman aimed carefully at the shoe, as though it were some strange reptile creeping into the house. She fired a trifle to the left, so that the pattern of the double-ought buckshot shell sprayed in a close mass into the sand. One pellet clipped through the leather, and a drop of blood sank placidly into the pine step. The man stared fascinated. His hand jerked to his mouth, like a wooden toy moved by strings. He stifled a sound, or tried to make one. The woman could not tell. He lifted a face dry with fear and backed down the steps.

It was necessary to walk widely to the side to avoid the heat of the burned car. He threw out his hands hopelessly and hesitated. The sun slanted orange and gold through the hammock. Beyond, there were already shadows among the dark pines. It would be twilight before he could be out of the flat-woods. He found voice.

"Matt," he whined, "how'll I git to town?"

The woman wiped her streaked face with a corner of her apron.

"Reckon you'll have to git there on foot, Mister—the way you come in the first place."

She turned her back and went into the house. The girl had come down the stairs and was flattened against a wall. Her face was brushed with a desperate knowledge. Matt jerked her head at the open front door.

"All right. I'm thu. You kin go on with him now."

"Matt——"

"Go on. Git."

The girl did not move. Matt pushed her headlong to the door. Elly took hold of the big arm with both hands, drawing back, and Matt struck her away. She went confusedly down the steps. Trax was leaving the hammock. He struck wildly through the pines. The girl took a few steps after him, then turned toward the woman watching from the doorway.

Matt called loudly, "Go on. Git."

The man had reached the road and was plunging along it to the north. The girl ran three or four paces in his direction, then stopped again, like a stray dog or cat that would not be driven away. She hesitated at the edge of the hammock. The small uncertain figure was visible between the twin oaks beyond the high porch. Matt turned into the house and closed the door.

She was strong and whole. She was fixed, deep-rooted as the pine trees. They leaned a little, bent by an ancient storm. Nothing more could move them.

The car in the yard had settled into a smoking heap. The acrid smell of burned rubber and paint filled the house. Matt closed the north window to keep out the stench. The glass rattled in its frame. The air was gusty and the spring night would be cold. There were swift movements and rustlings among the oak boughs above the roof, as though small creatures were pattering across the floor of the wind.

Matt shivered and kindled a fire in the front room. She looked about for the cat. The noise and disorder of the day had driven him to distant hunting grounds and he had not yet ventured to return. She drew close to the fire in her rocker and held her smudged hands to the blaze.

She thought, "I've lit a bait o' fires today."

That was over and done with. There would be no more 'shining among the palmettos; no more coming and going of folk; no more Trax and his owl-faced girl. She was very tired. Her square frame relaxed in its exhaustion. She leaned back her head and drowsed deeply in her chair.

When she wakened, the fire had burned to ashes. The moon rode high over the flat-woods, with clouds scurrying underneath. The room was silver, then black, as the moonlight came and went. The chill wind sucked through the pines. There was another sound; the sobbing of a lighter breath. Suddenly Matt knew the girl was still there.

She rose in a plunge from the rocker. She wasn't done with them yet. . . . She opened the door a few inches and listened. The muffled sound was unmistakable. It was the choked gasping of a child that has cried itself breathless. It came from the edge of the hammock. Where the pines began she could distinguish a huddle on the ground that was neither stump nor bushes. She closed the door.

Trax was gone—and Elly was here.

He had flung away and left her behind. She was discarded, as Matt had been long discarded. He was through with Elly, too. For the first time the woman was able to conceive of them separately. And the one was gone, and the other was here. She groped her way stupefied to the kitchen, lighted a kerosene lamp, and made a fire in the range. She wanted a scalding pot of tea to stop her shivering. She split a cold biscuit and fried it and sat down with her plate and tea-cup. She breathed hard, and ate and drank mechanically.

"He was done with her a long ways back."

He had driven off alone in the blue sedan, not to infuriate, but because there was nothing else to do with the girl. Matt chewed her biscuit slowly. She laughed grimly.

"I give him too much credit for smartness."

A flash of anger stirred her, like a spurt of flame from an old fire, that Elly should be now at the edge of the hammock.

"Trax wa'n't man enough to take off his mess with him."

She sipped her cooling tea.

She remembered grudgingly the girl's contentment. The shadow of the man, passing away, left clear the picture of a child, pulling moss apart and cutting paper dolls. Rage at Trax possessed her.

"I'd orter hided him for takin' sich a young un along his lowdown way."

In a burst of fury she conceded the girl's youth. Elly was too young . . .

"I'd orter been hided. Me an' Trax together."

Matt rose from the table and gathered up the few dishes. She stopped in the act. She looked at her hands as though their knotty strength were strange to her.

"Snatchin' off a young un's rations . . ."

She leaned heavily on the table. Emptiness filled the house.

She strode abruptly out the door and through the hammock to the pines. The moon had swung toward its setting and the rays lay long under the trees. The girl lay crouched against a broad mottled trunk.

Matt said, "You kin come on back."

The emaciated figure wavered from the ground on spindling legs. It tried to crowd close to the warmth of the woman's body. As they moved toward the house, the girl stumbled in the runover slippers.

Matt said, "Here. Gimme them crazy shoes."

Elly stooped and took them from her bare feet. The woman put them in her apron pockets. She went ahead of the girl into the front room and bent down to kindle a fire.

Cocks
Must Crow

I GOT NOTHING particular against time. Time's a natural thing.
Folks is a kind of accident on the face of the earth, but time
was here before us. And when we've done finished messing ourselves up, and when the last man turns over to die, saying, "Now
how come us to make such a loblolly of living?"—why, time'll rock
right on.

It's pure impudence to complain about much of ary thing, excusing human nature, and we all got a just complaint against
that. Seems like we could of got borned without so much meanness in us. But just as sure as cooters crawls before a rain, why, we
got no right to holler about such things as getting old and dying.

But now what I do hold against time is this: Time be so all-
fired slick. It's slick as a otter slide. And how come me to object
to that, don't be on account of you slip down it so fast, but you
slip down without noticing what time's a-doing to you. That's
what I object to. If time's fixing to change you, why, it can't be
holpen. But the road's greasy as a darky's cook pot, and what does
a feller do? He goes kiyoodling along it, and him changing, like
a man getting drunk and not knowing it. And here comes a turn
in the road, or a ditch you ain't looking for. And what do you do?
You think you got all your senses, and you ain't, and you do the
wrong thing and maybe knock your brains out. And if you only
had some sign, something to tell you you was drunk instead of
sober, something to tell you you was changed, why, you might
make it.

Now that happened to me with my Will. I come so clost to

losing the only man a woman like me could ever hope to get a-holt of, and a good man to boot, that I can still feel the danger whistling past me like a rattlesnake striking and just missing. And that's it. Time ain't got the decency of a rattlesnake. A rattler most times'll give warning. I almost lost my Will, and me a big fat somebody no man'd look at twicet lessen he was used to me. I almost lost him on account of I had changed and didn't know it, and time never give me the first sign to warn me. Merciful jay bird! No, sir, time's a low-down, sneaking, cottonmouth moccasin, drops its fangs without you knowing it's even in the grass, and was there ary thing I could do about it, I'd do it. Excusing that, I got nothing against time.

My Will married me—some say I married him—when I was a big feather-bolster kind of a gal, pink-cheeked and laughing and easy-going and heavy-eating. I will say, I always did have a tongue in my head, and loved to use it, just like a man with a keen knife loves to keep it sharp. But I used it fair and open. Some said I was lucky to get Will Dover, and some said he was lucky to get me. Will and me was both satisfied. I'd had men was more to look at, come courting me out at Pa's place in the flat-woods, and I'd had men come was nothing but breath and breeches. Will had a gold tooth in the front of his mouth, and I always was a fool for a gold tooth. I takened to the little feller first time I seed him. I was a heap bigger'n him even then.

Third time he come out of a Sunday evening, Pa tipped back in his chair on the porch and said to Will, "Better look out, young feller, Quincey don't take you for a play-dolly."

Will looked him square in the eye.

"You ever tried to hold a hawk in your bare hand?" Will said.

"Why, no," Pa said, "I'd know better."

"Well, a hawk's a heap littler'n you, ain't he? But 'taint his size or your size makes you leave him be. It's his nature. Now the gal ain't growed so big in these flat-woods, could take me for a play-dolly. I ain't got the size to hold Quincey, here, on my lap. But she shore as hell ain't going to hold me on hers."

Pa laughed and slapped hisself.

"Will Dover," he said, "if you want her and she don't take you, I'll lick her with my own hands."

"Ain't nobody going to lick Quincey but me," Will said, "and I aim just to reason with her."

"Ain't he something?" Pa said to me. "Quincey, I've always told you, you can't judge no man by the length of his suspenders. You got to judge him by the spirit in him."

And I done so. I takened Will first time he offered. The business he was in was just a mite in his favor. He run a livery stable in Oak Bluff, and he come courting in a light trap with a pair of black horses drove tandem. It kind of melted me. I hadn't never see a pair of horses drove tandem.

Me and Will hit it off fine right from the start. He was little and he acted gentle, but couldn't nobody press him no farther than he was o' mind to be pressed. And that was one thing I disremembered as the years went by.

When we was fresh-married I said to him, "You're soft-acting, Will Dover, but you got a will as hard as a gopher shell."

"You ain't fooling me none, either," he said. "You got a tongue as sharp as a new cane knife, but your heart's as big as your behind, and soft as summer butter." He looked at me with his head on one side, and them blue eyes as bright and quick as a mockingbird's. "And that's why I love you, Quincey Dover," he said.

Ary woman could get along with a man like that. I know now I don't deserve too much credit for us living so nice and friendly. But in them days I takened a mort of credit, on account of I was full of idees about handling men. They was good idees. I still got them. They was mostly this: Man-nature is man-nature, and a woman's a fool to interfere. A man worth his salt can't be helt to heel like a bird dog. Give him his head. Leave him run. If he knows he ain't running under a checkrain, the devil hisself can't get him to run more'n about so far away from his regular rations. Men is the most regular creatures on earth. All they need is to know they can run if they want to. That satisfies them. And that's what I had to go and forget.

Some things about me didn't never change. My tongue didn't never change and, truth to tell, I'd not want it to, for the times

I need it I want to know I can count on it. What Will called my big heart, I don't believe didn't never change; for I can't help being tormented when ary living thing, man, woman or dog, be hungry. I can't help feeling all tore up when another grieves. And when a old tabby cat has got no place to birth her kittens, or some poor soul in the woods is fool enough to be bringing another young un into the world, and not a piece of cloth to wrap it in, and a blessing if it was stillborn, why, I got to light in and fix a bed for that tabby cat or that fool woman.

What did change about me was my size. I had a mighty good start, and seems like a piece of corn bread with a slab of white bacon on top of it has a sweeter taste in my mouth than it do to one of them puny little old scrawny women. And seems like ary piece of rations I've ever ate has just wrapped itself around my middle and stayed there. The last time I weighed myself was a ways back on the scales in the express office, and it balanced two hundred and twenty, and I quit weighing.

"Don't let it fret you," Will said. "You was a big gal when I got you, and I'd purely hate to turn you back to your Maker without I had added something to the good thing was give me."

My Will has been a heap of comfort. Can ary one figure how I could be mean to a man like that? Seems to me, times, like growing into the biggest woman in the county had something to do with it. I growed so big, I reckon I got biggety too. Here was my Will, little and gentle, and here was me, big as Timmons' pond, and used to all Oak Bluff saying, "Go ask Quincey. See what Quincey think."

I can't no-ways recollect when the change in me begun. First time I remember cold-out bearing down on Will was about two years ago. I remember that.

He said to me one evening after supper, "The boys is having a cockfight down to the garage. Reckon I'll ease on down and watch it."

I said, "You'll do no such of a thing. Cockfighting is a low-down nasty business. Men that's got nothing better to do than watch a pair of roosters kill theirselves isn't fitten company."

Will looked at me slantwise and he said, "Don't you reckon I can judge my company, Quincey?"

I said, "Judge all you please, but you'll go to no cockfight."

He filled up his pipe and he tamped the tobaccy down and he lit it and he said, "Since when you been telling me where I could go?"

I said, "You heerd me the first time."

Now I felt mighty righteous about it. That's the trouble with changing, you still feel right about it. I'd never seed a cockfight, but I'd heerd tell they was cruel and bloody, and besides, it's agin the law.

Will rocked a while and he smoked a while and he said, "Nothing ain't worth quarrelling about. I'll just go on down to the station and wait-see do them automobile parts come in on Number Three."

I said, "All right, but don't you go near no cockfight."

He give me a look I hadn't never seed before, and he said, "No, ma'am," in a funny way, and he went on off.

Now I got to put this together the best way I can. I ain't like them story writers can make a tale come out as even as a first-prize patchwork quilt. Life ain't slick like a story, no-ways. I got to remember this, and remember that, and when I'm done it'll make sense. The Widow Tippett moving to Oak Bluff don't seem to have a thing to do with me and time mixing it. When she come, I sure as all get-out didn't figure she'd make no marks on my pie-crust. But move to Oak Bluff she did, and get messed up in my and Will's business, she done so. And that was about a year and a half ago.

First thing I knowed, I heerd a strange widow had bought the old Archer farm at the edge of town. I give her time to get nested down, and one afternoon I went out to welcome her. I takened a basket of my guava preserves and my sour-orange marmalade, and a bundle of cuttings from my porch plants. Minute she come to the door to greet me, I seed she had a chip on her shoulder. She was a quiet kind of a looking woman, right pretty if you like skimmed-milk eyes and sand-colored hair with a permanent wave put to it, and a tippy-tippy way of walking.

"Mis' Tippett?" I said. "I'm Mis' Will Dover. Quincey Dover. I come to welcome you."

"Pleased to meet you," she said. "I figured that was who 'twas."

I takened a quick look around. I never seed a place kept so careless. The front room looked as if a truck had just backed up to the door and dumped everything out together, and she hadn't never straightened it out and didn't aim to. She hadn't washed her dishes and a big old tomcat was asleep in the dishpan. There was cats and kittens and dogs and puppies strowed all over the house and yard. A Dominick hen was on the table, pecking at the butter.

"Set down," she said. "I hear tell Oak Bluff just couldn't make out without you."

There was something about her voice I mistrusted right off.

"When I see my duty, I do it," I said.

"That works good when ever'one sees it the same," she said. "You're the lady don't let her husband go to no cockfight, ain't you?"

"You mighty right," I said.

"Ain't it nice to have a man does just like you tell him?" she said.

I looked at her quick to read her mind, for there was pure sandspurs under that easy voice.

"I find it so," I said. "You're a widow, they tell me. Sod?"

"Water. Water and whisky."

"I never heerd tell of a water widow."

"He was drunk as ten coots and fell in the water and never did come up. A lake's as good a burying place as any."

"I'm mighty sorry about your loss."

"Don't mention it. I didn't lose much."

I said, "That's a right hard way to speak of the dead."

"So it be," she said, "and the dead was about as hard as they come."

I knowed from then on I didn't like the Widow Tippett and didn't mean to have no truck with her. I got up to go and I give her the preserves and the cuttings. She didn't offer me my basket back.

I said, "Pleased to of met you. Call on me if a need come," and I walked down the path. I turned at the gate.

"I hope you ain't fixing to farm this land," I said. "It's plumb wore out."

"I thank you," she said. "Just to keep folks from fretting their-selves to death, you can tell Oak Bluff I got steady insurance and aim to raise chickens."

I said to myself, "I'll tell Oak Bluff you're the biggetiest woman I know, to look like a curly-headed mouse."

What she thought of me, she told me when the time come.

Now if I'd of takened to her, I'd of give her settings of my eggs. I have game chickens, on account of they near about feed theirselves, ranging. They lays good, and they grows to fryer size the quickest of ary chicken. The breed is the Roundhead, and the roosters is some kind of handsome bronze and red, and now and again a long white feather mixed in with the shiny green tail. I have to eat them before they get much size to them, for I can't bear to kill them oncet they show up that reddy-bronze and grow them long tail feathers. 'Tain't everybody wants game chick-ens, on account of the hens'll steal their nests. Could be, I figured, the Widow Tippett'd not crave to raise Roundheads. I felt a mite mean, just the same, not offering. Then I put it out of my mind.

The next thing I can put my finger on was Will asking me for a couple of my frying-sized roosters. A year ago past spring I hatched me an early batch of biddies. They growed off big and fine.

"Quincey," Will said, "can I have a couple of them young roosters to give to a friend?"

"I raised them chickens to put in our own bellies," I said. "Any-body you want to invite to set down and eat fried chicken with us, that's another thing."

"I want to give them away," he said.

"Go catch a mess of fish to give away, if you want to feed the county," I said.

A day-two later he said, "Quincey, can I have a setting of them Roundhead eggs to give away?"

I said, "Now who in tarnation are you so fretted about them having chicken to eat?"

"A customer come to the garage."

"No," I said.

"I do pay for the chicken feed, Quincey."

"No."

"Nothing ain't worth quarrelling about," he said.

A week later one morning there wasn't an egg in the nests, and two of them frying-sized roosters never come up for their feed. I like to had a fit.

"A varmint likely went with them," Will said. "You'd of done better to of give them to me."

"Will," I said, "you reckon that varmint could of had two legs instead of four?" and I looked him in the eye.

He laid a dollar on the table. "Things has come to a pretty pass when a man has to buy eggs and chickens off his own wife," he said.

"Who's this friend you'd steal for?"

"Just a poor soul that don't have much pleasure in life."

"Well, you rob my nests and roosts one more time, and you'll get the living daylights displeasured outen you."

"Yes, ma'am," and he gave me that funny look.

A year rocked on. Twice he give me a quarter for a setting of eggs and fifty cents for two more roosters. I knowed there was a preacher he kind of looked out for when times was hard, and I figured it was him he was feeding. Then late this spring, the truth come out. The truth was a red chicken feather in a basket, and ary one thinks a chicken feather in a basket can't boil up hell in a woman, just don't know hell nor women.

I went out to the chicken house on a bright June morning to gather the eggs. I can't see the ground right under my stomach, and my foot catched in something. I backed off so's I could see, and it was a basket. I hadn't left no basket in the chicken house. I looked at it, and I picked it up and I turned it over. It was my basket. It was the basket I'd taken preserves in, and cuttings, to the Widow Tippett. She hadn't never come near me nor returned it. The first thing come to me was, she'd got ashamed of herself for not carrying it back to me, and she'd come and slipped it in my chicken house. But I hadn't seed no woman's tracks in the yard, and me raised in the woods, why, there ain't a polecat, animal or human, can make tracks in the sand of my yard and me not notice it. I looked at the basket again, and there was a bronzy-red chicken feather stuck to the inside of it. It was a tail feather off a Roundhead rooster.

I seed it plain. The slow-speaking, permanent-headed, butter-milk-faced widow with cats in her dishpan had done tolled my Will into her clutches. He'd done stole eggs and chickens from me, his loving and faithful wife, to take and put in her wicked hands. I set right down on the ground of the chicken house, and when I set down on the ground it's serious, for it near about takes a yoke of oxen to get me up again. I didn't even study about get-ting up again, for it seemed to me life had done gone so black I just as lief lay there and die and be shut of it. It's an awful thing when a woman has done builded her life on a man and she finds his legs is made of sand.

I thought about all the years me and Will had stuck it out together, him losing money on the livery stable, and cars coming in instead of horses, and finally him building the garage on credit, and learning a new trade, and me making a sack of grits last a fortnight. That were the only time in my life I come speaking-close to getting thin. Then things got good, and we prospered, and I fleshened up again, and seemed to me like man and wife couldn't of got along better together lessen they was a pair of angels, and if what they say about heaven be true, married angels couldn't of had near the nice time we had. My Will was always mighty good company.

I set on the ground of the chicken house and I studied. What had I done to deserve such as this? I'd been faithful. 'Course, there'd be them to say a woman as big as me had no choice but being faithful. But I'd been faithful in my mind, and 'tain't every woman goes to the movies can say the same. I'd worked, and I'd saved, and Will Dover hadn't never oncet come in from the garage, no matter how late, and the fruit trucks keeping him busy way into the night, but I had hot rations on the stove. I reckon a woman can put too much store by hot rations. A warm heart'll freshen a man a heap quicker'n hot rations, but all the hot rations in the world can't warm up a cold female tongue.

I set there. I boiled up inside like a syrup kettle filled too full. I boiled up hotter and higher than the fire in a sinners' hell, and I purely boiled over. That cooled the fire a mite, and I panted and fanned myself with my apron and I commenced to study. I laid me a trap for Will. I decided to watch-see when he done ary thing was different from what he generally done, and when I caught him at it I aimed to follow him. I got a-holt of a wall beam for a lever and I finally got myself up off the ground. If Will had of come home then, I like as not wouldn't of held my tongue. When he come in that evening, I was quieted down and set myself to watching, like an alligator watching for a shoat he knows comes to water.

Now the things a suspicioning woman can imagine different about a man would make a new man of him. That evening Will didn't stir from his rocker, just set and smoked. I thought, "Uh-huh, you know I'm watching you." The next evening he put on a clean shirt when he come in from the garage. I thought, "Uh-huh, dressing up for the widow." He didn't have much to say, and it come to me he hadn't been saying much to me for quite some time. I thought, "Uh-huh, saving up them cute things you used to say, for the widow." After supper he eased on out of the house, and I thought, "Uh-huh, I got you now." I followed along a half hour behind him and, bless Katy, there he was setting on the bench in front of the grocery store, visiting with Doc and Uncle Benny.

I said, "I forgot I was out of shortening," and I got me a pound of lard at the store.

Will said, "I'll go on home with you. I come down to hear the fight on the radio, but it's put off."

I thought, "Uh-huh, I just come too soon."

Sunday morning he takened me by surprise. He didn't shave, and he put on the same shirt he'd wore the day before. But he did get out of bed extra early and he acted like he had ants in his pants. I didn't think a thing about it, for he do that, times, of a

Sunday. He's a man is restless when he ain't at his work. I never studied on a thing, until I seed him slip off to the fireplace and pull out the loose brick and take out all the money we keep there. Banks is all right, and we got a account in Tray City, but there's nothing feels as safe as a pile of dollar bills under a loose brick in the fireplace. I seed him stuff them in his pocket and look around as sly as a 'possum.

He come to me and he said, "I'm going on down to town. Don't look for me back to dinner."

My heart lept like a mullet jumping. I thought, "Merciful jay bird, now's the time."

I said, "You're missing some mighty good black-eyed peas," and he went on off.

I give him about forty minutes' start and I lit out. I walked the two miles to the Widow Tippett's like a road-runner snake on its way home. I was puffing and blowing when I got to her gate, and I was just as blowed up inside as out.

I thought, "In a minute now I'll see Will Dover setting beside her and holding her hand, and he ain't held mine since spring."

I stopped to figure what I'd do; would I just crack their heads together, or would I say, proud and stiff, "So! This be the end."

While I was panting and studying, the Widow Tippett come out with her hat on.

She said, "Why, Mis' Dover! You look powerful warm."

I said, "I be warm. Tell me the truth, or you'll figure you never knowed what heat was. My Will here?"

"No," she said, "he ain't here."

I looked down in the sand by the gate, and there was his tracks. "He been here?"

She looked me up and down like a woman trying to make up her mind to step on a cockroach. She throwed back her head.

"Yes," she said. "He's been here."

Now folks talk about seeing red when they're mad. 'Tain't so. Nobody on earth couldn't of been madder'n I was, and what I seed wasn't red. It was white. I seed a white light like looking into the sun, and it was whirling around, and in the middle of it was the Widow Tippett. I closed my eyes against the light.

I said to myself, "O Lord, give my tongue a long reach."

I looked at her. I takened my tongue and I flicked it, like a man flicking a fishing rod. I takened it like a casting line and I laid it down right where I wanted it.

I said, "You figure I aim to leave a man-snatcher like you stay in Oak Bluff? You figure I aim to leave you go from home to home stealing husbands, like a stripety polecat going from nest to nest, stealing eggs? You takened my husband and never returned my preserve basket, and that's how come me to catch up with you, on account of a red chicken feather in that preserve basket. And what I aim to do to Will Dover is my business and not yours, but I ain't aiming to let you clean Oak Bluff out of husbands, for could be they's one or two of them worth keeping."

She tipped back her head and begun to laugh.

I takened my tongue and I drawed it back and I laid it down again. I said, "Devils laughs. Devils with buttermilk faces is the ones laughs. They laughs right on through damnation and brimstone, and that's what'll be your portion."

She said, "You should of been a lady preacher."

I takened my tongue and I purely threw it.

I said, "I comes to you with a basket of preserves and a bundle of cuttings, and what do you do? You don't even send back a empty basket. Not you. What you sends back is a empty husband. You figure I aim to leave the sun go down on you in Oak Bluff one more time? The sun ain't rose, will set on you in Oak Bluff."

She quit laughing. She licked her lips. I could see her drawing back her tongue like I'd done mine. And when she let it loose, seemed to me like I'd been casting mine full of back-lashes, and not coming with ten yards of putting it where I aimed to. For she takened her tongue and she laid it down so accurate I had to stand and admire a expert.

"You was likely a good woman oncet," she said. "You know what you are now? You're nothing but a big old fat hoot-nanny."

I like to of crumbled in the sand. She stepped down off her porch and she walked up to me, and there was nothing between her and me but the gate, and nothing between our souls at all.

She said, "I aim to give you credit for what you was oncet. I come to Oak Bluff, hearing the first day I come that you was a woman wouldn't leave her husband go to no cockfight. I thought, a husband leaves his wife tell him what to do and what not to do, ain't a man no-ways. And then folks begun telling me about you. They told me you was a woman with a tongue sharp enough to slice soft bacon, and a heart like gold. They told me all the good things you done. And they told me you was always a great one for leaving a man go his man's way, and seemed like you bearing down on yours was something had slipped up on you."

I said, "Go on."

She said, "Who be I, a stranger, to tell you to give a man his freedom? Who be I to tell you a man that has his freedom is the man don't particular want it? And the man drove with a short rein, do he be a man, is the one just ain't going to be drove?"

I said, "Tell me."

She said, "I'll tell you this. I got a man of my own. We're marrying soon as he sells out the stock in his store and crates up his fighting chickens and moves down here. I don't want your man nor no other woman's man. Now you quit your hassling and pull up your petticoat that's showing in the back, and I'll carry you where you can see just what your husband's been a-doing behind your big fat back."

She stalked out the gate and I followed her.

"Where you carrying me?" I said.

"To the cockfight."

Now if ary one had ever of said, "I seed Quincey Dover going to the cockfight on a Sunday morning," I'd of figured what they seed come out of the bottle. And if ary one had ever of told me I'd be walking along humble behind another woman, feeling scairt and as mixed up inside as a Brunswick stew, I'd of figured they was cold-out headed for the insane asylum.

But that's what I was doing. The Widow Tippett was purely stepping it off. It was all I could do to keep up with her.

I said to her back, "I ain't of no mind to follow you, without you tell me what to expect."

She never answered.

I puffed and I blowed and I said, "You could tell me how far we got to go."

She kept right on going. The sun beat down and I begun to sweat. The Widow Tippett was about ten yards ahead of me.

I called out after her, "If you aim to carry me to the cockfight, you got to wait a minute, else I'll be toted in as dead as one of them poor roosters."

She stopped then and we set down under a live-oak tree to rest.

I said, "I be blessed if I see how I can go to no cockfight. I've stood out against them things all my life. I cain't go setting up to one of them now."

She said, "Can you climb a tree?"

I said, "Can an elephant fly?"

She said, "Then you'll have to let folks see you there," and she got up and give me a boost to get me up and she set off again.

The place where she takened me was out in Wilson's Woods. We come up on it from the south, and here was a clearing in the woods, and a cockpit in the sand, with a wooden ring around it. On the north side was some men standing, and the trees was between us and them.

The Widow Tippett said to me, "Now how come me to ask you could you climb a tree, is on account of that big camphor tree has a flat bough leans right out over the cockpit, and could you oncet make that first crotch, you could get you a ringside seat and watch the show, and nobody ever know you was near if you set quiet. I aim for you to see the show. Then oncet you've seed it, what you do is your business, for I'm done with you."

I said, "If you was to push me a mite, could be I'd make the crotch."

She said, "You ain't asking much, be you?" but she put her shoulder under me and pushed with a will, and I got myself up into the camphor tree. Like she said, it was easy going oncet I was off the ground, and I pulled up a ways and found me a fine seat part-ways out the bough, with another bough right over me to hang onto.

"Now keep your big mouth shut," she said, "and with that green dress you got on, nobody won't no more notice you than if you was a owl. A mighty big owl," and she went on over to where the men was standing.

I hadn't no more than made it, for directly men begun coming in from all over. Most of them had gamecocks tucked under their arms. Some was Roundheads, like mine, and some was White Hackles and Irish Grays, and some was Carolina Blues. They had their combs trimmed and their spurs was cut off to a nub about a half-inch long. Their tail feathers was shaved off till the poor things' butts was naked.

I thought, "Merciful jay bird, them fine roosters throwed to the slaughter."

After I'd looked at the cocks, I begun craning my neck careful to look at the men. Heap of them was strange to me, men had come in from other counties to fight their chickens. And after I'd watched their faces it come to me there was two kinds of men there. One kind had the fighting mark on them. They was men with cold hard eyes and I knowed they'd fight theirselves or their chickens merciless. They had a easy kind of way of moving, a gambler's way. I knowed this kind of man would move slow and talk quiet, and fight until he couldn't get up. And he'd bet his last dollar and his last farm, did the notion take him. He was a kind of man loved to give a licking and could take one, and it was a hard kind of a man, but you had to give him your respect.

Then there was another kind of man there. This kind of man was little, and his eyes was gentle. And I thought to myself, "Now what's that kind of man doing at a cockfight?"

I inched around on my limb so I got a better peephole through the branches. The men milled around, not talking much, just cutting their eyes sideways at t'other feller's chickens. I seed money change hands. The men that was getting their cocks ready was as nervous as brides sewing on their wedding clothes. I could see one man good. He was wrapping little thin strips of leather around the nubs of his rooster's spurs. Then he takened a pair of sharp pointed steel things I knowed must be the gaffs, and he fastened them on, and wrapped them like they was a baby's bandage.

I thought, "Why, them things ain't as cruel as the natural spurs."

I could see they'd go in quick and clean, and if they didn't reach no vital spot they'd not be much more'n a pin prick. It was like a boxer's gloves; they look terrible, but they don't do the harm of a knuckled fist.

A gray-looking feller with his hat on the back of his head stepped into the pit. He drawed three lines acrost the sand with his foot.

He said, "Let's go."

Two men come ambling into the pit with their chickens. They turned their backs one on t'other. Each man on his side of the pit set his cock down on the sand, keeping holt of its wings, and let it run up and down. The cocks lifted their legs high. Their eyes was bright. They was raring to go.

The referee said, "Bill your cocks."

Seemed like electricity goed through all the men. All the easy-going limpness was done gone. They was all stiff and sharp and that high-charged to where you could of lit a match on ary one of them. The two handlers goed up to each other with the cocks cradled in their arms. They poked the cocks' bills together and one cock made him a pass at t'other.

Somebody hollered, "Two to one on the Blue!"

The cocks pecked at each other. Their hackles rose.

The referee said, "Pit your cocks."

The handlers set the birds down, each one on his own line.

The referee said, "Pit!"

The cocks flew at each other. They met in the air. When they come down, one just naturally didn't get up again. The men all relaxed, like a starched napkin had got wet. The handlers picked up the birds and went out. Money passed here and yon.

I thought, "Now nobody much got their money's worth outen that."

The next fight was a dandy. Right off, I picked a big Carolina Blue to win. I never did see such a fight. I'd seed men box and I'd seed men wrestle. I'd seed dogfights and catfights. I'd seed a pair of old male 'coons having it. I thought I'd seed fighting. But them game roosters was the fightingest things I ever laid eyes on. They knowed what they was doing. One'd lay quiet for t'other, and he'd flick up his feet, and whip his wings, and pass a lick with them gaffs.

I thought, "Now them fool roosters is following their nature. They're having them some kind of a good time."

I begun to get uneasy about the Blue I'd picked. Seemed to me he was dodging. He lay still oncet when he had him a fine chancet to hit a lick, and I almost hollered, "Get him now!" Then he kind of shuffled around, and next thing I knowed he laid out the enemy plumb cold. I come near shouting. I was so proud I'd picked the winner. There was three more fights and I picked two of them. I was breathing hard. I leaned back a mite on the camphor bough.

I said to myself, "Quincey Dover, take shame. You're purely enjoying yourself."

'Twas way too late to feel shame. I couldn't scarcely wait for the next fight to begin. I didn't even mind the camphor bough cutting into me. But there was a delay. I could see men look at their watches.

I heerd one say, "He knowed he was to fight the Main."

The Widow Tippett called out, "Yonder he comes."

And who come walking in to the cockfight? Who come walking in with a big red Roundhead rooster tucked under his arm? My Will come in, that's who come.

Now I can't say I was plumb surprised to see him. I'd figured, the way the Widow Tippett talked, I could look to see him here. I'd a'ready figured that's what she meant about what-all he'd been a-doing behind my back. But I sure didn't look to see him walk in with no fighting cock. I cut my eye at that chicken. And I recognized it. It was one of my prime young roosters, growed up into the biggest, finest, proudest gamecock I ever did see, and the marks of battle was on him. Seemed to me if a rooster had the choice, he'd a heap rather grow up to fight than perish in the cook pot.

Right off I knowed two things. I knowed the Widow Tippett hadn't done a thing but leave Will raise his chickens, and train them, at that sloppy, easygoing place of hers. And I knowed another thing. I knowed my Will was one of them second kind of men come to the cockfight; the little gentle fellers I couldn't

make out why they was there. Well, you'd of thought 'twas the
Lord of the Jay Birds had come in to the cockfight, 'stead of Will
Dover. The men parted a way for him to go into the pit. They
closed in after him, talking and joking and asking questions about
his rooster.

Will called out, "I got a hundred dollars says this is my day."

I like to shook the camphor tree to pieces. I near about climbed
down to say, "Will Dover, don't you go betting that money from
under the fireplace on no cockfight." But I didn't dast give myself
away. And truth to tell, I kind of hankered to see could that
chicken fight.

Didn't take long to know. The fight was the big fight of the
day. Seemed like Will's rooster was a old winner, and the men
figured it were his turn to take a licking. Odds was mostly two
to one against him. T'other cock was a Carolina Blue, and directly
I seed him my heart sank.

"Bill your cocks," said the referee, and Will and t'other feller
billed their cocks. They like to of fought right then and there.

"Pit!"

Nobody didn't have to give his rooster no shove. That pair was
mixing it time they hit the ground. Will's Roundhead got hung
in the Blue.

"Handle!"

The Blue's owner got him a-loose. "Anyways," I thought, "our
chicken got in the first lick." Then they was at it again. Now if
I hadn't of seed them other fights first, I'd not of appreciated this
one. It was a pair of champions, and they both knowed it. They
was both shufflers, and it was as neat as a pair of boxers that
knowed their footwork. Didn't neither one waste no energy, but
when the moment come one seed him a chancet, he was whipping
his wings and striking. Now and again they'd both fly up off the
ground and pass their licks a foot in the air.

"Handle!"

I wanted to holler so bad I had to put my hand over my mouth.
If our Roundhead takened a licking, that Blue was going to wear
me out doing it. Both chickens was breathing hard. Will picked
his up and run his mouth down along his feathers, from the top

of his head on down his back, cooling him and soothing him. He blowed on him and he dipped his bill in a pan of water.

"Pit!"

I mean, anybody that ain't seed a champion cockfight ain't seed a thing.

All of a sudden the Blue begun to take the fight. He got in a lick to the head and while the Roundhead lay hurt and dazed, the Blue followed through with another.

"Time!"

I takened my first breath in about two minutes. I'd of popped directly.

"Pit!"

This time it looked like it was all over. The Blue come in like a whirlwind and he done a heap of damage. He got hung in the Roundhead's back.

"Handle!"

This time when Will turned him a-loose he talked to him. He made queer little sounds, and one of them sounded like a hen a-clucking, like as if he knowed the cock'd fight better if he figured a faithful wife was encouraging him.

"Pit!"

He set him down, and the light of battle was in the Round-head's eyes. He fought hard and game, but next thing I knowed the Blue had him out cold, with one wing broke. "He's dead," I said, for he lay on his side just scarcely breathing. I could of cried. Seemed like a thing that noble and that fearless had ought to live to be husband to a hundred hens and daddy to a thousand biddies. The referee begun to count. The Blue give the Round-head an extra lick as he laid there, and everybody figured that finished him. The men that had bet against the Blue reached in their pockets for their money. I begun to sniffle. I didn't someway even mind Will losing the money. I just couldn't bear to see that Roundhead take a licking. Well, I reckon he figured the same. He opened his eyes and he drawed a breath and where he lay he reached up and he put them gaffs in that big Blue standing over him, and the Blue dropped like he'd been shot.

A grunt come outen the men like as if it was them had been hit. And you know that Roundhead wavered up to his feet, dragging that broke wing, and he climbed up on that Blue, and his head wobbled, and he lifted it up, and he flopped his one good wing, and he crowed! He'd won, and he knowed it, and he crowed.

My Will picked him up and stroked him, and wiped the sweat off his own forehead. He kind of lifted up his face and I could see the look on it. And that look made me feel the funniest I've near about ever felt. It was a deep kind of a male satisfaction. And I knowed that without that look a man just ain't a man. And with it, why, he's cock of the walk, no matter how little and runty and put-upon he be. And I knowed why Will loved a cockfight, and I knowed why all them other little gentle-looking fellers loved it. They was men didn't have no other way to be men.

A shame came over me. Times, it's life'll do that to a man. Mostly, it's his woman. And I'd done that to my Will. I'd tried to take his manhood from him, so he didn't have no way to strut but fighting a rooster. Now he'd won, and he was a man again. And I knowed that cocks must crow.

And about that time you know what happened? I reckon I'd been doing a heap of jiggling around in that camphor tree, and a camphor tree's right limber, but there's a limit to what it can stand.

I heerd a creak and then I heerd a crack, and the limb I was setting on busted off as neat as if you'd put a ax to it, and I slid down it, and I catched holt of the limb below, and I slid down that, and I plunked off down outen the camphor tree right smack in the middle of the cockpit.

I reckon everybody thought it was the end of the world. Nobody couldn't do nothing but gape at me.

"Well, get me up off the ground," I said. "You sure as the devil can't fight no chickens with me in the middle of the pit."

Will run to me then, and two-three others, and they hoisted me up. I brushed off my skirt and the Widow Tippett tidied me up. I looked her in the eye.

"I'd be proud to call you my friend," I said to her.

"All you got to do is call it," she said.

I turned to my Will. His face was in knots. The Lord Hisself couldn't of told what he was thinking.

"Well, Will," I said, "we sure got us some kind of a fighting rooster. Now I'd like a mite softer seat for the next fight."

He drawed a long slow breath.

"We ain't staying for the next," he said. "You're like to be hurt. I'm carrying you home."

The men that had lost to him paid him off. He crammed the bills in his pocket and he tucked up the Roundhead under his arm and he led me off to the car. He cranked up and headed out.

The Roundhead kind of nested down on the seat between us. Directly Will reached in his pocket and he handed out the money and he dropped it in my lap. I counted out the hundred he'd started with and I put it back in his pocket. Then I divided the rest in two piles, and I put one down inside my blouse and put the other in his pocket. He didn't say the first word.

"Will," I said, "I figured you'd been on-faithful to me with the Widow Tippett."

He shook his head.

"I should of knowed better. You ain't that kind of a man. But something in you had drawed off from me."

He nodded.

"I know why you drawed off," I said. "I'd done drove you to it. And I knowed better than to treat a man the way I'd got to treating you."

He never answered.

"Will," I said, "I hope it's in your heart to forgive me. I didn't use to be thataway. Time changed me, Will, and I didn't never notice it. I'd be proud if you'd blame time for it, and spare me."

He kind of blinked his eyes, like he was fixing to cry.

"Will," I said, "you ain't got to go raising no chickens behind my back. I'll raise them for you."

"No, Quincey," he said, slowlike. "No. I reckon I'll quit cock-fighting. It's a foolish business, for a man can loose his shirt at it. And you didn't happen to see one of them long, bloody, ugly fights, makes a man sick to watch it. No, Quincey, I'm done." He looked at me. "Seems like something inside me is satisfied."

Well, I busted out crying. The excitement and the camphor limb cracking, and finding I hadn't plumb lost him, and all, I couldn't stand it. I blubbered like a baby.

"Oh, Will," I said, "I wisht I was young again. An awful thing has done happened to me. You know what I be? I be nothing but a big old fat hoot-nanny."

"Why, Quincey," he said. "Why, Quincey. Don't you dast say such as that. You're my good, sweet Quincey, and I love every hundred pounds of you."

And we busted out laughing.

"Quincey," he said, "you remember when I come courting you and I told you I aimed to fatten you up, for a man couldn't have too much of a good thing?"

I blowed my nose and he put his arm around me.

"Will," I said, "we're on a public highway."

"It's a free road," he said, and he kissed me.

"Will," I said, "home's the place for such as that."

"Ain't I headed for home fast as I can go?" he said, and we laughed like a pair of young uns.

My Will ain't much to look at, but he's mighty good company.

Jacob's
Ladder

T HE NIGHT was sultry for square dancing. The Florida summer
hesitated sullenly between continued heat and the equinoctial
need of change. The dancers in the Jacklin cabin sweat as they
shuffled and wheeled. Tie-tongued Pinny called the figures in a
high minor wail intelligible only to experienced dancers.

" 'hoo' a coo'!"

There were grumblings.

"Dogged if it ain't too hot to shoot-the-'coon."

Alternating couples shot the neighboring girl through to her
partner, languidly. The figure was usually danced violently, so that
the lighter girls often sprawled on the rough pine floor, and it was
all a man could do to brace himself to catch his partner if she were
buxom.

The tune was plaintive, "Comin' 'Round the Mountain," and
lent itself to the suffocated daze in which the dancers moved. Feet
"sluf-sluf"-ed flatly. The bellow of a bullbat sounded outside the
window, a hoarse bass to the squeak of the fiddle and the whine of
the harmonica. Marsh frogs tinkled intermittently like the jangle
of a jew's-harp.

"Bir' i' a ca'!"

Bird-in-the-cage was always popular. Dull eyes brightened. The
tempo of the dance quickened. The middle-aged men held themselves rigidly, shoulders back, chests expanded, moving only their
feet and their long arms. The young bloods danced with their
heads lowered, reaching belligerently far ahead of their slight

bodies, their heels flicking up behind them. In the night's wet heat they sent forth the odor of their own pointer dogs, overlaid with the acridity of plug tobacco, the musk of mules and of the soil, with here and there the sharp sweetness of corn liquor.

Old Jo Leddy was the only man drunk. He claimed that "he couldn't no more go thu a set than a barbecue 'possum, lessen he was good and likkered." His partner tonight was his newest girl, the widow Boone. With the adjacent couple that formed his square, he made a cage about her. She shuffled rhythmically as the other three whirled around her. The cage broke to let her out. Old Jo moved in to take her place. The circling three chanted briskly:

> "Bird out—buzzard in!
> Purty good bird for the shape he's in!"

They tittered. The figure was amusing when the "buzzard" was drunk.

"Ha-hey!"

The dancers sashayed. The individual couples concentrated on each other, shoulders pressed together like wrestlers. The whole dance was violent, earnest, without levity.

"*Sluf-sluf! Shuffle-shuffle! Sluf-sluf!*"

The music stopped as abruptly as though the instrument had been struck from the fiddler's hands. The dancers fell away from one another wherever the end of the set found them. Some of the couples loitered out into the sultry moonlight, fanning their hot faces with handkerchiefs and slapping at the mosquitoes. The older women dropped down on the sides of the white iron bed in a far corner of the room, where old lady Jacklin sat sewing pieces for her interminable quilts.

The kerosene lamps flared up sootily as a quick gust of air sucked from window to door. The palmettos rustled their fans a moment above the cypress shingles of the roof. The fiddler tilted back in his splint-bottomed chair and dozed between sets. The men spat in the empty fireplace. Old Jo Leddy passed around a pint, then the night's closeness absorbed even his exuberance.

Suddenly the flickering voices of quarrelling females flashed like lightning in the thick atmosphere. Old Jo's former sweetheart was threatening the widow Boone.

"Celie's fixin' to crawl onto her," commented old lady Jacklin delightedly.

Jo jumped to the doorway, moistening his loose red lips. His eyes hardened. He snarled impartially at both angry women.

A thin girl in a ragged brown calico dress loosened herself from the confused group on the stoop and entered the one-room cabin for the first time. She flattened herself against the wall, as though, like a chameleon, she wished to fade from sight. She was conspicuous for the extreme poverty of her clothing and for her emaciation. Her body had the graceful ease of any thin wild animal. Her chipmunk-colored hair hung loosely about her neck. Her eyes were bright and quick. Above the pointed cheekbones and sharp chin and nose they gave her very much the look of a young squirrel. For all her gauntness, she was not unlovely.

Old Jo stopped to glare at her as he swaggered into the cabin again. He had pushed both Celie and the widow Boone off the steps in the perfect justice of his arbitration.

"Git on outen here, Florry!"

The girl was gone as quickly as she had come.

"Jo!"

Old lady Jacklin shrilled him to her across the twenty feet of cabin.

"Who's that gal?"

"My gal young un. Hain't never carried her nowheres before. Done carried her with me tonight, did I git the notion to git too drunk to go home alone."

"Jo Leddy, you be the sorriest ol' Cracker I know. Ain't she a pore leetle puny thing!"

"Jest thin-like. She's strong."

"Unh-unh! Reckon it's true, then, I heerd tell you works her loggin' in the cypress swamps, like a man. Up to her shoulders in swamp water, times."

"Shore I works her. Why not? Womenfolks is good for love or for work, one. My ol' woman makes a die of it and don't leave me nothin' but a gal young un. No boys. You bet I've done worked her. Loggin' ain't hurt her none."

The next set was forming. Old Lady Jacklin threw insults at his indifferent back.

" 'Stead o' spendin' what sorry leetle you makes on liquor an' women, you'd orter buy that gal some store clothes and carry her to the dances decent-like."

"She wouldn't go noways," he laughed. "She don't favor me none. She's rabbity!"

The dancers were in position. The fiddler struck up the favorite tune, brought to the Florida interior long since by Georgia and Carolina ancestors, "Ten-Cent Cotton."

Old Jo cut a buck-and-wing as he swung toward his partner. He thundered out the opening phrase.

> "Ten-cent cotton an' fifty-cent meat!
> How in the Hell kin a pore man eat!"

The dancers roared with laughter.

"Old Jo's a sight. He shore kin cut the fool."

The girl Florry looked up from her solitude on the steps at a shadow in the doorway. A young Cracker in torn blue pin-checks, as ragged almost, almost as gaunt, as she, came hesitantly out of the light and music of the room.

"I'll set down by you, if you don't keer," he said. "I don't aim to worry you none. I—I be rabbity, too."

They smiled together a moment.

She was both alarmed and attracted, like all young woods things in their first intimate contact with man. Until this terrifying night, when old Jo had ordered her to follow him the six miles to the dance, she had seen perhaps a dozen white men. None had spoken to her except the sleepy old fellow who drove a team of buff oxen in to their clearing to load their logs; the manager of the lumber mill, splendid, scarcely to be called human, in dark store clothes and driving an automobile; and a fat range rider.

Florry and the youth sat without speech. Their thoughts moved brightly toward each other, like fireflies in the darkness. She decided, as she usually did when anything startled her, that she was not afraid. Fearlessness was her defense against the world. She was conscious neither of happiness nor of unhappiness. When any new aspect of the disagreeable presented itself, she asked herself only whether or not it was best to run from it. Against the background of old Jo and the cypress swamp, very few things seemed formidable.

Assuredly, compared with the other things she knew, this lean, tattered young man was nothing to fear. She grew accustomed to the sweaty smell of him beside her, the rise and fall of his breathing, the comfort of his silence. She placed him, the first human being to enter there, in the corner of her mind that contained things definitely pleasing. These were: grits when she was very hungry; wild game, always; Sport, the hound; all flowers; trees in bloom, particularly the sweet bay and the magnolia; facts new to her, that she could be sure she understood; the taste of running branch water, for their well was sulphurous; a lighter'd fire on a cold night; Negro babies—she had never seen a white one; and a certain sort of day, cool and blue and wind-swept; a day in fall, when the summer's heat was done, and the red-bugs and mosquitoes were gone.

Such days must be due now. Wet heat like this meant storm. The moon, white as the belly of a dead fish, had a great ring around it. It was a wet moon, a moon of impending change. Out of the night's heat puffed another quick gust of air, fresh and chill. The palms rustled wildly, the tops of the pines lashed a moment, a ribbon of black cloud trailed across the moon. Then the night was still again. A hoot owl sobbed throatily. A whippoorwill, late or persistent with his courting, sounded his nocturnal mating call uncertainly.

Florry spoke.

"Hit's September a'ready?"

"Yessum!"

The youth's voice was eager. Speech was as difficult for him as for her, but he longed to attempt it.

" 'Bout the fust week. Shore will be good to git the skeeters blowed out. I mean, they's a pain, nights, and days too, places over in the hammock."

"Hit's time for the high winds?"

"Yessum. Shore is. Wouldn't surprise me none to see 'em beginnin' tomorrer."

"Wouldn't surprise me none," she agreed.

"Yessum. 'Bout crack o' day, mought git up and hear the palmeeters shakin' theirselves to pieces, and the ol' pine trees a-crashin', and the rain fair fallin' sidewise, if the high winds has done come."

"Well, I reckon it's time."

"Yessum. Hit's time."

They were silent again. Suddenly the girl knew that this man was not a stranger. He was like herself. More, he was a part of herself. She was a part of him. It was altogether natural that they should be sitting together in the hot, swarming night, while other folk thumped their feet and tossed their heads to fiddle music.

The last set was called and ended. The young man moved cautiously away from the girl, inside the cabin. The fiddler was ready for a snort of old Jo's 'shine, now his night's work was done. Old Jo was reeling. The widow Boone left him and went home with a man who had a mule and wagon.

Florry helped her father down the steps, her mind full of other things. His condition was of no importance. He beat her, drunk, and worked her, sober. The beating was more painful than the logging, but it was sooner over. She accepted old Jo, his 'shine, his women, as part of the general pattern of life. They came and went across her like the heat and the mosquitoes, like the waters of the swamp. She had no more control over them than over the impending hurricane.

They had walked the six miles from their clearing to the Jacklins' in an hour and a half, old Jo leading the way smartly through the familiar pine-woods. Dawn was breaking before they were home again. Florry had to go ahead through territory unknown to her for the first four miles. She picked an instinctive trail, often quitting the dirt wagon road altogether for a northeasterly short-cut through the open flat-woods. Jo stumbled behind her, the effort absorbing all his breath, so that he had none left with which to curse. When he dropped too far behind, she waited without looking back, her eyes strained ahead in the umbrous twilight that was the moon's setting.

When they plunged into the hammock south of the clearing, Florry could move more surely. The gusts of air that had been puffing at them on their way had blended into a long sweep of wind, rising and falling like the surge of surf. As the moon set behind them and the east lightened, the sky showed itself a bedlam of scudding clouds, rushing pell-mell south by west. Birds were stirring sleepily in the clearing. A red bird trilled richly from a sweet gum. A pair of turtle doves whirred from the long-leafed pine where they had nested for the night. In the cypress swamp to the north, jorees began to crackle. A covey of young quail emerged in single file from the night's shelter of thick brambles back of the cabin. The hound pat-patted his tail on the sand to greet them, but did not lift his sleepy head from his paws.

Old Jo tumbled into the rough pine bed at the side of the main room and snored thickly at once. Florry did not light the lamp in the gray dawn, but walked through the open, covered breezeway to the kitchen at the rear. This was the hour at which they arose when they were getting out logs and she was hungry. Jo was probably at the beginning of a long drunk. At any rate, he would not log today nor tomorrow.

There were a few embers of live oak in the small wood stove, but she did not trouble to stir them to life. She poured a cup of thick cold coffee and chicory in a tin cup and drank it, munching a slab of cold gray cornbread, a slice of cold boiled bacon and a few left-over greens. A very little satisfied her, for she was accustomed to working hard on light rations, but somehow she wanted more. She split a leathery biscuit and soaked it with home-made cane syrup. It was last year's boiling and was souring a little. Old Jo would give her the devil if he could see her pouring out so much syrup.

Near the stove was a pallet on the floor, covered with crocus sacks stuffed with black moss. Florry took off her stiff boy's shoes and black cotton stockings, the ragged brown dress, and her drawers made of sugar sacking. She lay down in her short shift of the same material and drew a quilt over her head to keep out the mosquitoes. She was not sleepy. She knew that things awaited her for which she must be prepared with sleep. The pines were hissing. The water-oak scratched long boughs across the cypress shingles of the kitchen roof. High winds were coming. They would sweep across her, move her on. When they were gone, she would not be in this place.

The girl was awakened by the tumult. It was broad day, and the outer perimeter of the hurricane was moving across the section. The yellow-grayness of the sky was tinged with green in the west. The roar of the wind was a train thundering nearer and nearer. The palmettos thrashed their fans in frenzy. Rain was pounding on the roof as though it would beat it open. On the gutters it flailed like bird-shot. The thunder no more than boomed above the downpour. Beyond the kitchen window, the gray flood was a curtain across the piney-woods. The world outside the cabin was obliterated.

Shingles ripped off with a dry rattle. The winds seemed to be the worst she could remember. This was the first time they had taken the shingles. Good, heavy, hand-hewn cypress, they weren't ready by twenty years to give way. The sugar cane would be flat. They'd have to grind right away to save it, fully ripe or no. Old Jo would have to grind——

Sport darted into the kitchen, his spotted coat blown into bristles. He whimpered. He was always afraid in a storm. She set the plate of cornbread on the floor and he gulped it, his ribs heaving in and out. He came back to her, quivering. She listened for sounds from old Jo. She could hear nothing in the tumult, in any case. He could be screaming for his rations and she didn't believe she could hear him. She opened the kitchen door to get fresh water and the wind lifted it from its makeshift leather hinges as if it were a leaf in her hands. She was all but taken with it as it hopped across the sand. The gale sucked her from the house. She pulled herself back into the confused open kitchen by great effort.

She washed her face and hands in the basin of water she had used last night. She put on her drawers and dress and made a lunge across the breezeway. She couldn't remember ever having to fight so hard across it before. The winds were bad last year, but not like this. Her lean body bent almost at right angles. The last few feet she was lying on the wind, like a swimmer in the water. Her strong bony arms pulled her along. She sprawled breathless into the main cabin. Old Jo still lay in the sagging bed, his red lips open, his breath rising and falling heavily, too deep in sleep to hear if the roof should fall about his head. Well, she thought, let him lie.

"I better be fixin' to clean up whilst he's quiet-like."

She was filled with the need of putting the place in order. She brushed the rough pine floor with a broom-grass sweep. The dirt was largely loose sand which she brushed into the fireplace. She picked up old Jo's wide-brimmed black felt Sunday hat from the floor and hung it on a wooden peg on the back of the door. A bunch of yellow daisies from the flatwoods was dead in a coffee can on the bare deal table. She threw them in the fireplace and poured the fetid water on the tin cans of plants on the two window-sills. They were wild ferns and jasmine vines. The rain was beating down too fiercely to set them out in it. Her porch plants in lard pails were being whipped to pieces. Two of them had been knocked over and rolled toward the wall of the cabin, where they thumped and banged. She moved Jo's twelve-gauge shotgun to a corner by the clay fireplace. There was nothing more in the room to put in order. There was indeed nothing more there.

Florry made a rush back to the kitchen. The gale lifted her across the breezeway as though great hands lay under her armpits. Moved by an obscure instinct, she overhauled her wardrobe. She patched the brown calico dress and took a few stitches in her other shift and drawers. The cockroaches had been at her ancient coat. She shook it out and brushed off the summer's white mold.

The young Cracker arrived in the lull of the gale. Like a bird-dog guided by scent, he came direct to the gaping rear door, where he stood hesitant. The rain washed through him from shirt to shoes. He pushed the dripping brown hair back from his eyes.

"I mean, hit's a toad-strangler of a rain," he proffered.

"I mean!" she agreed.

"Reckon your daddy'll keer, me a-follerin' this-a-way?"

"Reckon he mought." She looked him fearlessly in the face. "Hit don't worry me none. You couldn't git you no wetter," she said, "iffen you'll go yonder to the wood-pile and fetch me some lighter'd and a handful o' them turpentine chips, I kin make you a fire to dry you out a leetle."

"I shore will do that thing."

He dragged back the door and propped it against the opening. The wet wood steamed and popped in the iron stove. Sport stretched luxuriously closer, groaned in his sleep. The smell of the man, the smell of his garments, filled the room in rich waves. Florry sat by him on the pallet.

"Them ol' winds didn't waste no time a-comin'," he said.

"Seems like us mought o' brought 'em in, like, a-talkin' of 'em."

He shook his head.

"They was ready to come. I seed the signs."

She nodded.

"I kin feel them things a-comin', a long ways. I could kind o' feel you comin'," she added gravely.

"I studied some you mought be proud to see me."

They listened to the irregular surge of the rain on the shingles. The wind seemed to be picking up again. The chinaberry crackled ominously in its old brittle limbs. The boughs flailed the roof. The storm enclosed them, boxed them in together. It was inconceivable that they had ever been afraid, that they had ever been separate.

"My name be Martin," he said. "I be called mostly Mart."

"Mart," she repeated.

"You want to go off with me?" he asked.

She was not startled. She had sensed its coming, as she had sensed the coming of the gale. It was strangely a part of the storm. It was part of the inevitable change.

"I reckon."

"Git your things. Le's go."

She made a bundle of her belongings.

"What about your daddy?"

"I reckon we'd best jest ease out. He mought raise up a turrible fuss iffen he knowed I was goin'."

"Kin you write out a letter to leave for him?" he asked.

"No. I cain't write ary word."

"Nor me," he said.

"I got my name writ out," she suggested eagerly. "That Yankee at the sawmill done printed it for me on a white paper."

"I got no use for a Yankee," he said dubiously. "Reckon it's writ wrong, or means somethin' else?"

"I don't think. The range rider kin read, and he said it done spelled 'Florry.' If I leave it where Pappy kin find it, he'll know it means I done went."

She withdrew the slip from her bundle and smoothed it out on the kitchen table, weighting a corner with the coffee-pot. Mart nodded approvingly. On the step he hesitated.

"Hit don't seem right, takin' you off in sich a wind and rain."

"Hit'll mebbe fair off tomorrer. Hit don't mean nothin' to me, gittin' wetted. We got to git in the clare whilst Pappy's likkered."

"That's right. We got to git in the clare."

As he turned to replace the door behind them she darted back and set a pan of rain water on the floor for the hound.

"A thirsty animal be so pitiful," she explained.

The second circle of the hurricane was on them as they fought their way through the piney-woods, riotous with the hissing of pine boughs. The northwest section of the State was only getting the fringe of the great upheaval.

"On the east coast," Mart cried in her ear, "they tell the palmeeters gits flatted smack to the ground, times, like, and over in the scrub they says the trees 'll done be bended."

They stopped for breath under the comparative shelter of an overhanging live oak.

"There wa'n't much there," Florry told him, "but I be ashamed, I plumb forgot to git you some rations."

"Don't let it worry you none," he assured her. "I don't eat regular. You got you a long whiles to git me rations in."

His lean brown face was bright with his smile. He grew serious.

"I figgered on gittin' over to Levy County and gittin' us a parson there, mebbe tonight."

She grew anxious.

"Don't it cost money to git married?"

"I reckon."

The subject was delicate.

"Mart, I ain't got me a dime. Have you got ary cash-money?"

Turning his back to the driving rain he emptied his pockets. There were two paper dollars and some loose silver that proved too complicated to count accurately. It did not seem to total another dollar.

"Mart, I ain't too pertickler about standin' up in front of a parson. Hit's sort of a church-business, like, and I don't know nothin' abouten sich things. We could fix to git married some time when you got plenty cash-money."

"I'd ruther you'd feel right about it, Florry. Hit shore don't make no difference to me. When we was sittin' together last night with the air so hot and restless, I studied then on you and me goin' off. All two of us so kind o' rabbity, like your daddy said. I shore gits lonesome, times, like."

She nodded.

"I shore feels all right about it. I'll be your ol' woman and you'll be my ol' man, right on. I ain't no leetle mite skeered."

He put one hand on her bony shoulder and peered fiercely at her.

"Leave me tell you," he said. "I ain't studyin' none on quittin' you, no ways, nohow—no time——"

They made a new venture into the storm, working always south.

"If we don't make Levy County," he called, "I know a 'shiner'll put us up. He done borried my gun and I got to git it one time. Mought as well git it now. These high winds this time o' year is like to last three, four days."

"And then them fine, blue days," she shrilled back. "Jest breezy-like and clare, and no red-bugs or skeeters."

"That's right."

They fought on.

"I shore feel mean about leavin' ol' Sport," she said. "Pappy'll starve him to death."

"Ain't he a good rabbit dog? Cain't he ketch hisself rabbits?"

"I reckon." She pondered. "I reckon ol' Sport kin make out on rabbits."

II

FLORRY SAID, "A marsh sure is the crawlin'est thing."

She was a little homesick for the high piney-woods. The marsh seemed low, as though she were living in a sink-hole. The air was oppressive. The October night when Mart had brought her to the cabin in the lakeside hammock had startled her by its manner of falling. She had been looking idly at the streamers of salmon and gold in the sky above the close-set live oaks and sweet gums. Mart was repairing the sagging square shutters, so that they might be swung to, like casements, and hooked from the inside. The night air must be kept out, for it bred fever.

Suddenly, it was twilight, and in a moment, dark.

A brief panic touched her. The day was gone, and she was unable to see its going. All her life she had watched the sun burn fire-red through the long-leafed pines; drop inch by inch to a discernible oblivion. The close vegetation of the hammock turned the good sun unfriendly, a little treacherous.

She felt, at first, insecure in her footing. The piney-woods had been firm and dry. Following Mart along the marsh, in and out of the swamp, barefooted, the soft muck gave alarmingly under her. Here and there Mart pointed out a bubbling seepage and warned her of quicksands. She remembered the cypress swamp, where she had moved carelessly in brown water shoulder-deep. To her memory it had been surer, but she decided that a stranger might have been uneasy there. The cypress waters, amber-brown like a fine clear coffee, had been open. There was no undergrowth. The marsh edge, the very waters of the lake, until they were a half-mile out, were a thick, slippery mass of lilies, marsh-grass and coon-tail. Frogs splashed everywhere. Small fish darted in and out, brushing cool against her bare legs. Water moccasins slid like oil into the water.

In a brief time she grew intimate with the marsh Mart called a prairie. The marsh gave them their living, for in the cool autumn crispness Mart began to trap along its borders. The lake in front, the jungle hammock behind, enclosed them in what came to be a delightful safety. Rations were still scanty at times. Hunger was not new to her belly, but it was on the whole rather unimportant. A deep peace filled her. Sights and sounds and odors moved her as they had not done before. They were all associated with the pleasure of knowing that Mart was there; never more than a mile or two away.

Mart came in with a soft-shell cooter. The turtle was new to her. It had come out of the marsh to lay its eggs.

"Mart, a thing with a ugly ol' head like that un, shore ain't fitten to eat."

"I mean, shore is!" he insisted. "Hit's a sight sweeter meat than chicken."

"Hain't it a fishy ol' thing?"

"Nary a mite. Go on, Florry, cook it. We ain't had no meat in so long."

He drew out the long leathery neck with a hooked wire and cut off the sharp-beaked head with his knife. He separated the neck and four thick legs deftly from the shell, trimmed off sections of the translucent border, flexible like thin gristle. The female was full of yellow fat and still yellower eggs, some of them encased in paper-white shells, ready for depositing in a hole in the sand.

" 'Coons and skunks is wild for cooter eggs," Mart told her. "You kin allus tell when it's fixin' to come a rain, for a cooter's got sense enough to lay jest aforehand, so's the rain'll wash out her tracks and fool the varmints."

"Be cooter eggs fitten for folks to eat?" she inquired distastefully.

"I mean! And here's a question my daddy allus asked and nobody couldn't never answer. Why do a soft-shell cooter lay a hard-shelled egg, and a hard-shell cooter lay a soft-shelled egg?"

She marvelled duly at the conundrum without an answer.

Mart cut out the heart and the plump liver. The heart continued to beat in its regular rhythm. Florry's eyes widened and Mart laughed silently at her astonishment.

"Jest you wait 'til you see what happens in the pan," he chuckled.

In the face of her ignorance, he did the cooking. He boned the pieces of pink and white meat, dipped them in meal and salt, and fried them in the black iron Dutch oven that was their only cooking utensil. The lid vibrated alarmingly and in a few moments he lifted it to show her the heart still beating in the bubbling grease and the muscles of the legs twitching spasmodically.

"Mart," she protested, "dogged if I wants to eat arything you has to stand on the lid to keep it from poppin' out o' the pan."

But when the meat was fried golden brown and tender, she agreed, after a first cautious nibbling, that it was plumb noble rations. The left-over pieces, with the shell-less eggs, Mart made into a stew the next day, with a little wild garlic for seasoning. The shell-eggs he boiled in salted water.

"They ain't done thu," Florry declared.

Again he could laugh at her, for the white of a turtle egg will not solidify, not though it be boiled a week and a day. The eggs were slightly musty in flavor, but fine eating. After that, Florry, too, kept watch for cooters, come on shore to lay. She delighted to poke one with a stick and watch the flat brown pancake body lunge viciously forward and the evil, snakelike head snap futilely. She had to be fast on her feet to run one down before it could reach water ahead of her; quick to flip it on its back.

The cabin, with trapping rights, Mart rented for a percentage of his hides. They went hungry often through December while he acquired a few skins and reinvested them in more traps. A dozen traps were needed to show a profit. Game was plentiful. Cool weather had set in early and the pelts were thick and glossy. In the hammock were 'coons and 'possums, skunks, foxes and an occasional wildcat. In the marsh were mink and a few otters. The mink were of poor quality, but the rare otters were large and fine.

Mart showed Florry an otter slide on a slight clay elevation.

She wanted to come and watch the play the next moonlit night. Mart said she was foolish and set his largest trap at the top of the slide. A big trap with inch-long teeth was necessary to hold an otter in the full of his strength.

"Hit don't seem right," Florry said, "a-settin' trapses where a creetur plays."

But he trapped one very seldom, and when he received thirty dollars for a fine pelt, in January, she forgot her scruples. "That's a powerful piece of cash money for a varmint hide," she said.

They ate 'coon meat only when there was no 'possum. It had a strong taste. Yet a 'coon was clean and a 'possum was a scavenger. But when a 'possum was fat with persimmons and pilfered pinders, his flesh was more succulent than the juiciest young pork. Sometimes Florry cut one in pieces and smothered it in the Dutch oven. Mart's favorite way was to turn it on a spit over a bed of live-oak coals.

Florry's only quarrel with Mart was over his taking of the skunks. He insisted on bringing them home to skin, as he did the other varmints. Florry swore she was half ill from the stench. Mart seemed indifferent to the odor. In the early spring he found a young skunk caught only by a toe. It enlisted his interest by showing no fear. He brought it home alive. Old Negro Will showed him how to remove the musk. It was a clean and pleasing pet. Florry was beginning to feel a warm surge of pleasure in its white-striped little black form, when a wildcat made off with it one night, defenseless without its primordial weapon.

She went every morning with Mart to visit the traps. He did the skinning alone, but she helped him tack the hides to cure on the wall of the cabin, or stretch them over shingles. They must be stretched good and tight. All through the winter the unpainted gray walls were covered with drying skins.

Mart had the owner of the cabin send his name to fur houses in New York, St. Louis and New Orleans. Catalogues and postcards came to him in the mail. The fat prices offered were read off to him. He sent bundles of hides to the various houses, but the money-order sums he received back did not tally with what had been offered. He found he did better at the fur dealer's in

Manitopy. He had to walk some miles, fording a shallow river, or rent or borrow old Will's gray mule for the trip. It paid to do it.

Florry walked with him one crisp bright day in February and bought herself some red-spotted percale for a dress. There were many people walking up and down the streets. Some of them stared at her. They looked at her split coarse shoes, her ragged dress and caught-back soft hair. She was panicked, distraught, like a squirrel caught in a room. She could scarcely make the storekeeper in the village dry-goods store understand what she wanted. She picked the material at random, took her change and bundle blindly and scrambled out into the open. Her one thought was to meet Mart quickly and get away again. He came out of the fur dealer's dusty little building to find her crouched against the wall like a frightened dog. He was very little more comfortable than she. He bought snuff and pipe tobacco and they walked home without speaking. She did not go with him again.

It was hard for Mart to keep within boundaries at his trapping. A warm spell in February, with the sun beating down on the chilled hammock ground until it began to steam, brought out an old male rattlesnake for a few days. He caught or frightened away most of the small game in the immediate territory. One week of a diamond-back meant a deserted area. Mart looked longingly at the adjacent cultivated field, a Yankee's forty acres. There had been watermelons and corn there through the summer, pinders and chufas through the fall. 'Coons roamed the plot, seeking expectantly the next fresh crop of vegetables.

"Hit won't do no harm jest to work the edge, like," he decided.

Gradually he put his traps farther and farther in, until one day the Yankee caught him at it and ordered him off.

"Them 'coons shore'll eat up your next crop," Mart found courage to protest.

"That's my business. I'll do my trapping if I want any done."

"How about trappin' on shares, like?"

The landowner looked distastefully at the youth's brown, unshaven face, at his bare feet with the torn blue breeches turned up above them.

"No. Now get out and stay out."

Mart walked into the cabin with his clear brown eyes clouded with hate. He threw his traps on the bare pine floor.

"Hit don't hurt no man to talk polite," he grieved. "Not a man that owns forty good turned acres, free and clare, it don't hurt him none."

He breathed heavily with the shock of the encounter.

"Florry," he burst out, "the dogged biggety bastard done sended me off like I was a nigger!"

She sorrowed with him. He brooded long over it, bitterly.

Cold weather sent the rattler back to his hole and the game returned. Just before the season closed Mart filled his traps several times. Tempted, he trapped on for another ten days, but word came through Negro Will that the game warden was making the rounds. He hustled his hides to Manitopy. He oiled his traps and put them away in a lean-to back of the cabin.

They had enough money, buried in a glass fruit jar, to last them until trapping should open again the coming November. The fur dealer figured it out for Mart.

Spring was a delicious thing, invested with a new benevolence. It was unreal to have money under the porch. Unreal, to be able to idle all day. No work to do. Grits to cook once or twice a day, white bacon to crisp to otter-brown, fresh-caught fish to fry, late sour oranges to gather from the three wild trees in the hammock, so long hung as to be almost sweetened. No cypress logs, tearing at the muscles. No eddying brown water under the armpits. No old Jo.

The lake turned musical overnight. The frogs piped up and down the length of their small silver song. Hoot owls over the marsh boomed with the vibrancy of a bass viol. The cranes and loons cried dissonant, not quite inharmonious. On a night of full moon in April, Mart and Florry sat on the cabin steps. The palms were silver in the moonlight. The new growth of the oaks was white as candles. An odor grew in the stillness, sweeter than breath could endure. It seeped across the marsh like a fog of perfume. It filled the hammock. Yellow jessamine was in bloom.

When in the brightness a mockingbird began to sing, Florry put out her hand to Mart with a quick awkward motion. In the richness of her content, it was vital to her to touch him. It was as though she needed to be sure that he was there. Deep-sunk in her was a wisdom warning her that beauty was impermanent —safety was not secure—the money under the steps would not always be there. Nothing good stayed forever.

The mosquitoes were bad that summer. They slept with the cabin doors closed, the square shutters swung tight. They sweltered on hot nights on the pine bedstead Mart had hewn by hand and laced back and forth with strips of hide. In July the rains stopped. Both night and day were suffocating.

Florry awoke once at dawn, scarcely able to breathe. In the dim gray light she could see the sweat glistening on Mart's face. She slipped outside for air. Swarms of mosquitoes settled on her like a cloud. When she came down with chills and fever a few weeks later she knew of course that it was because she had exposed herself to the night's vapors.

The ordinary chills, the ordinary fever, striking her like a knife every afternoon, were matters of no particular alarm. Mart went to Manitopy for a bottle of Black Drought. She took it and grew worse. When she came to be out of her head for hours at a time, fighting phantoms, and wasted down to even more skeletonlike a figure than when Mart had taken her away, he lost all caution. He went to Manitopy for the doctor and paid willingly the staggering fee of thirty dollars for the half-dozen trips and the medicine. The iron and quinine took hold and by mid-September Florry was strong again.

The trapping money, however, was gone. The careful allotment of three dollars a week for rations and snuff and tobacco had been useless.

III

THE SEPTEMBER gales were not so fierce as usual. Summer moved into autumn without harshness. After the first quick distress, Mart and Florry were not disturbed that the money jar was empty. Mart made an alliance with the lake fishermen. They would not be forced to move on. Florry began to plant flowers and ferns and cuttings in tomato cans.

The fishermen were willing to have Mart join them on the terms by which they sold their fish to the storekeeper in the nearest village. He understood that hook-and-line fishing was only a pretense. A man could not be sure of catching half a dozen fish a day. They trapped and seined. This was illegal. The danger depended on who was county sheriff and who was the local game warden. At present Cap'n Tack, the storekeeper, who peddled the fish to city markets, had the game warden taken care of. A change of wardens would mean trouble.

Cap'n Tack owned the two seines, a hundred and fifty yards in length. They were worth a couple of hundred dollars. He provided the material for traps, a fine-meshed wire which the fishermen made into barrel-like traps with a funnel in each end. The fish swam idly into one of the funnels, and seemed content to make no great effort to escape. But if a trap were left unemptied on the lake bottom too long, the fish swam out again. Cap'n Tack allowed the fishermen five cents a pound. He sold the fish for twelve. This did not seem disproportionate to the men. They could not buy seines themselves. When an unfriendly warden pulled up their traps and destroyed them, Cap'n Tack bought new ones.

Mart was allowed fishing shares in a rowboat with the half-grown son of fisherman Boyter. He took Florry with him, half expecting to be told to send her home. No one seemed to object. Most of the time she paddled the boat, leaving Mart and young Boyter free to pull up and empty the traps.

The lake never lost its charm for her. They reached it by way of Crab Creek, two miles of winding channel to the lake. The Creek was a dark, lovely dream leading to the bright open of another world. The hammock pressed close on either side. Sometimes the rowboat scraped against cypress knees. Sometimes the moss-hung boughs of a live oak brushed like hands across it.

The channel was always sweet of odor. In season the jessamine perfumed it, the waxy white magnolias and the smaller blossoms of the sweet bay. In the rare intervals when there was no bloom, the clean smell of pines filled the Creek, or the rank reptilian richness of the marsh. The Creek was always alive with birds. Blue and gray cranes took fright slowly. Often white egrets sat without moving as the boat slid by. In a great dead hickory lived a pair of bald-headed eagles, crying weirdly on moonlit nights. Ahead of the boat the coots took off like clumsy seaplanes, threshing the water with their feet long before the incompetent wings lifted the dark bodies into the air.

The channel passed between rows of tall cat-tails just before it reached open water. The lake came before Florry suddenly. Each time, into the open, she felt its unreality, as though she were transfixed in space. It was of the blueness of space. A mile out from shore it was so solitary— The roar of a bull 'gator was like thunder in the heart of solitude. The gray and green and red of the distant hammock merged to form the semblance of tall cliffs, like prehistoric walls. The palms topped them like shaggy heads, far away. The blue sky was illimitable. Except for the rainlike rush of the coots and the dip of the paddle, the lake was a blue pool of silence.

The boat moved here and there about the bonnet patches, in and out among the floating tussocks. It was often difficult to locate the traps. Mart marked the spot where a trap had been dropped into the water, by beating the lily pads with the oar, cutting the edges of the thick green leaves. But time and wind and worms had a trick, too, of eating off the edges. He often groped futilely with a pole with a nail in the end.

When a trap contained many pounds of live fish, it was heavy lifting. It loomed large over the side of the boat and Mart and the boy tugged and toiled to get it in and open the small wire door to empty out the contents. They trapped much stuff for which they had no use, mudfish, eels and jacks. Sometimes Mart took the jackfish in to Negro Will. The jackfish flesh was white and sweet, but only a Negro had the patience to pick out the endless fine bones.

Their main catch was big-mouthed bass, which they knew as trout, perch and bream. There was a brief closed season, but they managed to slip out now and then at night. Cap'n Tack could always sell the catch as coming from Lake George, where there were no restrictions.

Old man Boyter said, "A man cain't stop makin' hisself a livin' jest a-cause the law be meddlesome."

The seining must be done at night. Hauling in the heavy nets was too lengthy a process to risk by daylight. Trapping by day, the movements of strange boats could be watched.

In March Cap'n Tack got drunk and talked freely in the wrong house. The friendly game warden was deposed. Zeke Teeter, from the village, was named in his place. It was not dreamed of that he would attempt to interfere with the local fishing faction. He took his authority seriously. He not only found and destroyed twenty traps his first week, but he began to lie in wait for the fishermen along the shore.

Mart's boat lay alongside that of old man Boyter. They were emptying their traps leisurely when the sudden *put-put* of an outboard motor exploded and Zeke bore down on them. Old Boyter dropped the incriminating traps overboard not so much with discretion as with astonishment. Zeke cut off his motor and faced them a little sheepishly.

"If Mart here didn't have his wife along, you Zeke you, I shore would git you told!" old Boyter sputtered. "Sneakin' up that-a-way on fellers you was raised with!"

"I don't keer," Zeke insisted, "I'm enforcin' the law on this lake."

"Well, you go do your enforcin' some'eres else. You don't belong to be enforcin' it on me."

Zeke withdrew before the old Cracker's wrath, but war was declared. It was agreed that with Zeke acting up it would be just as well to fish the traps by night and avoid trouble. When a camp-fire was observed of nights on Black Island, opinion was divided as to whether Willy Butler, recently escaped from the penitentiary at Raiford, was in hiding, or whether Zeke was fool enough to be lying there. Strong spiritual necessity alone would put a man in that jungle nest of rattlesnakes.

Old Boyter said, "Hit must be Willy. Zeke knowed there was a nine-foot shed of a rattler seed there lately. A man wants to be on Black Island bad, to risk them things."

But the inhabitant of Black Island proved to be Zeke, set on ingratiating himself with the county authorities by bringing in the lake's offenders.

Trapping by night, Matt refused to let Florry go with him. During a hot spell in April, young Boyter came down one afternoon with an early attack of fever. Mart set out alone that night, paddling softly to the bonnet patch where he had half a dozen traps. There was a murky half-moon. A water turkey, disturbed, flew off with a clatter of wings. Frogs splashed into the water from the lily pads.

As he reached for a bonnet to act as anchor, a boat moved in on him from either side. Quick hands in the darkness turned his boat over. He flailed wildly in the deep water. The two boats moved silently away. He thrashed about, trying to reach his rowboat. Rifle shots flicked across his head. One grazed his knuckles as he put a hand on his boat. He let go and swam in the opposite direction with a strong dog-paddle that was the only stroke he knew. He caught the drift of voices.

"Serve him dogged right if he do git drownded."

It was the voice of old man Boyter, in ambush since early morning. Mart understood that, alone, he had been mistaken for warden Zeke. He raised his voice in a Hullo, declaring himself. After an astonished pause, the two boats came to him. Old Boyter told it in the village as a prodigious joke. It came in due time to Zeke's ears. He was frightened. If they had caught him, he would surely have drowned. He let them alone most of the summer, until his courage oozed back in him, like sap rising again in a tree.

Mart lied to Florry. Some private knowledge of him told her when he came in at dawn that things had gone wrong. She looked at his blood-caked hand.

"A pure accident," he said, and washed it carelessly.

"Hit ain't neither," she said shrewdly. "Did Zeke git you?"

He shook his head.

She had a basic fear of treachery.

"Mart, Boyter and them ain't turned on you?"

"No. Now Florry, don't git worrit up over nothin'. They ain't nary thing the matter."

She could get no further satisfaction. In her isolation from the village life, five miles away, the tale did not reach her.

After a summer of brooding inactivity, Zeke took heart to go after the fishermen. He had a sullen nature, and long pondering through the hot dog days finally inflamed him. He appeared on the lake restlessly, day and night, with an obtrusive shotgun. He had been taunted here and derided there. Cohorts of the fishing faction laughed at him openly. His own friends advised him that it was a job for a man from another part of the country.

Cap'n Tack decided to end the matter once and for all. He drew out his several hundreds of dollars in postal savings and invested in a fast little motorboat for the use of the seiners. Old man Boyter planned the campaign. His headquarters were in the Pocket, a lake-cove deep-indented in the hammock on the north shore. No one could slip in unobserved. Cap'n Tack and old Boyter decided to concentrate. The fishermen gathered in all the traps and piled them high in the Pocket. They would not leave them in the lake for Zeke to pick off, like a chicken-hawk picking off biddies. All the men were assigned to a few boats, and intensive seining was done openly, in the daytime. They dared Zeke to trouble them.

In the unbearable, sultry days of early September Zeke foamed at the mouth. His motor followed the big new one around and around the lake. When old Boyter was through for the day, he shot in to the Pocket, and Zeke, frenzied though he might be, kept out.

The first day of the September gales lashed the lake into the peculiar fury of inland waters. It was impossible to venture out more than a few yards from shore. The wind was followed by a tropical deluge of rain that obscured both water and land. It was agreed by the fishermen that Zeke in his cowardice would be sitting safe by his light-wood hearth fire. They left the Pocket and went home to their own.

"Mart," said Florry, after the rain had lifted, "ain't that smoke yonder in the Pocket?"

Zeke had gone in by land and made one gigantic bonfire of traps, seines, rowboats and the new motorboat.

"You buzzards should of knowed better," Cap'n Tack said mildly. "You should of had you some watchment. I'm thu with fishin'. I got no cash money to start off agin. Go git you a job for hoe-hands."

IV

RATIONS had been regular the year Mart fished with Boyter. When a fishing week was lean, Cap'n Tack let them have grits and white bacon and water-ground meal just the same. With plenty of fish and wild mustard greens, they had lived well. Mrs. Boyter had a scrub milch cow and sometimes sent Florry a can of clabber-milk. Blackberries were plentiful that summer, and huckleberries and blueberries, for the piney-woods had not been burned over. Long, sweet paw-paws were ripe in August. Florry's lean frame took on a few pounds of flesh. The malaria did not return and her golden-tanned cheeks were like sun-ripened guavas. Her quick squirrel eyes were clear and bright.

Well-nourished, strong, conception took place within her. It was strangely fortuitous. Neither was amorous of nature. Passion for her seized the man as briefly, if as necessitously, as flames that lick the turpentine pines when forest fire moves through. The meager delights of her spare body were no more to him than the pleasures of a drink or two of the hot, raw 'shine old Boyter sometimes passed around. If they were together, side by side of pleasant nights on the stoop of the cabin, it was usually comfort enough.

"A young un won't make no pertickler difference, I reckon," Mart said.

He was driven to finding work not so much with conscience toward the coming child, as because, with credit stopped at Cap'n Tack's and Florry on short rations once more, she dropped back rapidly to her old gauntness. She made no complaints. If the growing belly pinched her with hunger, she borrowed a little of Mart's snuff to lip. That satisfied for the time. If it had not been for Cap'n Tack's sardonic injunction to the fishermen to take jobs as hoe-hands, it would perhaps never have occurred to Mart to hire out to another man. He was not of a breed that took to work for others.

He had been thinking over his problem when the Yankee came to him. The man did not seem to recognize Mart as the trapper of two years before, whom he had ordered off his forty acres. Crackers, like Negroes, looked much alike to his complacency. The Yankee did not get along well with the Negro help. The other unemployed white men had all refused him. His last tenant farmer, a Negro, had walked off. He needed a man to live on his place and work his orange grove. He could not pay an inexperienced man very much—four dollars a week, his house, and land to garden for himself.

Mart's impulse was to send the man about his business. Florry's lean face with the quick, wild-animal eyes flashed before him. He accepted the job. He was depressed as he told Florry what he had done. She was in a fiercer panic at the thought of living close to another house; close to Yankees. But a canniness for the child moved her, and she found courage to follow Mart to the dirty tenant house in the orange grove.

The Negro family had left the house a sty. The Yankee owner had not troubled himself to determine its condition. In her bare, clean life it was Florry's first experience with filth. She found refuge from her unhappiness the first week in scouring the place from end to end. She ran down cockroaches one by one. The sagging walls were crudely papered by former occupants with newspapers and magazine pages, glued to the wall with a gummy paste made of flour and water. Spiders and roaches were thickly nested behind them. Mart made her a new shucks scrub, dried corn husks inserted in holes in a block of wood, the handle set in at a convenient angle. She took satisfaction in its thick wet swish on floors and walls.

"I kin hear you a-scrubbin' t'other end o' the lot," Mart said.

The Yankee home was occupied from September to May. Cap'n himself was mean and miserly, but his family, headed by a young wife, made holiday through the winter. There was a constant coming and going of high-voiced people. The front gate was just within range from Florry's sagging front porch. Carefully concealed, she watched brightly dressed women get out of automobiles and walk up the path, shrieking with pleasure. The Cracker speech was soft as velvet, low as the rush of running branch water. The foreign voices were a constant alarm.

Florry kept out of sight whenever possible. The sulphur well that supplied the tenant house was a hundred yards away. When she went for water, a pail in either hand, her graceful tread stiffened self-consciously into rigidity. When one of Cap'n's family appeared on the distant side porch facing the tenant house, she darted inside.

The Yankee walked over one day and called them both out of the house.

"Wonder if your missus will take on our washing?" he asked Mart. "I'd expect to pay her extra, of course."

In his first week Mart had learned there were many things the Yankee did not know. He forgave him much for his ignorance. He stifled from expression the hot wave that swept over him.

He wanted to say, "No white woman don't ask another white woman to wash her dirty clothes for her nor to carry her slops, neither. 'Course, for a favor, like, a woman'll do most ary thing for a woman in trouble, sick-a-bed. Or for her own kin-folks."

He dared not. He shook his head. The Yankee shrugged his shoulders and walked away.

"Hit shore will be a pain, tryin' to work for that catbird," Mart said.

"I mean!" Florry agreed. "Hit'll be a pain right on."

Florry marveled that Mart was able to go out among strangers and talk up to them. It distressed him, but he could force himself to it. He hated the grove work, not because it was hard, but because it was unfamiliar. He could not seem to learn fast enough to please the owner. When he was pruning, the Yankee constantly complained.

As a matter of course, Mart got out his traps, cleaned them up and set them at the far edge of the hammock grove near the lake edge. The Yankee's cow stepped in one and lamed herself

a little. The Yankee recognized Mart. He raged just short of firing
him. He would not have him trapping on his land and on his
time. Mart pointed out that he was up at his traps before dawn.
That made no difference.

But the fur money, sheer profit, was too tempting. Mart slipped
closer to the lake and set his traps where the Yankee would not
find them. Cap'n smelled the hides drying in the tenant house.
He railed constantly. Mart's revolt was no more than held in leash.

"Florry, I swear me an' some Yankee's goin' to git mixed up
some day," he confided to her. "I jest got no use for one."

"I know how you feels," she said. "I git the same feelin', times."

"After the young un gits borned," he said hopefully, "mebbe
we kin git out."

They decided against having a doctor. The last experience had
been too financially disastrous. Negro Will told them his old
woman had helped birth many a child. She was better at bringing
children than any white doctor. It seemed reasonable. It did not
occur to them even to mention the matter to Cap'n or his wife.
Old black Martha slipped in to stay with Florry when she began
to have spells of faintness. She stayed in the house and no one
knew she was there. Cap'n would perhaps not have permitted it.
The old Negress nursed Florry with a kindness that was like
warm sun.

"You sho' is po'ly, chile," she said, disturbed, "po'ly as a snake.
You wants to eat good and flesh up. You time 'bout come."

"Hit shore don't seem long enough," Florry puzzled.

"Mebbe you's to be took a little soon. Chile," she asked sus-
piciously, "you isn't done anything to git rid of it?"

She shook her head, wondering.

"Tha's right." The old woman sighed, relieved. "These days
so many ladies don' want they chillen. I'se raised all my gal chil-
lens to live right and mind they manners wid de men. But I'se
often tole 'em, 'Iffen one o' you does do wrong, now mind, iffen
you does, and gits you'se'f in a way you hadn't oughta—why,
you be lady enough to bring the chile into the worl'!' "

The child was born on a chill evening in January. The temperature had hung just above freezing all the dank and cloudy

day. The Yankee kept Mart hauling wood, to fire the grove at night if necessary. At dusk a changing wind brought that rare phenomenon, a Florida snow. It hissed on the cypress shingles like a shower of pine needles. It blew in under the eaves of the flimsy tenant house and lay in scattered white flakes on the cold floor. Martha had a roaring fire on the hearth in the bedroom, but the other room was bleak and cold. Mart came in after dark. The temperature was still just thirty-two. They would not need to fire. He noticed the light fluff at his feet.

"What you spilt, Marthy," he asked wearily, "meal or salt?"

Weighted as she was with the announcing of his son's birth, she smiled at him.

"Snow new to you, son, ain't it? You don' know its ways. Dat snow on the flo'. Fust snow I'se seed in thutty year. Done come in thu the eaves. Snow's a searchin' thing. Searches in thu the eaves and thu the cracks. You got you a boy-chile, Mist' Mart, but he puny. Po' li'l Mis' Florry too scrambly-scrawny. The chile cain' live too long. You look at that snow good, boy. Snow be's like sorrow—hit searches people out."

The puny boy-child lived all spring and most of the summer. Florry could have been almost content if Mart were not like a wildcat sullen in a cage. Mart hated the grove, but she loved it. Trees were gentle. The sounds they made were lovely sounds. The susurrus of the palms, the sibilance of the pines, the roar and rush of great winds through the oaks and magnolias, were the only music she had known. A holly tree, shining with glossy leaf-points, with green or red berries alive like eyes, was to her a bright friend. When a tree ripped and crashed in a storm, its death was pitiful, like that of an animal. Anywhere among trees she would be at home.

She had known wild oranges. The green richness of the culti- vated grove was new to her. There was rhythm to the hexagonal planting, so that whichever way she looked, the trees made straight and marching rows. When the golden globes of fruit were picked, unharmed after the snow, it was as though bright lamps had been turned out around her.

The grove was in bloom when she was first able to sit out on the porch with the baby in her arms. The oranges and tangerines, the spicier grapefruit, the wild-roselike bloom of the thorny trifoliata, drenched the world with their sweetness. The scent was more powerful at night. As soon as the sun withdrew its dryness, the bloom sent its odor into every nook and cranny of the air. It was inescapable. Still weak and dizzy, for weeks she dropped off to sleep at night, drowning in perfumed waters.

The jessamine was too far away in the hammock for more than a breath to reach her. It was tantalizing to get only a whiff of it. Compensation came in May. A magnolia sixty feet tall shaded the tenant house. It was covered from top to bottom with tall white candles that burst wide into dazzling glories, opening from the top down, like a Christmas tree being slowly lighted. The blossoming was leisurely. The great white blooms were above her head for weeks. Then the white petals began to drop down and turn russet on the ground. The yellow stamens fell. The huge green leaves, brown-faced, drifted down with a soft rattling on the roof. In summer, the white candles shone red. Tall red cones were thick with glistening seeds and the birds rustled in and out among the branches. The Yankee complained about Mart's clothing. He wanted his hired man to look trim, like a servant. Mart had three sets of blue pin-check pants and blue denim shirts. He changed twice a week. There was no use, he said, in changing every day when he was wet with sweat an hour after he had begun to work. In his brown face and hands and arms, his bare golden chest, in his blue work-clothes, he was like a patch of good loamy soil covered with a mat of blue flowers. He had the smell of earth, with man-sweat and mule-sweat over it.

He handled the mules well. It was one thing Cap'n could not criticize. The Negro ahead of him had almost ruined them. He had beaten them about the head, so that it took Mart weeks to make them stand for bridling. Slowly, easily, he gentled the team until they were as amenable as oxen. Cap'n was pleased. When Mart had such a way with the animals, when he was so handy at repairing tools and harness, the Yankee could not understand why he didn't get the hang of the grove work better. Why, when a task was done, he didn't come for further instructions, but went straying off with his wife in the near-by hammock or down to the lake. There was something about him the Yankee could not control, could not quite put his finger on, to make discipline take hold. He was like an old bird-dog, that, when you are not paying attention, goes pattering off, hunting for himself.

Mart had to wear boots at his work. He was in and out among brambles, over the evil cruelty of sand-spurs, in danger of stepping on rattlers and moccasins. He needed their protection, although they chafed his feet and heated his ankles. Cap'n had started him off with an old pair of his own. As Mart saw them wearing out, he tried to save a little each week to send off to the mail-order house for a new pair, but he could not get enough ahead. He had felt obliged to give old Martha five dollars, although she had professed herself willing to help out for nothing. A white man ought to pay a Negro. He had to buy unbleached muslin for sheets and towels and underclothing for Florry and the baby. The baby choked and gagged a great deal and he bought a bottle of colic medicine once a week.

His toes were out of the boots. Cap'n looked at them and laughed.

"Those look like nigger-shoes, Mart," he said. "Tell you what I'll do. I've decided to put in spring beans. If you'll stick by the crop and not go prowling off half the time, I'll stand treat for a new pair of boots."

They made good money on the beans. Mart forced himself to nurse the crop, doing long hours of working and hoeing he felt a Negro should be helping with. He felt some little interest in the rich, quick growth.

"I mean, we made beans," he said proudly to Florry.

Nothing more was said about the boots. The soles were loose. He tied them to the uppers with binder twine, but they continued to flap under him. He decided to speak.

"How about them bootses, Cap'n?"

"Oh, yes." The man frowned impatiently.

Mart saw him glancing over the mail-order catalogue. When the boots came, Mart could see they were so flimsy they would not last the summer.

"Them soles is paper," Florry said. "One good wettin', like, 'll jest turn 'em to mush."

Mart drew them on and laced them slowly.

Florry went barefooted always. When she kept out of the sand-spurs, the light sand was soft under her feet. Her toes were spread wide. Her thin muscular legs were strong and straight. Even when she carried the baby lightly on one shoulder, she walked erect and firm. Her gait had the quality of a trot, so that she seemed to be walking with determination to some certain place.

One afternoon Negro Will stopped by with a post-card ad-dressed to Mart that had been left in his box. It had a picture of a red house and some printing on it. Mart had gone to town with the mules to get feed. He would not be back before dark. It might be something very important. She lipped a little of Mart's snuff and pondered. Better find out. She tucked the baby over one hip, his little wizened head hanging down, and walked over to the side porch of the Yankee house. The Yankee woman saw her coming on her first call. There was something a little alarm-ing in the fixed swing forward, the steady Indian-like tread of the lean body.

Florry said, "Evenin'," and thrust out the card.

The woman turned it over, uncomprehending.

"Will you please read hit?" Florry explained.

The card was an advertisement from a raw fur house. It quoted probable prices for the coming year. Florry listened gravely as the woman read aloud the list of wanted skins.

"Be that all?"

"The name of the firm and their address."

"Read hit."

Then, "I thank you." The girl reached out to take the card again and turned to go.

The Yankee woman had a strange feeling of bafflement.

"How are you getting along?" she called to the straight thin back.

Florry half turned.

"Purty good." Then, truthfully, "Nothin' extry."

"Is your house comfortable?"

"Hit'll do, now I got it cleant." She paused. "The antses is bad. I cain't keep the antses out o' Mart's breakfast."

She paced back to the tenant house.

The Yankee's family went north early and in late May he followed. The mosquitoes in the grove were very bad. The tall grass, which Cap'n did not want cut until August, bred them. They came up from the marsh in high-singing droves. All night they sounded like a high-pitched machine. The few old screens in the tenant house were gaping with rusty holes. Florry stuffed the door-cracks with paper and tried to block the paneless windows. But the old house itself was settling, wall from wall, beam from beam, timber from timber. They could see sunlight through the gaps by day and stars by night. They kept smudges going in the yard, but there was no keeping out the mosquitoes.

Mart bought enough mosquito netting to make a little canopy for the baby's pallet on the floor. It would cost more than he could get together to buy enough for their own bed. Cap'n sent him his wages each week by mail, and by the time he bought rations and colic medicine and snuff and tobacco, there was nothing left. He got young Boyter to write him a letter to the Yankee asking for money for a mosquito bar. The Yankee did not answer for a long time. At last he wrote, reminding Mart that he'd never had a mosquito bar in his life and if he indulged him now Mart would expect too much of him.

"First thing you know, Mart," the Cap'n wrote, "your wife'll be wanting running water in the tenant house."

That day Florry saw Mart walking around and around the Yankee house.

"What you lookin' for?" she asked.

"To see kin I git in. If I kin git in, we'll shore sleep on the floor in there. We'd jest go in and out to sleep, like, and not do no harm."

But he could not make an entrance without ripping off a door or a barred shutter. Florry was not willing to have him do that.

The mosquitoes were of a feverless variety, but sleeping under covers on the hottest nights to keep away from them weakened her. She had only begun to be strong again. She had recurrent fever attacks. Her milk grew scant and poor. The undersized baby had grown very little. It was blue-white in color. The unhappy small face scarcely seemed to recognize the mother. Even its cry was not a lusty one. It whimpered and fretted. In mid-August, Florry was feverish for a week. One morning the baby turned blue, then black, and merely failed to draw again the threadlike breath that all along had been its dubious hold on life.

They had half-expected it to go, but there seemed nothing to do about it. Old Martha had seen it once or twice, had exclaimed "Do, Jesus!" and made it some herb tea. She had assured them there would be no raising it. But when it was actually gone, a dull knife turned over in Florry's vitals and for long months would not give her rest. She stroked the small cold body over and over while Mart sat in a corner, whittling a stick unhappily.

"Well," he said at last, "mought as well go make it a grave."

They had never given it a name. It seemed always too indefinite to need one.

"Dig it where the varmints and the hogs won't git to root it," Florry called.

They decided that back of the house, in the grove itself, would be safest. Mart knocked together a small pine box—it was astonishing how little room the body took—and lined a hole in the sand with bricks from the chimney of an old smoke-house. Florry washed the baby and dressed it in clean clothes. She trembled a little as Mart piled bricks on top of the box and threw in three safe feet of sand. He stood back and looked at her questioningly.

"No need to mark it," she said faintly from pale lips. "Cap'n mought not like it and then we'd have to dig it up agin."

She dug up some petunias from the Yankee garden and planted them above the pine box.

"They'll seed theirselves, even after the land be ploughed," she explained.

With the rainy season, the vegetation swelled overnight. The red-top was man-high. Dog-fennel lined the roadway like a green wall. The coffee-weed was thick in the pasture lot. Mart mowed hay and stored it in the barn. The citrus sized up rapidly. By late August the grapefruit boughs were bending to the ground.

The slim branches of the orange trees were freighted with more than they could bear.

Cap'n came down early in September, just after the high winds had come and gone. Whole sections of trees lay cracked to the ground, a quarter of the crop flat and ruined. Growth conditions had made the limbs too brittle for the immense crop of fruit. He called down frenzied imprecations on Mart's head.

"You Cracker fool," he finished, "when you saw what was happening, why didn't you prop the limbs?"

"I allus reckoned trees could take care of theirselves," Mart said quietly. "I allus thought trees jest takened what come."

He went to Florry gravely.

"Florry, I got a bait of it. I got eight dollars. Le's us go down to the Gulf and see kin we make us a livin' salt-water fishin'."

She hesitated, her thought on the petunias growing purple and white.

"Hit suits me," she said at last.

They packed their few belongings in cardboard cartons and set off on foot before dawn. The sunrise came on them as they crossed the prairie west of the lake. The waters were rosy and the white egrets circling up from the reeds were tinged with pink. The man and woman cut a little north through a stretch of flat-woods.

"Hit's done been a sorrowful year," Florry said. "I shore be proud to git shut of it."

V

THE WHARVES of the last westerly town dropped slowly behind Mart and Florry in the rowboat. They set out downstream at the full of the tide. Mart had bought a sunken boat for fifty cents, raised it and repaired it. It was too make-shift for fishing, but it would take them down the tidal river to the Gulf.

Mart rowed with jerking, powerful strokes. The current was with him, yet it was hard going until the tide should turn. Florry sat in the bow, the high afternoon sun in her face, the river dazzling, flipping its spray over her now and then. The oppression of the town, of the ever-alarming contact with folk, lifted from her. She felt light-headed. She hummed a little, "Jacob's Ladder."

A rush of vital force surged through the man. The escape from the town, the push of the river-current toward new ground, the sound of Florry's small, sweet voice, stirred him. He picked up the song from her.

> "Jacob's ladder's steep an' ta-all—
> *When I lay my burden down!*
> If you try to climb, you boun' to fa-all—
> *When I lay my burden down!"*

There was no burden. The sorrowful year was over and forgotten. The tide was turning. Tide and wind and current were taking them down the river to a deep sea thick with fish. Florry dipped her fingers in the river water and tasted it. It was brackish. They were coming closer to the Gulf.

The river lost its identity reluctantly. Its banks followed it far into deep water. Toward the mouth, the banks broke up into a succession of shell and limestone islands, where Spanish bayonets fought with palmettos for a footing. Cactus showed among the undercover. Cedars twisted and writhed and grew sturdy on bare rock. Florry studied them, like new strange faces.

They reached Alligator Joe's island at sunset. Alligator Joe's name was now only legend, but the high ground of his island home was fine camping. Some other fisherman had been ahead of them, for a camp was built. It was a good sign, warming, like a welcome.

Pine saplings had been nailed together to make the bare framework of a shack. The peaked ridge poles were thatched with palmetto fans. The walls were of palmetto fans, closely overlapping, nailed by the stems upside down, so that no amount of wind or rain could beat through them. Square openings were left for doors and windows. The builder had not camped there long and he was not long gone. The palm fronds had scarcely finished drying. Their gold was still streaked with sage-green. They rustled constantly, for there was a breeze as steady as the Trades. Day and night, the whole shelter murmured as though it were alive. Small gray lizards were already at home in the thatched rustling roof. The rustling of the palmetto fans seemed the voice of the river— the current, the marsh grass and the tides made audible.

Mart made sure his patched boat was safely moored. Florry cooked bacon and grits with a Gulf sunset riotous beyond her. It was fine to see the sun go down again. She waved a thin arm about her.

"Be this Mexico, Mart?"

"Not yit. This be Floridy right on." He pointed. "Yonder, jest out o' sight, down to the end o' the river, be the Mexico Gulf. But Mexico's a furrin country. It be way yonder, acrost them miles o' waters."

She stared, trying to make out the Gulf, and maybe Mexico.

Sleep was sweeter here than she had ever known it. The cool salt air cradled her. The dried palm leaves' whispering overlaid the suck of the tidal water on the shingle. She roused up once at night, only to breathe deeply of the sibilant peace, to touch Mart gently, to make sure he too was there.

He intended to start off the next morning alone. Florry begged to go.

"They'll be a bait o' times when I won't git to go, when you git to fishin'," she pleaded. "Hit'll make me feel acquainted-like to go when I kin."

It was not the folk she longed to know, but the river. The small islands were entities with whom she would become familiar. The river seemed uninhabited as they rowed to the mouth. After the wild-life of the piney-woods and the populous hammock, it was strange to see no live things moving, no birds, no small furry faces turned to her for a brief moment. After she had lived on these back-waters of the Gulf for a few weeks, she would know where to look for the few shy birds and animals. She began to distinguish a human habitation here and one there. There was only a handful of families on the lower river. Houses on islands were often sunk out of sight among palms and cedars. Others lay up the winding salt creeks and were not visible from the river.

The chief of the small fishing clan lived up Channel Creek. The creek was no more than a canal connecting two of the tidal rivers. It wound interminably, like a tangled thread. The reeds and grasses were so high, the route so tortuous, that the boat seemed to be making no headway, land-bound and forgotten between flexible green walls.

Cap'n Harper's house sat back in the marsh, reared high on stilts. A swaying plank walk sagged for two hundred yards from wharf to house. The wharf was over an old oyster bed. It was low tide and the shells showed thick in gray muck. A sizable fishing dory with a sturdy in-board motor rocked at the wharf.

Mart was not gone long. He came back to report that Harper had just come in from a night's fishing, sleepy and a little ugly.

"He didn't shore enough promise I could fish for him," Mart said. "He done tol' me to come along an' fish with 'em a whiles, thouten no shares nor wages, to see could I git the hang of it."

"You kin git the hang of it all right," Florry said confidently. "You done good on the lake. You belong to do good at it."

"Hit's all right," Mart said. "He's got to see does my ways suit his ways. He'll likely give me fish and we got rations for a while and a leetle more cash money. They ain't no hurry."

"No, they ain't no hurry," Florry agreed comfortably. "No use a-hurryin' no ways, no time."

When Cap'n Harper told them they might stay, Mart rowed Florry in and out among the islands at the mouth of the river, house-hunting. They had their choice of several deserted houses. The island they chose was on the incurve of a cove. High, it still was not visible either from Gulf or river. Florry liked the feeling that no one could look in. No human life came within her vision, but there would be enough to see. Far out she could glimpse the fishing boats. There was never anything else. The steamship lanes were farther west.

Her house had once been very fine. It was two tall stories of weathered gray cypress, with gables and chimneys. A broad-columned porch spread across the front, sagging at the corners. There were endless gaunt rooms. The house was sunk almost out of sight in oleanders, shell-pink and fragrant. The gray-limbed bushes grew taller than the roof. The flowers dropped their soft pink petals all over the gray shingles.

Straggling in exotic borders on either side of the path leading to the water were venerable fig trees. Fat yellow figs hung dripping, like great beads of amber. Some had dried on the trees without falling and these were withered and honey-sweet. Mart and Florry stuffed greedily, hungry for fruit and for sweets.

Florry found a sunken pot of geraniums alive by the back steps. Some one had lived here recently. After they had been in the house a few days, the aromatic smoke of cedar logs curling up from the chimneys, an immense black and brown house-cat emerged from the woods. It skirmished about, watching for hours from the thicket. It had been deserted by the planter of geraniums three years before. It was sleek and fat. Small game was plentiful on the island. When Florry called, it yowled distressingly, as though it would have her understand that it longed, but feared, to come. At last it came to her. It kneaded its paws and beat its head against her.

Harper told them they had chosen a good place. It was even possible, he said, to grow a little garden in the few inches of top-soil above the shell and limestone. The droppings of the live oaks, the cedars, the bay, the palms, and the myrtle, had finally created a layer of humus.

"And they ain't nothing there to watch out for," he encouraged them, "excusin' rattlesnakes. Tell you what I'll do for you. Give you a leetle shoat from my new litter. Too many for the ol' sow to nuss. When it grows up it'll clare the place of ary snakeses."

Florry made a pet of the small runty black porker. Wherever she went, the pig trotted behind her, and the immense cat with its tail high in the air.

"I got me enough comp'ny now to suit anybody," she said.

She raised the pig on cornmeal and water. For lack of milk it did not grow. The blue cedar berries had fallen to the ground, and the live oak acorns. It soon found these and made a living for itself. It slept with the cat under the house. Florry felt as though she had lived here a long time. Now and then she saw a familiar bird, a red-bird in a cedar, a gray or white crane in the marsh.

Marsh chickens, smaller than quail, walked daintily on the shore of the island, picking up food in the mucky sand. Mart made spring traps and they caught all they wanted to eat. On the uninhabited islands lived water-turkeys and pelicans and black nigger-geese. The gulls came and went.

Florry thought the army of fiddler crabs at the edge of the water came to know her. When she walked among them they no more than moved out of her way. When Mart came, they rushed to the grasses or into the water. Their movement made a hissing sound, like the rustle of a stiff silk. Sometimes units of them paused, and lifted their single large claws up and down in rhythm. They became an orchestra, sawing without sound on invisible fiddles.

Mart felt a free man again. Taking the fisherman's orders was quite different from laboring under the alien cloud of the Yankee's displeasure. Harper turned over to him a flat-bottomed skiff and a gill net black with age. Mart would have to fish on shares. He had no money for equipment. Even the old rotten net was worth twenty dollars. Mart was assigned Cully Johnson for partner. Cully was a tall youngster of fourteen. The Johnsons were kin to the Harpers. As on the inland lake, Mart was being utilized to help a younger member of the tribe add to the family profits. He was an outsider and he was willing to take what was left. If fishing was good over any considerable length of time, even on third shares he could save up for a net and boat of his own.

He found Cully a good partner. His slim brown body was almost as strong as a man's. He could pull in his share of the great net, loaded with fish, as competently as Mart. There was a trick to paying out the net over the stern of the dory, a trick to handling it in again. On land, it must be spread just so on parallel poles to dry. There was a trick to fanning it—gathering it in folds so that it would dry evenly. It was a matter of rhythm. One man alone could handle the net when he knew his business. Often, when the fish were running, Mart took the boat out alone by night and Cully took it out by day.

After Mart came to feel sure of himself, he took Florry with him when he fished alone. It frightened her a little to pass from the river into the open Gulf. The mouth of the river was an end and a beginning. At a certain point it could be said, "Here, now, the river is alive." A few yards more, past the last wind-beaten cedar, there was no longer any river. There was only the blue horizon. As it is told of a departing life, the river was not ended, but was become part of the sea's infinity.

More than ever at night, the boat was precipitated into a dark eternity of waters. The last receding islands loomed immense. The black heads of the palms towered above the earth. The water was black as death itself. On moonlit nights the world was silver. Flecks of silver dotted the Gulf as far as Florry could see, so thick, so glittering, it seemed she could gather them by handfuls. The islands behind were silver, and the palm trees. The fish in the net flashed silver.

It was slow work finding the net on dark nights, finding the way in and out of the river. All the work seemed slowed up by a great dark hand. Fishing, day or night, was on the low tide. The boats went from one to four miles out in the Gulf, fishing the flats. Sinkers along the bottom edge, corks along the top, made the long straight nets stand like wavy fences down in the water. In calm weather they stood as erect as though posts held them. The fish swam into them and were hooked by the gills in the small meshes.

The usual catch was an assortment of sheep'shead, drum, mullet, butter-fish, needle-fish, sea-trout and mackerel in season. Stingarees were a nuisance in the nets. Mart's only complaint was over the painful necessity of removing them. The fat blue crabs were a pest. They tore the nets as if they were feasting on a choice bait. Mart and Florry could not believe it when Harper told them there were people who ate the meat.

"Them spidery things! They cain't be fitten!"

When she was alone, Florry sometimes took the old patched boat and rowed in and out among the winding cross channels. On each inhabited island nets were hung in the sun to dry, cream-colored, tan, gray or black, according to their time of service. Once a porpoise leaped and blew in the river near her. Cully told her a porpoise often came in and fished out the river.

"Reckon this un was jest traipsin' around, a-visitin'," she decided.

She and Cully were good friends. He was solemn and mature. She saved him pieces of corn pone and let him talk to her of what he thought the world was like. The world to him, as to her, was the rest of Florida. He took her one day to visit his family. Florry sat painfully on the steps of their shack and answered questions. The place was dirtier than hers and the family seemed poorer. So many children ate up a heap of rations.

Cully took her around the Johnson island to show her the sights. He led her with pride to a small rectangle planted with vines, with a rickety cross at one end.

"This be Bob's grave," he said. "He got kilt dead by the pneumony."

Florry found herself suddenly weak.

"I got me a grave," she told the boy. "Back yonder to the east I buried me a young un, a leetle ol' baby no bigger'n a cat."

No bigger than a cat, but the old pain was on her.

In the late winter Mart fell into a great piece of luck. Harper's son Eph was away, 'shining, and Mart was given a place in the motor dory for a week, on fourth shares. They ran unexpectedly into huge schools of pompano. The pompano ran for two days and two nights. The slim silvery fish announced their coming half a mile away, raising the surface of the water visibly. The boat was ready for them. The motor was fast enough to throw out one end of the net and circle around the fish, ahead of them. They must be taken quickly, or they were gone forever.

The dory took in hundreds of pounds in the forty-eight hours of the aristocrats' passing. Pompano had been scarce for two years. They brought twenty-five cents a pound at the wholesale market. The whole town came to the docks to see the dory unloaded. Boats put out feverishly from all the tidal rivers, but the pompano had passed.

Mart's share of the big catch was enough to buy the net and rowboat he was using. He was now the capitalist. When Cully fished alone, Mart had half of the catch coming to him. His own catches need no longer be shared. Until early summer he prospered.

Then the fish, of a sudden, simply were not there any more. It was astonishing. Mart and the Johnsons and the Harpers lamented together.

"There's nary fish by day and there's nary fish by night."

"Hit's them pound-net fishermen north up the Gulf," Harper decided. "Them big ol' pound-nets, with traps in the bottoms, they jest scoops in everything. 'Course, them fellers has the right to make a livin', but it shore makes fishin' sorry down here."

Two or three days often passed without a catch. Times were lean. The fish house paid three cents a pound. When twenty pounds of fish at this price had to be divided two or three ways, there was not enough to buy grits and meal. Mart and Florry were better off than the rest. Johnson said that if fishing did not soon improve, he would have to give away his two younger boys. He could not feed them.

The Johnsons and the Harpers had no gardens on their bare soil. They could no longer buy greens. They grew sallow from the steady diet of fish and corn pone. Mart had planted a garden back of the old house, where the soil was thickest on the shell. Florry tended it. They had collards and cow-peas and pole beans. They shared as far as they could.

Harper fought the fish house to get four cents a pound.

"This is Saturday," the dealer answered. "If I have to pay you men four cents today, the fish house won't open Monday morning."

Fishing would pick up. They knew that. The fish would run again. It was a question of how long they could all hold out.

Perhaps despair made them careless. Harper must have known the signs. He had seen too many September gales drive in across the wide sweep of the Gulf not to know a fuzzykin. In the daytime that mass of black cloud, low-slung in the south, full of wind and thunder, was ominous but not alarming. Time could be gauged, and distance. At night, seeing that certain sign of high winds, Harper should have had the small fleet put in at once.

Wind in the south—and thunder. Especially at night. This time of year. They should have scurried in ahead of it, hell-bent. The first squall caught them from the southwest with the saved-up force of hundreds of miles. The black rain came in sheets. The gale seemed to pile half the Gulf into the two shore-miles. Harper in the motor dory set out for the mouth of the river, calling to the slow boats to follow. Cully wanted to pull an oar but Mart took both.

"This be work for a man, son."

Mart had not known such effort was in him. He was fighting the Gulf of Mexico, with all the winds of the Caribbean behind it. The wind seemed to move him at a terrific speed, but the waves caught up with him and spat venomously into the flat boat. Cully bailed fiercely. His young wet face, white in the night, showed the sternness of an old man.

Harper looked back. A long flash of lightning showed the small boats foundering. Ten men bailing could not have kept them from swamping. One by one they filled to the gunwhales. Harper put back and took the men on board the dory. The dory put into Channel Creek and the men slept that night on the floor of Harper's house. The next morning, although the gale still raged, he took them to their own islands, working through the maze of cross channels.

Florry had not slept. She had been afraid for Mart for the first time. On the north point of the island she had tried to build a signal fire as a guide for him. It was useless in the roaring downpour. The west end of the porch roof had blown in. She could not have slept long in the din, at best, but whenever she lay down and dozed a moment, she was awakened sharply by a black vision of Mart swimming in the Gulf—then going under. When he landed at the foot of the path below the fig trees, like a phantom in the rain, it was as though he had come back to her from the bottom of the Gulf. She stirred up the fire on the hearth and moved the coffee pot closer to the coals.

"Leetle boats is gone," he said after he had eaten.

"Nets, too?"

"They was in the boats."

"Won't they float, with all them big corks?"

"Mought. But they'll likely git all tangled up with the boats. If they does float, they'll drift on beyond where we could ketch 'em at."

They sat silently by the window with rags stuffed in the broken panes and watched the palm trees bend and the cedars flatten. The Gulf seas thrust long gray claws up the river. The wind roared steadily. Florry shook the sound of it off impatiently. Wind had once been only wind, a good sound in the trees. Now it was something else. A brief moment of resentment against it came over her, like the rare flickers of hate she had once felt for old Jo. Her thoughts came and went uncertainly in her mind, like fish far down in a dark pool.

The high tide was due in mid-afternoon. As the time approached, the Gulf seas swelled to appalling size. The gale was at its height. At three o'clock, with a great heaving and rolling, there came in what is still known on the river as the high salt tide. It writhed up the river like a sea-serpent, in and out among the islands, and flooded land that had never been submerged before.

"Mart," Florry asked, "we kin stay here right on? You kin fish with Harper's? Or the fish-house mebbe credit you on a boat and net?"

Yet she knew the answer. He shook his head.

"Reckon not. Harper cain't no more'n use his own kinfolks in the dory. He's studyin' on movin' down to Cedar Key. Fishin's some better there. The fish-house feller was down to Harper's this mornin'. He's closin' up."

"We could ketch enough fish for our own rations," she persisted, "and we got a fine garden comin' on. I seed yestiddy the beans was up, and the cabbage jest comin' thu."

They walked back to the kitchen window to look out at the garden on the low slope back of the house. The high salt tide was on it. The new green sprouts just had their heads above the sucking water. Tomorrow the brine would have made black wisps of them. Florry's lips twitched.

"Hit'll be plumb destroyed," she whispered.

Mart looked at her curiously.

"Ain't yo gittin' to be a froggy leetle ol' thing?" he said. "I got me good plans. Eph Harper ain't been gittin' but seventy-five cents a gallon for his 'shine. He says there be good money in 'shine in the right place. He's fixin' to clare out for Putnam County and start him a still in the scrub. He says Putnam County likker bring a fine price, two, three dollars a gallon, if you take time to run it thu twicet, so it ain't raw. He says he'd as leave carry me with him as not. I ain't never been in the scrub, but I allus hankered to see it. You'd like it fine."

She pondered.

"Would I jest leave the ol' cat here, like I found it?"

"Shore. You cain't tote cats from one county to another. They allus runs away."

"Kin I carry the pig?"

"Eph wouldn't want no pig messin' up his flivver. Tell you, Florry, we kin barbecue the pig jest afore we starts and carry it for rations."

"Mart, dogged if I could eat ary mouthful o' that leetle ol' critter. The longer I chawed it, the bigger it'd git."

He frowned.

"Hit's take it that-a-way or leave it, one. Pigs was meant for eatin'. Hit'll git et some'eres else if we don't eat it. Hit'll jest be pork when it's dead. Now don't you take on, Florry," he soothed her. "Hit don't make no special difference where we goes nor what we does. Rations is rations, right on. Hit don't make no difference where we squats to eat 'em."

"No," she agreed, reassured. "Hit don't make a mite o' difference, do it?"

VI

THE RIVER folk who knew Eph Harper could have warned Mart, if they would, that a year with Eph would be a year of treachery. In the vast silence of the scrub country, with cabins in clearings sometimes twenty miles apart, it would seem that there would be no evil for Eph to do; that two men would cleave together, in any case, for safety. But it was in the man to betray.

Florry was in no danger from him, although at first the three shared a shack in the high region above the Ocklawaha. When Mart's back was turned and Eph made tentative overtures, she did not even understand. He watched her afterward with wonder in his square yellow face, squatting on his haunches, his long arms dangling from his bunchy body, like a frustrated ape. Besides, a different kind of treachery was to his taste. He was a born informer.

Their location was good for liquor making. Eph set up his still on the bank of the river, so deep in saw palmettos that the approach of federal invaders would be announced far off by the loud rattling of the sharp fronds. They were equally safe from the river side. The clear cold river water ran swift under overhanging buttonwoods and cypresses and swamp laurel. It eddied against banks riotous with wild scarlet hibiscus and white spider lilies.

The shack they lived in was high above, up a steep bank where cooters came to lay their eggs, and skunks and 'coons to dig them out and eat them. The variegated growth along the river gave way, back of the shack, to dense virgin scrub. Scrub oaks and pines stood as close as matches in a box, match-lean, with myrtle and rosemary at their feet. The scrub was always shadowy, except where the deep sand roads cut through in blazing sunlight. Areas that had been burned over by forest fires were shadeless; the scrub naked and exposed, marked only by the tracks of deer and wildcat.

Mart had not begun to understand that Eph was using him for the mean work necessary; for the carrying of water; for the setting of the mash; for the long watches when the mash was slow to heat, slow to cook, and the drops of water-clear liquor at the end of the copper coil dripped as slowly as turpentine sap.

Eph found him a red-lipped girl in the scrub, a half-wild thing who would always mate here and there like any rabbit. He moved with her into another shack, five miles down the river, and left Mart with most of the labor of the still. Florry began to help in Eph's place. The arrangement seemed logical enough. Eph owned the still. He had to take what shelter he could find for his girl, and five miles was quite a distance to come to light a fire under the boiler. Eph took the finished liquor to a house some miles east of Palatka, where it was picked up for further relay.

Until uneasiness at being dependent on Eph came over them, Mart and Florry were contented here. No human voices came to startle them. Eph brought their rations with him on his return trips. The shack was on higher ground than they had ever known and it was a treat to look across the river valley to blue and purple distant ridges. The scrub was soft underfoot as a carpet. Pine needles and oak leaves, undisturbed on white sand, gave beneath their bare feet with a delicious yielding. There was game again to eat; wild turkeys, rabbits and 'possums, and young squirrels fat on hickory nuts and pine mast.

Mart shot a 'coon in the early spring. There came snuffling up to the dead body a young one, no more than a few days old. It let Mart pick it up as if it were a baby. When he took it home to Florry it nested in her lap snugly, then cried to be fed. The creature seemed half-human. The palms of the fore-paws were marked like a child's. When it tussled with Florry a little roughly, and she slapped it in punishment, it ran off whimpering with an an un-animal distress. She added canned milk to her list of rations for Eph to bring. It ate the things they ate, more daintily than they.

It washed its face and hands in the wash basin, like a well-trained child. It snuggled as soft in Florry's arms as the baby she had lost. Its pointed face with the black mask peered into hers with a recognizable affection. It liked to sit on her shoulder and rub its soft nose and long pointed hands across her neck. They kept it in the house at night, for fear of wild-cats. It fought persistently to sleep next to Florry in the bed, but Mart found this distasteful.

"Hit's a cute leetle feller," he admitted, "but hit's a varmint right on."

Florry fixed a padded box for it on the floor beside the bed. When Mart was asleep it slipped stealthily under the cover on the edge and lay mouse-still all night, its enigmatic face close to hers on the moss pillow. At day-break Florry put it in the box again, before Mart wakened. It looked up at him smugly when he arose.

When Mart and Florry went off into the scrub together they taught it to stay at the house, driving it back with switches. It ran around and around the shack in protest, its longer hind legs giving it an awkward gallop. Then it reared up, its forepaws in the air, and craned its neck after them. Occasionally it disappeared in the scrub for a few hours. They found they could not eat 'coon meat at all any more. There was enough of other meat, in any case, through the winter season. Twice they had the small black bear of the Florida scrub. The deer seemed scarce and wild.

Old-timers in the scrub said to Mart, "You cain't git no deer in the open season. Them hunters from all over is a-stirrin' up the woods with their dogs an' their fuss an' their shootin'. They thinks it's a big thing, do a whole camp get 'em a deer. You jest wait 'til the law closes down. Closed season is open season for us what lives here. The deer gits to be a plumb nuisance in the spring and summer. You cain't make cow-peas, nary a crop, the deer is so crazy for 'em. They'll leap ary fence to git to 'em. You kin git all the deer you want. You jest wait."

It was the venison that gave Eph away. He was ready to get rid of Mart. He had his market for his liquor, his price established. He was ready to move the still close to his own cabin, let his girl do some of the work, and collect the profits instead of sharing them.

Mart had been timorous about shooting deer out of season. The meat was more than they could use before it spoiled. Tales had reached him of the high fines imposed for out-of-season shooting. But in the first heat of May, Florry had not been well. She was languid, without appetite. They had had no fresh meat for some weeks. A young buck paused within range of Mart one afternoon. Before it could show its white scut and flash away, Mart had brought it down. He broiled the choice steaks over live-oak coals. Florry enjoyed it and ate plentifully. She thought it made her feel a little livelier.

The next morning, on his way down the river to help old man Bradson round up hogs, he carried a hindquarter of venison to

Eph. He was pleased to bring such a fine gift to his friend. Eph took it with thanks. As later testimony brought out, he and the girl gorged on it that day and the next. Then Eph drove to Waleka, looked up the game warden and turned Mart up. Eph swore to an affidavit that to his personal knowledge one Martin had shot a buck deer on May the eighteenth.

The trial is still talked of. All over the scrub, through Marion and Putnam counties, one man says of another, "He's as good a neighbor as Eph Harper," and it is known at once what depths of treachery are implied.

The lawyer who had volunteered to defend Mart questioned Eph's girl.

"How can you swear the meat was deer meat? Venison is very similar to beef."

"Well," she hesitated, "I seed a deer-hair on hit."

The crowded courtroom stirred.

A venerable Cracker announced audibly, "Dogged if that ain't purty fine swearin'."

Before Mart was put on the stand, old man Bradson rose majestically in court.

"Somethin's jest come to me," he announced.

The judge rapped for silence.

"That affidavit this here Harper has sweared to, do I understand the date be May eighteenth of this year?"

A hunter himself, the judge recognized the river patriarch. He looked at the document before him.

"Yes, Mr. Bradson. Do you wish to testify?"

"I shore do."

"Swear him—. Now, then, Mr. Bradson?"

"I got me a Coca-Cola calendar in the kitchen an' I jest happened to be studyin' it this mornin'. Wa'n't the eighteenth a Sat'day?"

"It was."

"Well, then, Jedge, I cain't swear I'd know deer-meat by a hair on hit, but I shore kin swear by God A'mighty that on Sat'day, May the eighteenth, this man Martin was to my house the whole day. He come soon in the mornin' to he'p me round up some hogs an' he worked with me to good-dark. My wife done give him a bite o' supper, seein' as it were so late. He didn't have no gun nor no deer meat, nor I didn't see no deer hairs on him. He didn't shoot no gun on the way home, nor pick up no deer, for I went home with him 'count o' bein' on my way to my son's house for Sunday."

The record shows that the judge had to silence the roar of delight that shook the courtroom. Eph's yellow face was white. Old Bradson's word was unimpeachable. Mart had indeed worked for him on that day. It was only a perfunctory matter for him to testify that he had no means of telling one date from another, but that if the date named on the papers was the date he had worked for Bradson, the papers lied. Eph had made the mistake of assuming that Mart had shot the deer the same morning that he brought him the meat. The case was dismissed.

It was known generally that Mart had shot a deer out of season. Eph's crime was greater. He had broken a frontier law more fundamental than the game rules. Yet Mart's safe return from the hands of the law was to Florry miraculous.

Because neither knew how to change the arrangement, the two men continued to 'shine together. It was their joint livelihood. Mart worked silently, watching Eph constantly for fear of attack. Eph was surly.

"He'd shore be proud to shoot me in the back, behind a clump o' palmeeters," Mart told Florry, "but he ain't got the chidlin's."

Chance probably played into Eph's hand, for he would not have planned to betray Mart at the expense of losing his still. It is certain that the Federal men merely nosed out the still. Eph was heading for it when he saw the agents creeping toward the bank where the odor of the sour mash rose strong. Florry caught a glimpse of him running toward home. He did not warn Mart, as he might easily have done. Mart's only escape would have been the river. The agents hand-cuffed him and smashed the still. They allowed him to speak with Florry before they took him away.

"Git on outen here afore Eph gits to harm you," he told her. "Go to work for ol' man Bradson whilst I be shut up. I'll come for you. Git Bradson to find out how long they put me in for. When the time's up, you be ready and we'll git back to the hammock where we fust come, when we went off together. I been studyin' on the way up the hill. We'll go back to the hammock and go to trappin' agin, come winter."

He was gone.

When he came back on foot a month later, Florry was not at Bradson's. He found her still in the shack above the river, with the 'coon. She was gaunter than he had ever known her.

"I didn't aim to be with folks," she excused herself. "I had me your gun and I felt safer-like here. I made me some box-traps and caught me rabbits, and I fished some. Eph ain't bothered me."

"Hit wa'n't right," he said slowly, "but it cain't be he'ped now. You ready? Le's go."

"Mart," she pleaded, "I don't aim to worry you none, but I shore would be proud to carry the 'coon with us."

The 'coon was half-grown and fat and heavy. Mart looked at it wearily. He was already tired.

"You be quare, Florry," he said. "I hates to refuse you, but dogged if I kin see ary sense to totin' a half-growed varmint."

"Hit's hard to leave somethin' behind, ever'time we goes," she said patiently.

As they walked off, she looked back at the 'coon, sitting reared up on the cabin door-sill. As far as she could see behind her, its quizzical masked face was visible.

VII

D UST LAY yellow on the palmetto scrub. The rattler coiled in its uncooling shade was almost invisible. Florry's bare feet padded close to him. He lifted his head, weaving it somnolently. The whirr of his rattle was faint, like a far-off cacophony of dry castor-beans. He was indifferent to her passing, sluggish, an old snake weary in the September heat.

Her lean body was sweaty with carrying a bucket of drinking water from the spring-fed branch two miles away; two miles of hammock, whose undergrowth whipped her face and whose wild bamboo vines left bleeding trails across her arms and legs. Her sun-bleached hair clung wet on her forehead.

She pushed aside the gray curtain of Spanish moss that canopied the live oak beneath which she and Mart had made their camp, waiting for November. The long gray fingers gave such privacy to the clearing that the camp would scarcely be noticed from the clay road a hundred feet away. Three walls of a pine shack were still standing under the oak. The flooring was intact. The shingle roof, drooping like an old hat where the fourth wall was gone, gave a certain shelter. It would do until trapping began. Then they could rent the old cabin in the hammock.

Ordinarily Florry pulsed with vague pleasure whenever she stepped within the cool shade of the oak, but the shade today, as for the past weeks, was a dusky delusion. It was more stifling than the open glare of the sun. After putting the bucket of water on the shady side of the camp and laying a palmetto leaf over it, she dropped down on the clean sand carpeted with oak leaves, panting like a dog. The blood beat scalding in her throat and cheeks. It had been hot and dry too long, longer than folks could bear.

The creak of a hand-pump sounded across the road like a seagull's cry. If the people in the new house were natives, she could get water from their well, but they were Yankees. They made no offer and she did not ask. She was not anxious to remind them of the camp's existence, for she was not sure whether or not they owned the land. Yankees were queer. They put up signs and warned people off.

She peered through the moss. The Yankee's small boy and girl were rolling discarded automobile tires for hoops down the roadway. They were tanned to the golden-brown of ripe pears. They moved with a dancer's grace, lifting their small arms free from the shoulders, like bird wings.

She watched them with a dull hunger. They were tiring in the intense heat. She saw that their faces were crimson. If they were hers, she'd make them lie down while it was so hot. The children trotted in like hot and weary puppies. The boy turned and latched the wooden gate after him.

Florry thought, "Ain't it fine to have a gate and a house with doors."

The only good house she had ever lived in had been old Jo's cabin in the piney-woods. Her mother's grandfather had built it and her mother's father had put a new shingle roof on it. The front door was soft gray cypress. The kitchen door was pine and it had blown off the hinges the day she went away with Mart. She had been glad to go. She hadn't minded the make-shift camps and cabins since, nor the storms that moved them on to other places. Nobody had anything to say about such things. Mart hadn't been treated right. But you couldn't help other folks' meanness.

She had minded leaving old Sport behind, and the cat and the 'coon, and butchering the pig for rations. She minded the puny baby lying on a Yankee's land, under a Yankee woman's petunias. It came to her that if Mart had stayed on the clearing, in old Jo's cabin that she had a right to, she would still have the hound, and it might be the baby. They had let their fear move them on.

Maybe, she thought, the winter's trapping would be good and they could buy them some land, free and clear; an acre or two from which they could not be driven by wind or circumstance. It would be fine to have Mart own a piece of ground, and a cabin with good doors to it. She lay motionless under the live oak, closing her eyes against the sand gnats. The summer had been so long. It had bothered Mart. She thought uneasily that he was late returning.

He was trading at Cap'n Tack's store in the village, four miles away. He had a string of perch and catfish he had caught in the lake. They came to sixty-six cents in trade. The storekeeper gave him a chunk of white bacon, five pounds of grits, a sack of meal and a can of Railroad snuff. Mart hesitated in the hot, dark store, odorous of rancid salt pork, of sour tobacco juice, of fish hummed above by swarms of flies. He wanted to ask some questions but the thick heat dulled his brain.

"This be September, eh?" he asked.

The storekeeper nodded.

"The tenth."

"How long 'til the season gits opened?"

"End o' November."

Cap'n Tack had gone over to the law since the loss of his fishing equipment. He hoped to be appointed game warden this year.

"Plenty o' ducks flyin' over jest afore dark," he commented slyly. "Fixin' to do a leetle shootin'?"

"No," Mart said, "I done a piece o' trappin' a few miles from here, afore I fished for you. I got my trapses yestiddy from the nigger I left 'em with. Jest fixin' to oil 'em an' git 'em ready."

He wanted to reassure Cap'n Tack that he was a man with property and good for his bill.

"I see. Col' drink afore you goes?"

A thought stirred in the storekeeper's shrewd brain. He lifted the lid of the ice-box. A wave of cold air washed over Mart's face. He was tempted.

"Shore would cool my gullet——"

He hated to get in debt another nickel. Cap'n Tack had already given him more than five dollars' credit. Storekeepers were smart that way. They worked your bill up, when a cold drink would feel so good. You thought, Only a nickel. There flashed across the weariness of his mind old Martha's chant——

> "Fi' cents in my pocket, ten cents on my bill.
> If I don't git no better, I'se boun' fo' Sugar Hill."

He smiled to himself.

"Reckon not today," he said.

The ice-box lid dropped down. He thought of asking for a chip of ice to suck, but he hated to. It was a Negro trick. If he was Cap'n Tack, a day like this, he'd lift that lid and just lie in that box, all through the heat of the day. He'd let the ice strike through him until his bones were cold.

When he set out down the road, the sun was at its zenith. It struck through the holes in his broad-brimmed straw hat. It made a golden inferno of the clay road under his calloused feet. It was an effort to keep a grip on the sack of rations and the strip of bear-grass on which he had kept three perch for Florry. His fingers prickled. The four miles were endless. Now and then he stopped by the side of the road to rest. He felt hotter than when he was in motion. Dry heat crawled over his body. He didn't believe he was sweating enough. It was always cooler when you could sweat.

He stepped off the road into the ditch to get out of the way of a truck he had seen gassing up in the village. The driver had been drinking cold pop at the gas station. Mart had noticed him fishing around for his favorite flavor in a great circular tank that held hundreds of pounds of ice and dozens of bottles. As the truck rattled past, the driver finished a final bottle and tossed it into the ditch. It lay at Mart's feet, still frosted, with a few mouthfuls of brown liquid bubbling in the bottom.

He picked it up, wiped the sand from the mouth and drained it thirstily. The last drops trickled down his parched throat in cold pin-points of ecstasy. Ice made it feel that way. Warm pop was no better than sweetened water. He fondled the frigid glass of the bottle. He passed his dry lips over it. He laid it against his throat. Its coldness passed into him and the bottle became tepid. Only the concave bottom was cold and he slid it inside his shirt and back and forth across his belly. If he could choose between ice and 'shine, he would choose ice. Maybe not in the winter, but certainly now, in September, while it was so hot. He wished he had bought a cold dope of Cap'n Tack.

He remembered the look in the storekeeper's eyes. They had been talking about trapping. Suddenly the sweat started out of him. In a moment he was wet all over. The last thing in the world he should have mentioned was his traps. Cap'n Tack would take them away for his bill. He was always making off with some Negro's shotgun, or even his mule, and white men's too, when he could. He always took something that was worth several times the bill, but when you owed him money, what could you do?

Mart thought maybe he and Florry had better get out right away. The traps were all he had. If he lost those, there was nothing left. Yet he knew no place to go, no good trapping place, where Cap'n Tack wouldn't hear about it and run him down. He'd heard the storekeeper was thick with the sheriff these days, doing low tricks together. No use having the law after him again.

He was worn out now from those thirty days on the gang, road-building in the blistering summer sun. He'd been hot ever since, and tired.

As he turned off the road to the camp, he noticed his neighbor out working. He was painting his new house, slapping bright yellow paint on its fresh pine boarding. Sweat streamed down his face and arms. Now and then a drop spattered into his paint bucket. Mart laughed noiselessly.

"Paint! Yaller paint on fresh pine!"

Nothing was funnier than a Yankee coming down here with his money in the bank and trying to paint fresh pine. His fine paint would be flakes in the sand, this time next year. Nobody but a Yankee could help knowing that. Over his shoulder Mart saw the Yankee woman come out of the screen door with a pitcher of water. He could hear the ice in it clink against the glass. He had never wanted anything that didn't belong to him, but he couldn't help thinking how good it would be to have your old woman bring you ice water in the heat of the day; and when you were through your work, to sleep behind screens away from the sand flies and mosquitoes.

Florry sat up, hands on knees, as his familiar step crackled through the bone-dry underbrush. He placed the sack of groceries in a box nailed to a tree. Bull ants began at once to climb the trunk to wave their feelers about the sack of grits. He took off his hat, drew his faded blue sleeve across his damp face. He lifted the palmetto leaf over the drinking water, already lukewarm, dipped a rusty tin cup and drank again and again, his head thrown back. Drops of water fell crystal on the amber of his throat. He replaced the covering and laid the fish on it. He had cleaned them at the lake, because fish guts around the camp drew flies. He lay down with his head and shoulders against the trunk of the oak tree.

"Florry, I done played me the fool."

"How come?"

"I done let on to Cap'n Tack I had me my trapses here. He'll take 'em shore."

"Cain't you hide 'em gooder?"

"No use, now he know I got 'em."

"He mought not study none on takin' 'em. When kin we trap?"

"We kin crowd the trappin' a mite. If he don't bother me, 'bout a month from now I'll set me a few trapses. We kin hide the skins, like, 'til I kin sell 'em."

"A month be four weeks, eh?" she mused.

She picked up Mart's pocket knife from the camp table and cut a straight length from the oak limb overhead. She began to cut notches, to make a calendar, so that if the moon wasn't clear, to show them, they could tell when a month had passed.

"Sunday, Monday, Chewsday, We'n'sday, Friday, Satiddy——"

That was one week. She began over again.

"Sunday——"

Mart closed his eyes.

"Hit's powerful hot," Florry said.

"Don't seem like I kin breathe. Don't seem like it's ever been so hot so long. Seems like it's plumb wore me out."

"Mebbe you got the fever," she suggested.

"Mought be. Don't seem like I kin stand it. Seems like the only thing'd cool me'd be lyin' deep down in water, some'eres, with chips o' ice floatin' around in it."

He drew his hat over his face for protection against any rays of the sun that might filter through the leaves as the afternoon wore on. Florry resumed her outstretched position near him. In the fevered coma of mid-afternoon there was no sound, neither of bird nor beast, neither of grass nor pine nor palmetto. The September heat smothered them all against her parched, unbreathing breast.

A car stopping in the road wakened them from their siesta. Two men were pushing their way in to the camp. Mart reared to his feet. Florry stepped behind the oak.

"Hit's them," he said.

Cap'n Tack lifted a hand in greeting.

"Howdy, Mart," he called jovially.

"Howdy."

The storekeeper leaned down casually to pick sandspurs from his pants.

"Mart, meet the sheriff."

The sheriff was a sallow fellow with thin yellow hands always open for chance fees. He did his profitable duty mournfully, as though the expense and trouble fell all upon his hunched shoulders.

"Howdy, Mart."

Mart's eyes moved up and down the man's frame, noting the uneasy gesture of the nervous fingers toward the ponderous revolver in the hip holster. He did not acknowledge the sheriff's greeting. He shifted his weight to lean one shoulder against the oak tree.

As though he were the host, Cap'n Tack waved toward the upturned boxes about the camp.

"Set down, Sheriff."

The officer eased himself to a seat.

"Nice camp you got here."

"Couldn't git you one no sorrier," Mart said.

The sheriff looked about him. He caught sight of Florry's dark head leaning forward around the oak, her bright alarmed eyes on him.

"How do, ma'am. How you?"

She bobbed her head to him.

Cap'n Tack drew out his plug of tobacco and pared off a shaving. He held it out to the sheriff questioningly.

"Reckon I'll smoke a cigarette."

The officer passed his package. Mart hesitated and took one, lighting it quickly with his own match. Cap'n Tack worked up his chew. The cigarette smoke hung blue and heavy on the thick air. A buzzard wheeled in the hot sky. A hawk screamed from a near-by pine. Mart smoked thoughtfully, as though he were alone. The sheriff cleared his throat.

"Mart," he said, "I'm sorry to crowd you, but I reckon you'd best hand over your traps for your debt to Tack here. He says he's got no other way to collect."

"That ain't so. Soon's I kin git to trappin' I kin git ketched up." Mart spoke slowly, watching the end of his cigarette.

"I got no way o' knowin'," interrupted the storekeeper, "he ain't goin' to jest pick up an' go off, traps an' all."

"I ain't fixin' to go off."

"That's what he says." The storekeeper nodded suggestively to the officer, who nodded back.

Mart said flatly, "The trapses is wuth a sight more'n the bill."

"They don't bring nothin' when you sells 'em, Sheriff," Cap'n Tack insisted.

"That's right," the sheriff agreed gravely. He shook out a handkerchief and wiped his face.

"Tell you what I'll do for him," the storekeeper spoke amiably, slapping his knee. "I'll let him take back the loan of his traps come winter and trap for me on shares."

Mart stamped out his cigarette butt angrily.

"You jest figgered it out that-a-way," he raged. "Dogged if I'll do it."

"Reckon you will."

The two men glanced at each other and moved in together toward him.

"You two pilferin' pole-cats——" He spat contemptuously.

"Look out how you talk to the law," the sheriff warned him sadly.

Mart kicked at a pile of leaves at the base of the oak.

"Take 'em," he said, "an' git."

He turned his back and walked away.

Cap'n Tack raked out the dozen traps. The sheriff kept an uneasy watch on the contemptuous ragged back.

"I hates to crowd you," the storekeeper remarked cheerfully.

The two men made off smartly, increasing their pace as they approached the road. Mart wheeled.

"Look at 'em scat," he said bitterly.

He reached suddenly for his shotgun leaning against the far side of the tree. He lifted it, trembling. Then he laid it carefully down.

"Hit ain't wuth it," he said.

The sun set molten, beneficence gone mad. The evening was a soft gray velvet suffocation. Sand gnats and mosquitoes hummed and stung. Mart opened his shirt and fanned himself with its tails. Florry was wet with the labor of waving a palmetto leaf for fan. The fish for supper had made them thirsty. Their lips were cracking. Mart set the bucket of water between them. It was the temperature of the air, nauseating on the palate. Its leaf-flavored brackishness tasted slightly rotten. It was good neither to quench thirst nor to cool the throat. Only ice could make it fit to drink. Florry drank, but Mart pushed the bucket aside.

He sat down with his back to the tree and leaned his head despairingly against the gray trunk. He closed and unclosed his broad fists, then his hands relaxed and lay loosely on the ground. Florry moved to the camp table and cleared off the debris of supper.

"Save them cold grits, Florry. That sack o' rations is like to be the last you'll git."

She stared at him. In the faint light the sweat glistened on his face. She could see his pulse work desperately in and out from his knotted throat. She crouched beside him and peered at him.

"Mart! You be'n't afeered?"

"I ain't skeert o' nobody," he answered heavily.

"No, I knows that." She pushed the soft hair impatiently behind her ears. She fixed the bright squirrel eyes earnestly on him. "I mean, you ain't afeered o' not gittin' no rations? Not gittin' no place for us to be? You ain't afeered o' what-all kin happen to folkses?"

He did not answer. He closed his eyes and rubbed the back of his dark head against the roughness of oak-bark.

Florry thought, "Mart's in trouble, shore."

"I knows how you feels," she said comfortingly.

She moved away to build the night's mosquito smudge and sat down in the slow gray drift of smoke. She frowned anxiously, seizing at thoughts that swept by like the wild flight of doves. She had felt secure so long. Now security was slipping away. Mart's despair was quicksand under her feet. In the old days of the cypress swamp her courage had stood like a wind-break against old Jo and the chill brown waters. Since the day she had gone away with Mart, through wind and rain, she had not needed courage.

"*—burden down——*"

She had laid her burden down on his lean, strong knees. She thought, "I've done had me a rest, like." A burden laid down could be picked up again.

"Mart," she said, "likely you're worrit up about me. You belong to know I ain't skeert, not one leetle mite."

"You leetle ol' froggy thing, you," he said gently, "rabbity, like your daddy said——"

His voice turned harsh.

"You belong to be skeert."

He spat in the smoky fire and swung forward so that he sat on his heels, rocking.

"Hit ain't like I was a sorry thing wouldn't do a man's work nor a day's work, neither," he said passionately. "You know I've scratched like a hound dog at a gopher hole. Nor I ain't been pertickler what 'twas I done, fishin' or trappin' or 'shinin' or sich. Excusin' workin' for a Yankee," he corrected himself.

"I cain't work for folkses that-a-way, nohow," he said unhappily. "Do they git biggety, I git uppity, an' it's trouble shore. An' ever'thing I done, Florry, has got so messed up there wa'n't no straightenin' to it. Storms an' sich, a-spoilin' the fishin', an' other fellers' meanness a-spoilin' t'other things. Hain't done nary good to kep' a-workin', no more good than squattin' by a creek with a catfish line."

He wiped his wet face with his shirt sleeve.

"You belong to be skeert, a'right. There ain't nothin' left to try. There ain't no'eres left to go. We been a-climbin' ol' Jacob's ladder thouten no end to it."

"Them trapses—" she interrupted.

"Them trapses finished us off, shore," he said. "Did I try to trap on shares for that storekeepin' buzzard, I'd owe him twicet the hides, come the year's end. Him takin' the trapses finished us. An' the heat, Florry." His eyes rested on her appealingly, like those of a dog. "Seems like the heat's plumb wore me out."

His head drooped forward between his knees. Florry brushed away the mosquitoes on his hair. She threw a handful of oak leaves on the smudge.

"He's like to had the chidlin's beat out of him," she thought.

"I don't belong to be skeert," she said doggedly. "You done tol' me your very self, hit don't make no difference where we goes nor what we does, nor where we squats to eat our rations."

"If we got any——"

"An' that don't make no difference, neither," she persisted. "Goin' hungry don't matter. Nor a roof to git under don't matter. Nor folks drawin' in their necks an' strikin' like a rattlesnake. Them's all things you cain't he'p."

She wrinkled her forehead and rubbed her thin hands tensely up and down her thighs.

"But you kin he'p bein' afeered!" she said fiercely.

She reached in his pocket for his snuff box and lipped a pinch quickly.

"Folks is wusser'n storms," she pondered. "Git you a place you got a right to, a place you kin drive folks offen, steaden them chunkin' things at you—you ain't so likely to have trouble."

Mart lifted his head impatiently.

"Florry, you're talkin' wild as a coot."

"Mart," she said, "you know good I got me a right to Pappy's cabin, yonder in the piney-woods. Would you jest stand up to him one time an' mebbe framm him with them big hands o' yourn, we'd be safe-like right on. I got me my rights there."

"An' I done had me my rights, too," he said bitterly, "ever' time I been moved on." He stretched flat, an arm across his face. "Wisht that bucket o' water was cold an' fitten."

"Our well water had sulphur to it, but it shore were cold an' fine."

"Hit ain't a mite o' use, Florry. I ain't got the strength to leg it that far, jest to git th'owed out agin. Hit's goin' to a goat's house for wool."

"Be you skeert?"

"I ain't skeert o' your daddy." He was sullen.

She took a deep, slow breath.

"Well, I'm a-headin' for the cabin, come day. Reckon you'd bes' foller jest to take keer o' me."

"Florry, leave me be. I cain't hold out. I'm wore out. Damn that fire! Put it out! I kin stand the skeeters better'n a smudge tonight."

"You got you a tech o' fever. Hit'll do you good to git outen the hammocks. Hit's the last chanct, shore, Mart, headin' for the piney-woods. We got to try it. If we cain't stay there—" she did not finish.

"Mart——"

Her small voice was gentle.

"Mart, be you skeert o' what-all kin happen to folkses?"

He did not answer for so long that she thought he had gone to sleep in his weariness. She leaned over him to hear what he was saying.

"I got a right to be——"

VIII

FLORRY THOUGHT that she had moved through such a nightmare before. The trek to Dixie County was like the hot seas of fever in which she had once swum. The air, like that of delirium, was palpable, pressing on her bony shoulders an insupportable weight. Her straight muscular calves ached as though the flat roads wound forever up-hill. Old Jo's blows had never fallen on her head so heavily as the direct rays of the September sun. No cypress log had tugged so ponderously against her as the burden of Mart's heavy spirit. He followed her like a hound unwilling at heel.

The thought of the clearing drew her ahead, as resistless as the sun. If she could reach it before the storms caught them up, she would willingly lie down on the cabin floor and let old Jo flail about him. She was weak with longing for the piney-woods, where the sun dropped visibly behind the tall trees, and peace lay like a cloak of pine-needles, pierced only by the rhythmic pattern of the hoot-owl's cry.

She felt hurried. The thick heat was a warning of change to come. It had been hot too long. There had been no rain since the torrents of June, and these had long since sunk deep into the soil. The sand was like powder. The clay ridges were burned brick. The flat-woods were brown. The occasional hammocks were dried up except in the lowest swamps and along the edges of lakes and streams. The creeks were withered down to the brown beds, cracking wide with thirst. The frogs, who had sung all spring in the good damp, were silent under the ooze where they had burrowed. Across the roads the moccasins and king snakes moved all day in search of water. Now the winds had stopped, and there was no breath of coolness anywhere. September was so still, so hot, that the very elements could not endure it. In a little while they would explode. They would burst out with wind and rain, tearing the heat to tatters.

In Levy County they passed a gang cutting ties in the flatwoods. Mart said, "Mus' we stop, an' me git a job, two-three days?"

Florry shook her head.

"We got to keep goin'. Hit's time for the high winds. We'll git ketched shore, do we stop."

They travelled fast on light rations. They were worn down to assemblages of bones that kept moving forward. Florry's feet were blistered under the worn soles of her shoes. Whenever they left the highways and cut through on the dirt roads, she walked barefooted, treading surely with long, spread toes. The high cheekbones lay across her thin pointed face like sun-baked ridges. Her eyes were sink-holes filled with leaf-brown water. In rough going, her long arm, lean as a crane's wing, held aside thorny vines to spare Mart, shuffling dull-eyed and indifferent behind her.

At night they tried to camp near water, to cool their feet and wash the sweat from their bodies. They had now no change of clothing, and she washed their shirts by starlight or by moonlight, in running water. She cooked hoe-cake in a palm-leaf in hot ashes and roasted what fish they stopped to catch. They sat each night by their camp-fire, staring wearily at the embers. Mart crouched dazed, until his eyes closed and his shoulders fell back on the moss-pile Florry gathered.

"You got the fever," she repeated again and again.

"Don't seem like I kin stand it," he would answer.

Yet she knew that it was more than fever ailed him. Random fears scampered like young rabbits before her. Old Jo might meet them, first thing, with a load of buckshot. He might have let the house burn down, lying drunk before the fireplace. Violence was reasonable, concerning him. She had promised Mart security. If it was not there to give——

She watched the white, hot skies anxiously. She was sure of her directions, but they had been more than a week on the way without a landmark. A Georgia sweet-potato peddler offered them a lift in his truck. Timidly, they accepted. Mart sat talking with the driver, but Florry slept most of the day, joggling snugly on potato sacks fragrant with the smell of Georgia earth. When she roused toward sunset, she recognized a bridge over which she and Mart had passed in their first flight south. They had come far in the one day's travel. The peddler gave them a few pounds of potatoes. Mart shot a young 'possum as they camped at dusk. That night they feasted. The thick air smothered them, but in the heaviness a restlessness stirred at last, like a quiver of wind across still water.

The next day Mart began to recognize the territory he had once so briefly visited. They were in the open piney-woods, walking over brown pine-needles inches deep. Sparkleberry leaves caught spots of sunlight that filtered through the shadows. Gallberries shone black like small eyes. Quail ran ahead of them down the ruts of the wagon trail. Doves whirred from the tops of the pines in rose-gray flocks. Squirrels chattered shrilly from a safe distance.

Mart's eyes grew wide. He shifted his shotgun from the crook of his elbow to his shoulder, fingering the trigger.

"I mean, this is shore good huntin' woods."

Florry nodded.

"The squirrels is extry thick 'count o' this bein' seed year."

That night they talked late by the camp-fire. The abundant game stirred Mart to interest. She told him what she knew of trapping here; of logging; of cane-growing. Long after she had gone to sleep he sat hunched by the live-oak coals. At midnight a shiver passed across the lethargy of the pines. A sudden chill moved through.

When Florry wakened in the first silver daylight, she said, "We cain't no more'n make it."

The woods creatures were stirring excitedly, the squirrels scampering up and down the trees with a tail-whisking madness.

"They allus acts that-a-way afore a storm," she told him.

There was a breathless hush in the forest, but overhead gray clouds scudded wildly to the southwest. There was terror in the flight of these imponderable things, as though the forces pounding in behind them were those of a pestilence. The sky blackened, moment by moment. Twilight took over the woods; then dark. There was no morning; no day; no longer any time. The mottled bark of the pines spotted the blackness. Mart's face and Florry's floated white, detached from their bodies that were blended with the myrtle bushes and the dark trunks of trees. They were phantoms, hurrying unhappily through the endless piney-woods of space.

Florry said, "We got a mile to go."

She stared over her shoulder. As she looked, the black sky turned luminous. A green translucence filled the east. A gust of cold wind puffed in from nowhere and was gone. A few drops of rain flicked their throats. Florry pulled her gray cotton blouse together across her slim brown neck. Suddenly the air about them vibrated. There was no perceptible wind, but the pines quivered. Their needles rustled frantically a moment. Something like a shudder stirred in the palmettos. Florry laid a quick hand on Mart's bare forearm.

"Listen!"

Far off a giant sea of wind was pounding on the shingle that was the forest. A roar as of surf beat in, wave on wave, seething and angry. It was coming nearer. A rumble—a boom—as the gale moved close it climbed the scale until its voice was a high-pitched whine. It hung there shrieking, shrill beyond all mortal bagpipes. The sky was black and green glass. The storm was shattering it into uncountable brittle pieces. The sky crashed. Floods of rain fell slantwise. Chaos came in and ripped the piney-woods to pieces. This was the hurricane.

Mart tried to shelter Florry with his body. He pushed his side against the gale, pulling her along in the lee of him. The first rush of the storm deluged them. It drove blinding into their eyes and cascaded down their thin frames. The wind choked off their breath. Sometimes it was a great wall against which there was no moving. They stood balancing, heads lowered, until a hole broke in the wall to let them through. Their clothes were pasted flat against them, so that they were like wet dark statues. With her eyes wide, her soft hair plastered over her ears, her small pointed breasts and slender thighs, Florry had to Mart the look of a child.

He shouted, "Leave me tote you."

She shook her head.

"I kin make out."

Her voice, close against his ear, was a thin sweet flute above the scream of the hurricane.

Her knowledge of the ways of trees kept them safe. When an old pine, rotten of heart, crashed down, her quick eye caught in time the ominous sway. Against falling limbs, palmetto fans driven like spears before the gale, they could only keep their arms over their heads and take the stinging blows as they came. Their sleeves were torn in shreds. The rain washed the blood from their cuts as it ran. They fought ahead, tripping over logs and into holes made invisible by rushing water.

At noon they reached the cabin. Florry stamped the sand from her bare feet and wrung the water from her full skirt. She lifted the latch of the gray cypress door. Together they threw their shoulders against it. It swung violently open and thumped flat against the wall. Florry sprawled headlong into the room. Mart turned his back to tug the door shut again.

He heard old Jo's amazed curse and Florry's cry. He bolted the door and wheeled to see the old man lift a heavy lightwood knot from the clay hearth above the girl's thin shoulders. Fierce, not with anger but with a strange delight, he knocked the stick from old Jo's claw and closed his hands about the leathery neck. He tightened his grip until the bloodshot eyes grew wild and the strong old hands quit their beating upon him. A terrified whimper came from the scrawny throat. Old Jo's body drooped limply. Mart held him up by the jaws. The neck under his fingers seemed suddenly weak and small. He pushed the man from him, tumbling him across the sagging pine bedstead. Old Jo sobbed and gasped. Mart loomed over him.

"Ol' feller," he said, "mebbe you'll be a mite more pertickler about your meanness. Reckon you an' me's goin' to make out over the same pot o' grits."

Old Jo snuffled and wiped his nose.

Florry's blood stirred warm again, where for a moment there had been the old chill of fear. Jo was old; frightened, old and beaten. She stared at the unhappy huddle on the bed. He was mumbling miserably, his old face wrinkled in distress. The ancient terror was gone.

Mart strode about, appraising the bare room with satisfaction. His step, that had shuffled all summer, in spite of his weariness was hard and sure. Something of the shy delight was in him that he had brought to her in this place those several years ago. His wet clothes steamed as he moved closer to the hearth fire. The gale drummed fiercely on the shingled roof. The small-paned windows rattled like loose teeth.

"Ol' feller," he called to the sniffling heap on the bed, "is they rations in your kitchen?"

"There be meal an' sich," the old man proffered grudgingly.

"Let's go, Florry."

They dashed through the east door, across the breezeway, Mart pushing Florry ahead of him against the pounding winds. They burst into the kitchen, only to have the full force of the hurricane sweep in upon them through the gaping doorway.

"That ol' rascal," Mart yelled, "never put back that door blowed off."

She put out a hand to hold him, but he was already in the storm, freeing the fallen door from a tangle of weeds. He loped across the sand, searching out an implement for his uses. He picked up at last a rusty axe-head, and brought in a pine sapling to use for batten. The wind shrieked over the kitchen, but it was no longer blowing through. Mart had the door in place.

Florry called through the thin pine.

"Kin you make that sorry door stay shut?"

He thumped confidently with the rusty axe-head.

"Hit'll hold," he said.